POISONS IN YOUR FOOD

POISONS IN YOUR FOOD

Ruth Winter

with an Introduction by
Senator Walter Frederick Mondale

CROWN PUBLISHERS, INC.   NEW YORK

To

Rose Rich Grosman

Acknowledgments

The author gratefully acknowledges permission to quote from their works by:

Jay M. Arena, M.D., Poison Control Center, Duke University Medical School, Durham, North Carolina, and the *Journal of the American Medical Association* for "Poisonings and Other Health Hazards Associated with Use of Detergents," *JAMA,* October 5, 1964.

William B. Deichmann, Ph.D., Professor and Chairman of the Department of Pharmacology and the Research and Teaching Center of Toxicology, University of Miami, Coral Gables, Florida, for "Retention of Pesticides in Human Adipose Tissues—Preliminary Report," *Industrial Medicine and Surgery,* 3713, March, 1968.

Ben Feingold, M.D., Chief, Department of Allergy, Kaiser Foundation Hospitals, "The Recognition of Food Additives in Allergic Diseases," presented before the American College of Allergists, Denver, Colorado, March 27, 1968.

Stephen D. Lockey, M.D., 60 North West End Avenue, Lancaster, Pennsylvania, for case histories.

Charles C. Thomas, Fort Lauderdale, Florida, publishers of *Chemical Carcinogenesis and Cancers,* by W. C. Hueper and W. D. Conway, for extracts from that volume.

Contents

Introduction

Like poverty and hunger before it, the issue of health hazards in food is a matter discussed more by experts than by the consuming public. Like those other issues as well, the issue of health hazards is gradually commanding more attention through the pioneering efforts of writers like Ruth Winter.

Our knowledge about health hazards in food is like the tip of an iceberg. This book touches on much of the submerged knowledge.

Testimony on meat and poultry inspection legislation called attention to potential hazards, and available information on fish and eggs has convinced me that there is work to do in these fields as well.

But protein products are not the only problem. Mrs. Winter graphically summarizes information about agricultural chemicals, food additives, and water pollutants. And in her discussion of the potential problems of catering, vending machines, convenience foods, and home freezing, she brings forward information that has not been widely discussed before.

Poisons in Your Food is a compendium of information for consumers. Mrs. Winter has presented scientific literature in an eminently readable form, giving laymen a sense of the nature of the controversy and, by extension, an opportunity to participate in its resolution.

For housewives and husbands, industry representatives, legislators, public officials, and scientists are all consumers of the food Mrs. Winter is writing about in this volume. It will take the efforts of all of us to mount the campaign of action suggested in Chapter 10 of this book. Meat and poultry legislation passed in the last Congress is solid testimony to the effectiveness of the aroused citizen.

Behind the specifics is the underlying issue of the interaction of technology and society. Modern techniques of growing and processing the food we eat are remarkable. Today we may be on the verge of preventing worldwide starvation through this technology.

But *Poisons in Your Food* presents graphic evidence that this technology creates the possibility of detrimental effects as well. Tipping the balance toward human welfare requires genuine concern from all whose lives are touched.

That means those of us who produce and process must be concerned with the human impact of our practices. Those of us who use the products also have to defend ourselves.

All of us need information and the determination to force consideration of health and safety among those who seem to be unwilling to take such considerations upon themselves, whether in producing, processing, or consuming publics.

This book provides a good deal of the information. It should also provoke the determination.

WALTER F. MONDALE

1

Have You Had Your Poisons Today?

WHEN YOU SIT DOWN TO eat a meal in your own home or in one of the 540,000 eating and drinking places in the United States, you take it for granted that the food is wholesome and nutritious. Unless you have access to special knowledge—medical data, reports of qualified investigators, and findings behind the "vital statistics"—it may not occur to you that it is now impossible for you to eat an ordinary meal, or to give a child milk from a bottle, can, carton, or breast, that is not contaminated with pesticides.[1] The sausages, ham, hamburgers, or hot dogs you eat can be filled with hog blood, cereal, lungs, niacin, water, detergents, and/or sodium sulfite.[2] Even a baby's diet can be dangerous.

The bread you put in your mouth daily is literally embalmed to keep it feeling soft and fresh long after it isn't,[3] and the dessert you eat may be colored with a cancer-causing agent.[4]

The candy you put in the mouths of babies may not only be bad for their teeth but also dangerous because of contaminants such as wood splinters or rodent urine.[5]

"Impossible!" you are probably saying to yourself. "Our food is inspected and protected by law!"

But do you know that most foods from catering establishments, intrastate processing plants, and vending machines are almost never inspected?[6]

Do you know that only 10 percent of the foodstuffs adulterated with pesticides and chemicals or contaminated by insect filth and

1

disease organisms is condemned by Food and Drug inspectors? The other 90 percent gets through to unwary consumers.[7]

Do you know that 89.3 percent of the fish—despite the fact that some of it is kept aboard boats from eight to sixteen days—is not inspected and that the 10.7 percent that is inspected is done on a purely voluntary basis by inspectors paid by the fishing industry?[8]

The majority of food and drug inspectors are hardworking, grossly underpaid public servants. But despite the fact that most contamination and adulteration cannot be recognized without laboratory tests, 41 percent of the state milk and dairy supervisors and 71 percent of the state food inspection supervisors have no degrees.[9]

Although the food and drug inspectors may be responsible for overseeing the health standards of thousands of restaurants, retail foods and drugs, wholesale and manufacturing plants, meat inspection and radiation hazards, some states, such as Maryland, have only three state food and drug inspectors; Ohio has five; and North Carolina and Idaho six compared to Florida's 244.[10]

Many eminent physicians, university scientists, politicians, and industrialists contend that the American food supply is wholesome, safe, and nutritious and that it is abundant. Compared to what the starving peoples of the world must eat, and in contrast to the typhoid- or tuberculosis-contaminated food of the past, perhaps we should not complain. It is true that our food is abundant to the point that our taxes pay farmers not to grow crops. Our market shelves contain 8,000 items compared to the 1,500 they displayed before World War II. But this very increase in new items has created new dangers.

The National Academy of Sciences' Food Protection Committee warned in 1964: "Food scientists in industry and government are concerned about the increasing disparity between the rate of technological change in certain segments of the food industries and the level of efforts being made to evaluate and control health hazards associated with new products and processes."

Food poisoning in America is increasing at an "alarming rate," according to Dr. James Goddard, Commissioner of the Federal Food and Drug Administration. He points out that salmonellosis, a form of food poisoning, has increased more than 1,000 percent since 1951.[11]

The National Health Surveys have reported that digestive disturbances affect an estimated eight million Americans a year and that stomach upsets are the second leading cause of school absences. In fact, 42 percent of all illnesses suffered by man are foodborne.[12]

Even more dangerous than the obvious upset stomachs from food are the hidden illnesses, the unsuspected allergies, the irreparable damage to the cells of the unborn, and the slow poisons that are suspected of being a cause of cancer.

In the November 22, 1968, issue of *Science,* researchers from the University of Pittsburgh School of Medicine reported that a substance which causes liver cancer remained in the multiplying cancerous liver cells of rats "weeks to months" after it was removed from the rodent's diets. "For many different tissues," the Pittsburgh researchers said, "the required exposure time to a variety of carcinogens is considerably less than the shortest interval in which malignant cells can be detected with current techniques."

Dr. Goddard told a meeting of the Food Protection Committee of the National Academy of Sciences that food additives and pesticides are not now adequately tested for safety in humans before they are marketed. He said:

"We do not have the kind of clinical research underlying food chemistry that we have underlying drug chemistry." And animal studies, on which the food chemists must rely, simply won't reveal the same depth of detail about effects on human beings that they do in the clinical tests to which all drugs are subjected.[13]

Dr. Goddard is not alone in his warnings. Dr. W. C. Hueper, former Chief of the Environmental Cancer Section, National Cancer Institute, said: "Apart from the fact that most of the food, drug and cosmetic dyes used in this and other countries have not adequately and competently been studied for possible carcinogenic properties in experimental animals, no pertinent reliable and valid information has ever been published concerning such possibilities by surveying occupational groups and other specially exposed population groups for carcinogenic effects from these agents when present in a considerably more impure state than that required for food dyes. Such investigations, however, are urgently needed because claims have been advanced, based on epidemiologically deficient evidence, that the use of butter yellow in Austria and in some oriental countries for coloring foodstuffs was responsible for an increased or excessive death rate from primary liver cancer among the populations consuming such foods."[14]

Dr. Chauncey Leake, past president of the American Association for the Advancement of Science, and one of the nation's most distinguished pharmacologists, warned in 1963 that general use of new chemicals in large quantities has created a new hazard—subclinical poisoning—so insidious that physicians cannot connect the poison with the ailment.[15]

Rachel Carson warned in 1962, in her best seller *Silent Spring,* about the dangers of pesticides: "Malathion (beloved of gardeners) has induced severe muscular weakness in experiments on chickens. This was attended (as in ginger paralysis) by destruction of the sheaths of the sciatic and spinal nerves. . . .

"The widespread neglect of the problem of chemical mutagens is perhaps due to the fact that those first discovered were of scientific interest only. . . .

She described how fruit flies, the classic subject of genetics experiments, developed damaging and even fatal mutations when exposed to one of the common herbicides or to urethane. Urethane belongs to the group of chemicals called carbamates, from which an increasing number of insecticides and other agricultural chemicals are drawn.

"Two of the carbamates," she wrote, "are actually used to prevent sprouting of potatoes in storage—precisely because of their proven effect on stopping cell division."

Did Rachel Carson, a highly respected marine biologist, write her book in vain?

In "Protecting Our Foods," *The Yearbook of Agriculture,* 1966, the United States Department of Agriculture states on page 28: "Both Malathion and carbaryl are toxic to many insect pests. Unlike the chlorinated hydrocarbon materials they do not accumulate in tissues. Thus they can be applied up to or within a day or so of harvest on many human food and forage crops." (Carbaryl, like urethane, is a carbamate.) That Malathion has been approved for direct application to grain and to peanuts in the shell is described on page 146 of the same publication.

The United States Department of Agriculture has greatly reduced its spraying activities with DDT in the past ten years. In 1968, the Food and Drug Administration and the United States Department of Agriculture jointly recommended that the amount of permissible residue of DDT on thirty-six fruits and vegetables be reduced.

But no matter how much the residues are reduced or how many noxious chemicals are recognized and banned, for those of us already subjected to as many as ten pesticides with every meal, it is too late. It may even be too late for those children we may someday have. Our tissues have been storing a generous supply of pesticides.[16]

The human digestive system is in itself a chemical engine. As it moves food through its conveyor belt, it adds digestive juices and secretions from the gallbladder, liver, and pancreas. The human body is a wondrous thing. It can detoxify many poisons through its liver and kidneys. It can fend off many germs, and even cancer—that is, if it is young and healthy. But what about infants and the elderly, whose resistance is not great? What about those with damaged kidneys and livers? allergies? chronic illnesses?

The use of chemicals in foods has soared from 419 million pounds in 1955 to more than 800 million today. Each of us eats more than three pounds of food additives a year.[17]

Added to the intentional and unintentional chemicals in our foods are the chemicals we ingest as medicines. Americans are the most medicated people in the world. Every year we swallow 37 billion doses of therapeutic pills, powders, capsules, and elixirs.[18]

No one knows what effect the combinations of pesticides, food additives; and medicines may have. The American Public Health Association, in its "Safe Use of Pesticides," 1968, said: "Organic phosphates (common pesticides) affect promazine and chlorpromazine (very common tranquizilers), but what other drugs or to what extent we do not know."

In addition to the foods we eat and the medicines we take, we fill the sky with 130 million tons of noxious chemicals . . . carbon monoxides, hydrocarbons, nitrogen oxides, sulfur oxides, and particulates. Persons living in New York may inhale the equivalent of 730 pounds of chemicals a year.[19]

In addition to chemical purifiers, water today contains all sorts of pollutants, from detergents to sewage and industrial wastes.

Added to all the chemicals in food, water, medicine and air, a large percentage of the population smokes and/or drinks alcoholic beverages. Tobacco smoke may be an additional cancer-causing agent that breaks down the body's immunity, while alcohol may be a solvent that aids another noxious chemical.

Perhaps the many eminent, conservative scientists who warn

us that we may be irrevocably poisoning ourselves are alarmists. On
the other hand, before we draw that conclusion, we must rule out
such things as the role of pesticides in infant mortality.

At least 25 percent of the conceptions in the United States
end in intrauterine death.[20] Is it a coincidence that traces of pesticides have been found in the tissues of stillborn and unborn human
babies in the United States? In some cases the concentration of
pesticides in the fetus was almost as high as those of the mother
or of young adults of comparable age.[21]

The question of why millions of Americans have ulcers, gall-
stones, kidney stones, and cancer must be answered. Although
heredity is certainly implicated, so is diet.

We must ask ourselves why trichinosis is higher in the United
States than in European countries. Why the American export of
oranges has been endangered because the European Economic
Market set its permissible biphenyl (decay retardant) residue rate
40 percent lower than the 110 parts per million rate set by the Federal Food and Drug Administration.[22]

We must ask ourselves if we must accept the suffering and loss
of millions of hours from school and work caused by preventable intestinal upsets.

We hear much today of ecology; we worry about changes in
wildlife when the "balance of nature" is upset. Yet one of the world's
leading gastroenterologists, Dr. Burrill B. Crohn of New York, told
his colleagues at the Eighth International Congress of Gastroenterol-
ogy in Prague, in 1968, that the current high incidence of intestinal
diseases may reflect a "disturbed ecology of the human race." Com-
menting on the apparently altered pattern of gastrointestinal diseases
in the past three decades, he said:

"Where previously the beds of the hospitals were occupied
predominantly by cases of gastric and duodenal ulcer, we now note
the census of gastrointestinal cases as essentially intestinal. My own
office records of private patients include over 3,000 cases of ulcera-
tive colitis, 1,100 cases of ileitis and 260 instances of granulomatous
colitis."

He said that today 5 to 10 percent of the adult population on
routine barium enema will demonstrate diverticuli (pouches) in the
intestines.

Dr. Crohn, who is Professor Emeritus of Medicine at Mount

Sinai School of Medicine, said that he could not accept the view that the "upsurge" of these disorders could be laid to the stresses of the twentieth century. Other centuries have also been marked by stress, he said.

"Is the causation of these diseases to be found in the food we eat?" Dr. Crohn asked. "In the last decades of our ecology, our foods contain multiple chemical preservatives; our growing crops are sprayed with insecticides. We ingest multiple new drugs never before used, such as the coal-tar products of which aspirin and its derivatives are regular household remedies. The pollution of our drinking water might also be a factor."[23]

1 NOTES

1. R. E. Duggan and Keith Dawson, "Pesticides," a report on residues in food, U.S. Food and Drug Administration reports, *FDA Papers,* June, 1967, Vol. 1, No. 5. Tom Bogaard, chemist and general manager, Kenya Pyrethrum Co., interview with author, January, 1968. Dr. George Kupchik, Director of Environmental Health, American Public Health Association, tape-recorded interview with author, February 26, 1968.
2. William E. Jennings, director of the Division of Meat Inspection of New York, April 20, 1963, issue of *The National Provisioner.* Rodney E. Leonard, Deputy Assistant Secretary, Consumer and Marketing Service, U.S. Department of Agriculture, November 9, 1967, Congressional Hearings on Meat Inspection, Washington, D.C.
3. Howard J. Sanders, "Food Additives," *Chemical and Engineering News,* October 17, 1966. *Changing Times,* May, 1960.
4. W. C. Hueper, former chief of the Environmental Section, National Cancer Institute, and W. D. Conway, *Chemical Carcinogenesis and Cancers* (Springfield, Ill.: C. C. Thomas, 1965), p. 645.
5. Chocolate mint candy, Utah, packed under insanitary conditions; contains wood splinters, cloth fibers, metal fragments, *FDA Papers,* November, 1967, p. 36. Peppermint candy, South Carolina and Texas, on December 20, 1966, had rodent contamination, *FDA Papers,* April, 1967, p. 31.
6. Dr. George Kupchik, taped interview February 26, 1968.
7. *Ibid.*
8. Leroy Houser, Standard Development Section, Shellfish Sanitation Branch, Division of Engineering, U.S. Department of Health, Education, and Welfare (HEW), "The Role of Health Agencies in Fishery Sanitation," *Journal of Environmental Health,* National Association of Sanitarians, September–October, 1966.

9. "A Study of State and Local Food and Drug Programs," report to the Commissioner, Food and Drug Administration, U.S. Department of Health, Education and Welfare, February, 1965.

10. *Ibid.*

11. James L. Goddard, M.D., *Nutrition Today,* September, 1967, Vol. 2, No. 3, p. 3.

12. Robert W. Harkins, Ph.D., Chicago, *Journal of the American Medical Association,* November 6, 1967, Vol. 202, No. 6.

13. Reported in *Science News Letter,* December 10, 1966.

14. Hueper and Conway, *op. cit.,* p. 645.

15. *Medical World News,* January, 1963.

16. "Pesticide Residues in Food," Food and Agriculture Organization of the United Nations, 1967, p. 15.

17. Howard J. Sanders, "Food Additives," *Chemical and Engineering News,* October 17, 1966. James L. Goddard, M.D., FDA Commissioner, tape-recorded interview with author, May, 1968.

18. Pharmaceutical Manufacturers Association, Washington, D.C., fact booklet, 1967.

19. Essex County, New Jersey, Medical Society bulletin.

20. David Zimmerman, "Unmasking the Agents That Can Make Genes Go Wrong," *Medical World News,* May 17, 1968.

21. Harold Schmeck, "Pesticides Found in Unborn Babies," *New York Times,* Sunday, January 30, 1966.

22. United States Department of Agriculture news release, "USDA Studies Residue Control of Biphenyl-Treated Oranges," October 15, 1968.

23. *Medical Tribune,* August 8, 1968.

2

How to Kill Insects— and People

IT WAS A WARM JUNE day—warm enough for a young mother to keep the window open while she gave her five-year-old son a bath. Insecticide that was being used to protect the elm trees in front of the house was accidentally whooshed through the window, filling the bathroom with fumes. Both the mother and the little boy choked and coughed for fifteen minutes.

Eight months later, the child was taken to the family physician because a skin wound failed to heal properly. Worried about the slow healing and the boy's loss of appetite, listlessness, and enlarged spleen, the doctor had him admitted to the hospital for further tests. An examination of the child's blood marrow confirmed the dread diagnosis—acute granulocytic leukemia.

The child was treated by various means—the latest drugs, X rays, blood transfusions—but as spring was just beginning to fill the air and the elm trees in front of the house were once again proudly displaying their buds, the little boy died.

In the following February his mother was referred to the Mayo Clinic because of a suspiciously low white blood count that had first been noticed three months earlier, when she suffered an attack of the "flu" with a fever of 103 degrees. Her fever had cleared and she had felt well—that is, as well as a mother who has lost a child can ever feel. At the hospital, an examination of her bone marrow revealed acute leukemia. She was put on drugs, and received twenty-eight blood transfusions. But, nine months after her little boy died, she also succumbed to leukemia.[1]

9

High in the Andes of Colombia there is a town called Chiquin-quirá about which almost no one had heard until a day in November, 1967. Chiquinquirá, like farm towns everywhere, rose early for breakfast that particular morning. By 8:30 A.M., the first child was dead.

By afternoon, more than 130 persons, most of them children, violently sick and near death, were brought to the hospital. They lay on mattresses or straw tossed on the unpaved floors of an uncompleted wing of the San Salvator Hospital. Mattresses were frantically gathered from the local army garrison and every other available source. Fathers and sons, mothers and daughters, brothers and sisters lay two in a bed or on straw pallets. They were the lucky ones. With medical aid, many of them survived. But seventy-seven in the town died. Of that number, only four were more than seventeen years old. "For some unknown reason," the doctors said, "adults seemed more resistant to the poison."

What was the deadly poison? About a pint of the pesticide parathion. On the hundred-mile truck journey from Bogotá, a parathion container broke in its carton, and the insecticide leaked into the bags of flour. A baker used two of the bags of flour for his early-morning batch of bread. Within four hours, the first of the victims had died.[2]

Just a month earlier, the story had been the same in Tijuana, Mexico. There, seventeen died from bread contaminated with parathion.[3]

Parathion poisoning has occurred within the United States, although not as yet on such a mass scale. Shortly after the news of the Colombian deaths broke, the Health Department of New York warned that parathion was being sold by itinerant peddlers in the city as an insecticide. Health Commissioner Edward O'Rourke said that an eighteen-month-old child had swallowed the poison, which had been sold as a vermin exterminator in an unlabeled baby-food jar.[4]

Parathion is also used as an agricultural spray, particularly on vegetables and cotton. In its September, 1968, report, the Food and Drug Administration noted that 340 crates of celery had been seized in Florida because of contamination with parathion residue.

In the case of the mother and son, where inhalation of the insecticide was followed by leukemia, death took months to claim its victims. In the instances in Colombia and Mexico, where the insecticide was ingested, death was swift.

The awful question that haunts many scientists today is whether the one to a dozen pesticides we may ingest with every meal may cause or contribute to a slow poisoning of our systems and those of our unborn children.

In the leukemia cases, the physicians at the Mayo Clinic concluded: "Neither consanguinity [blood relationship] nor blood dyscrasias [abnormalities] were known among the relatives of the two patients with acute myelogenous leukemia described in their report. Both patients were exposed simultaneously and intensely to inhalation and contact with insecticides. . . . Moreover, both patients had acute myelogenous leukemia, commonly associated with patients exposed to toxic agents."

The Mayo Clinic physicians also cited two other reports, one in 1958 and one in 1962, linking insecticides and leukemia victims.

The American Medical Association Council on Drugs, which maintains a registry on blood dyscrasias, has a list of eighteen reports of major blood abnormalities associated with exposure to an insecticide, lindane, or benzene hexachloride (BHC). Dozens of other cases linking blood disorders and insecticides have also been reported.[5]

Since 1957, five Californians have died from aplastic anemia or related blood dyscrasias; each of them had been exposed to the chlorinated hydrocarbon pesticide known as lindane. None of the deaths was listed as due to lindane in the mortality statistics.[6] These deaths, which came to the attention of the California State Health Department, included that of a thirty-nine-year-old wife of a physician. The interior of her home had been treated, every three months for several years, by a pest-control operator who used vaporizing lindane. On one occasion, an insect was found just after treatment, and the application was repeated. A heavier than usual "white film" was found over the walls and surfaces of the home. After cleaning the house thoroughly, the housewife became seriously ill, and a diagnosis of aplastic anemia was made. On several occasions before her death, she noted relapses after eating in a restaurant where a lindane vaporizer was in operation.

For several hours a day, for several years, an eight-year-old girl occupied a kitchen in which a lindane vaporizer was operating. She became ill with aplastic anemia and also experienced a sudden relapse when patronizing a restaurant where a lindane vaporizer was in operation.

Dr. Irma West, of the Bureau of Occupational Health, State of California Department of Public Health, said before a Senate committee in 1963: "With the notable exception of the organic phosphate pesticides, physicians do not have laboratory tests available to confirm diagnoses of agricultural chemical poisoning. Diagnoses can be made on a clinical or circumstantial basis only. Signs and symptoms may be similar to many other conditions. Just about any illness can be attributed to chemicals and there is little help in confirming, refuting or clarifying the situation. Bona fide cases can be buried among the erroneous, and vice versa.

"There are instances of the most astute diagnostic skill and examples of the most dismal ignorance in the medical handling of pesticide poisoning."

She gave as an example the case of a young boy who had been applying an organic phosphate pesticide all day. He developed symptoms of poisoning. He was sent home twice in the course of several hours by the same physician—once with a tranquilizer for medication.

"The second time he came for medical help," Dr. West said, "the label from the chemical was presented to the physician, who sent him home again with several atropine pills, a first aid recommendation on some labels but an entirely inadequate treatment. The boy died during the night at home, still in his contaminated work clothes."

Rachel Carson, in her best seller *Silent Spring*,[7] made the world aware of the potential dangers of pesticides. For an all-too-brief period, there was a great public outcry for stricter laws and controls. Then reassuring books and articles flooded the market—most of them sponsored by pesticide manufacturers. Rachel Carson was accused of being a sensationalist, and the public settled back into apathy.

But even a cursory search of the scientific literature by an objective researcher shows that for every reassurance, there is a frightening contradiction.

In one year, United States farmers use an estimated 175,826,000 pounds of insecticides, averaging $250 worth per farm.[8] There are 500 chemical compounds used in more than 54,000 formulations for pest control alone.[9] Total pesticide sales were up 37 percent between 1964 and 1966. Domestic use of pesticides was up an estimated 15 percent in 1968 over 1967.[10]

Pesticides certainly have proved their economic worth. In the United States, some 10,000 species of insects are classed as public enemies. Of these, several hundred species are particularly destructive, and require some degree of control. The estimated cost of insect-control measures to protect our food and fibers is $704 million a year.

"Without insecticides," according to Agricultural Research Division entomologist C. H. Hoffman and Chief of the Stored Product Insect Research Branch L. S. Henderson, both of the United States Department of Agriculture, "production of livestock would soon drop about 25 percent and production of crops about 30 percent. Food prices might then go up as much as 50 to 75 percent and the food still not be of high quality."[11]

The fact that farmers are producing more then they can sell, killing beef and dumping milk to raise prices, is beside the point.[12] The real question is whether the price we are paying for insecticides may be cancer, birth defects, liver diseases, and even mental illness.

The age of organic pesticides began with DDT, still the most widely known and used pest killer. It combines chlorine with carbon and hydrogen. It is manufactured from chlorine (a deadly gas), benzene (a leukemia-causing agent), and alcohol (toxic to the liver), which react and combine to form the DDT molecule.

DDT was first described in 1874 by the German chemist Othmar Zeidler. Its insecticidal value was recognized in 1939 by Paul Mueller, a scientist working for the Geigy Dye Company in Basel, Switzerland. The Swiss potato crop was threatened that year by the Colorado potato beetle, and the company gave Dr. Mueller a sample of DDT for testing. The beetle was exterminated, and the value of DDT against other insecticides was heralded. Dr. Mueller's work won him the Nobel Prize in 1948.

The Geigy Company shipped samples of DDT to the United States for testing in 1942. The good results soon led to the importing of the insecticide. At first it was used only for the Armed Forces, but after World War II it was unleashed on the general market. DDT can now be found in the bodies of everyone reading this book.[13]

Penguins in Antarctica, elk on the high slopes of North America, oysters in Chesapeake Bay, and the owl in your attic—all now have DDT or traces of some other lethal pesticide in their systems. Ducks, bald and golden eagles, deer, perch, and shellfish—in fact, probably every living creature on this earth—even those separated from farmers by thousands of miles, by depths of oceans, by mountains and clouds, have pesticides in their flesh.

Pesticides used to control harmful insects are washed into streams or lakes, where they are absorbed by tiny plankton, which are eaten by small fish, which are eaten by bigger fish, which are eaten by birds, which in turn may be eaten by other creatures.

For example, E. G. Hunt, of the California Department of Fish and Game, Sacramento, described startling results at Clearlake, California, where pesticides were used to control gnats. Residue levels of the pesticides in the lake area after thirteen months showed 10 parts per million in plankton, 903 parts per million in smaller fish, 2,690 parts per million in carnivorous fish, and 2,134 parts per million in the fat of fish-eating birds. This represented nearly a 100,000-fold increase of harmful chemicals in fish-eating birds.[14]

Except for a few cannibals in remote parts of the world (they too probably have pesticides in their flesh), man is at the end of the food chain. The dose of pesticide he may receive from eating fish that have eaten smaller fish that have eaten plankton or from game and beef that have eaten insecticide-contaminated feed defies measurement. That is, except for rare instances, no one even tries to measure it.[15]

DDT is toxic to man and beast. How toxic and in what dosage is unknown.[16]

"Although DDT is the most widely used insecticide, its mechanism of action remains uncertain," said Cornell University researchers R. D. O'Brien and F. Matsumara in the General Medical Science's United States Health, Education, and Welfare Department report for 1964–1965. "However, the symptoms of DDT poisoning in animals —which include tremors, convulsions and paralysis—indicate that the poison attacks the central nervous system."

There is no doubt that DDT can cause deaths—the *Journal of the American Medical Association* in 1951 listed twenty-three cases of DDT ingestion, four of which resulted in death.

California, which uses 20 percent of the nation's pesticides, has about 1,000 cases of occupational diseases associated with exposure to them or other agricultural chemicals annually. There are about 150 pesticide deaths a year in the nation. How many children are poisoned by ingestion of pesticides can be gleaned from the fact that in California alone, 3,000 youngsters a year are treated in hospital emergency rooms for pesticide poisoning.[17]

Take the case of a three-year-old California girl who in 1965 was playing near where her parents were picking berries on a farm. She took the cap off a gallon can of 40 percent tetraethyl pyrophosphate, TEPP, a pesticide. She put her finger in the can and then sucked her finger. She immediately vomited, became unconscious, and was dead on arrival at the hospital. The estimated fatal dose of pure TEPP for an adult is one drop orally and one drop on the skin. The child weighed about thirty pounds. The postmortem examination revealed only constriction of the pupils and some lung congestion.[18]

In the state of Washington, a small boy was poisoned almost fatally from parathion that had survived the winter snow and rain after being spilled on the driveway of his home. The youngster had eaten mud pies made from contaminated soil that was found to contain 1 percent parathion.[19]

An eighteen-month-old child of a California agricultural aircraft pilot was found at home in a state of acute respiratory distress, semiconscious, and with pinpoint pupils. In the hospital, she was placed in a resuscitator and treated by a skilled physician for severe organic phosphate poisoning, from which she recovered. On the morning of the illness, her father had come home after applying a highly toxic phosphate ester pesticide. He was reported to have cleaned his boots with paper towels and then thrown the towels into the wastebasket and placed his boots in the bathroom. The child touched either the boots or the paper in the wastebasket.[20]

The preceding cases concerned relatively large amounts of pesticides as poisons, but what of even smaller residues?

A decline in the learning ability of quail given DDT-doctored food was reported by scientists attending a recent American Institute of Biological Sciences meeting.[21] The researcher Dr. Douglas James, Associate Professor of Zoology at the University of Arkansas, said the amount of DDT the birds ate had been considered safe.

Evidently DDT and another class of pesticides, organophosphate compounds, have similar mental effects on man—the worst effects when given in combination. A study at the University of Colorado Medical Center shows that men exposed to these pesticides over a long period have relatively slow reaction times and poor memories, tend to lose their vitality and become unusually irritable.

Reporting at a New York Academy of Sciences Conference on "The Biological Effects of Pesticides in the Mammalian System," Dr. David R. Metcalf, Assistant Professor of Psychiatry and head of the Division of Electroencephalography at the University of Colorado, pointed out that there are few hard neurologic signs of poisoning, such as sensory or motor deficits, but that there is a significant increase in the soft signs, namely: "Persistent, easily demonstrated slowness or thinking and memory deficit.

"We suspect that these findings do not necessarily represent true, irreversible chronic brain disease, but rather a slowly reversible deficit. Unfortunately, these soft signs are not usually given emphasis in neurological examination."[22]

A San Francisco psychiatrist, Dr. Douglas Gordon Campbell, of the University of California Medical School, said in 1963 that in taking a history, every physician should ask if the patient uses sprays in the home, in the garden, or on the job.

"Patients with obscure and seemingly neurotic symptoms are sometimes victims of chronic poisoning by such household sprays." He cited patients who, after "making the rounds of medical doctors," were found to have no organic disease to account for loss of coordination, blurred speech, and other neurological symptoms. "Then they were referred to me. Their symptoms did not seem to be caused by emotional stress. On a hunch, I had a pharmacologist study fatty tissue from one patient. It contained six times the average amount of DDT."[23]

The World Health Organization is very concerned about pesticide residues in food. Members of the WHO Expert Committee on Pesticide Residues and the Food and Agriculture Organization of the United Nations have been gathering reports and opinions of experts from around the world on the subject.[24] In their 1966 report, they said: "Monkeys given DDT orally in a dose of 0.2 mg/kg bodyweight for 7 to 9 months developed symptoms of hepatitis. After a year, the animals showed liver enlargement and hyperglycaemia."

An experimental study was carried out on the effects on man of prolonged ingestion of small doses of DDT in the form of oily solution in capsules or emulsions in milk. Administration was continued for as long as eighteen months. The authors of the study noted that the accumulation of the insecticide in the fatty tissues and the urinary excretion of its metabolite, DDA, were proportional to the dose of DDT ingested. A state of equilibrium was reached after about a year, and the concentration of DDT accumulated in the fatty tissues reached an average of 234 parts per million in subjects who had ingested 35 milligrams of DDT per day. No ill effects were noted.

The WHO report continued: "It has been repeatedly noted that women and cows secrete DDT in the milk. The content of DDT in cows' milk was found to be lower than in human mothers' milk." The World Health Organization concluded from their study of the information available on DDT in man that as much as 0.5 mg./kg. body weight per day for up to twenty-one months showed no effect apart from storage in the fat.

"However," the report said, "the possibility that the latter might have deleterious consequences later in life cannot be ruled out. In addition, it has not been demonstrated that metabolic changes in the liver cells comparable to those observed in the rat do not take place in man."

The World Health group pointed out that some of the metabolites or products of DDT formed by the body should at least be considered.

"At the present time, the Committee remains concerned about the storage of DDT which occurs in all species and about the cellular changes produced in the liver of rats by DDT and by other compounds chemically related to it."

Cousins of DDT in the family of chlorinated hydrocarbons are dieldrin, aldrin, endrin, toxaphene, lindane, methoxychlor, and heptachlor. All have the toxic potential of DDT. Take endrin, for instance:

At 1:00 P.M. on a Tuesday in July, a twenty-seven-year-old woman (we'll call her Mrs. Anderson) walked into the medical department of a United States Naval Medical Research unit because of a "tender" lump on her forehead. At breakfast, apparently, she was in her usual fine state of health. At noon, when she complained of a headache and feeling ill, the patient's husband discovered the prominent lump on her forehead. Neither she nor her husband could explain the swelling.

Upon admission to the hospital, Mrs. Anderson appeared acutely ill, complaining of a headache and nausea. She walked with slight assistance into the examining room. She became easily confused by simple questioning about her morning activities. Within five minutes, she suddenly became speechless and had a convulsion that lasted approximately two minutes. She frothed at the mouth and was confused for two or three minutes after remission of the convulsion. The patient remained semiconscious for fifteen to twenty minutes. After awakening, she could not even remember coming to the naval facility or the subsequent events.

On that same July day, a neighbor of Mrs. Anderson, a Miss Baxter, had a friend, Mr. Cummings, to lunch. About one and a half hours later, Mr. Cummings was found on the floor of his home, "frothing at the mouth, jerking and beating his head on the floor. After a short, semiconscious period, he vomited several times and then felt much better."

At 5:00 P.M., Miss Baxter saw the servant of Mr. and Mrs. Anderson walk from the house, stop, and suddenly fall to the ground with jerking movements, frothing at the mouth. Following several minutes of semiconsciousness, she was taken to a hospital.

Like Sherlock Holmes, the Navy doctors meticulously tracked down the source of the poisoning. It turned out that a servant of the Andersons had made bread the previous evening. Part of the bread had been given by Mrs. Anderson to Miss Baxter, who in turn served it for lunch. Miss Baxter remained in good health despite the fact that she had consumed the same quantity of bread, one roll, as did her friend Mr. Cummings, who developed convulsions shortly after the meal. Mr. Anderson had consumed even larger quantities of bread than his wife on the morning of her seizures. He had no ill effects. How much bread the couple's children ate is unclear, but they ate large quantities of cookies made by the servant at the same time that she made the bread.

The Navy doctors fed part of the bread from the batch eaten by Mrs. Anderson to a rat and two dogs. The rat died within twelve hours. The dogs began to salivate within two hours, then had convulsions, but recovered.

Mr. Anderson recalled that a case containing twelve five-pound sacks of flour purchased in March had been stained. An investigation of flour from one of the stained sacks was made. Flour from the sack was fed to a dog. Within thirty minutes the dog began to salivate. Two hours later, the dog was dead.

The stain proved to be endrin. Ironically, when the blood, serum, and urine of all the persons involved were studied, eight pesticides were found. Why the others who ate the bread did not suffer the convulsions was not clear, but perhaps they were lucky to have missed the "stained" flour or they were resistant to the poison.[25]

In their article about the case in the *Journal of the American Medical Association,* the doctors said: "The toxicity of endrin to humans appears to involve stimulation of the central nervous system. Other than neurological damage secondary to inadequate ventilation during seizures, the only suggestions in the literature of permanent injury directly due to endrin are:

"1. A possible synergism [joint action] of endrin and DDT believed to be responsible for a peripheral neuropathy [nerve damage].

"2. A patient whose course and electroencephalograms indicate brain stem injury.

"No specific findings at autopsy of humans or animals have been reported from acute poisoning, but chronic endrin poisoning may produce liver changes."

How toxic are endrin's cousins aldrin and dieldrin? It depends on where you look. For instance, quoting from the article "A Summary of Work on Aldrin and Dieldrin Toxicity at the Kettering Laboratory," by Dr. Frank P. Cleveland of Cincinnati, in the *Archives of Environmental Health,* 1966:

"It is my opinion that aldrin and dieldrin are neither carcinogenic nor tumorigenic. In a long-term experiment when aldrin and dieldrin were fed in various concentrations to rats, the incidence of tumors in the experimental animals was similar to that of control rats. . . .

"While these substances are highly toxic to insects and experimental animals, no definitive evidence is available that any harm has resulted to mankind. . . ."[26]

From the "Evaluation of Some Pesticide Residues in Food," published by the Food and Agriculture Organization of the United Nations World Health Organization, 1966:

"The primary site of action of aldrin and dieldrin is the central nervous system. CNS stimulation is the cause of death in acute poisoning. Signs of CNS stimulation are also seen after repeated high doses. Repeated doses at lower levels give rise to liver damage, and in this respect, young dogs are more susceptible than older dogs.

"In one long-term feeding experiment in rats there was a general increase in tumor production in the experimental animals at the lower dosage levels as compared to the controls, but the liver was not particularly affected. Liver tumors, however, significantly increased at dosage levels of 10 parts per million in one strain of mice susceptible to the development of these tumors."[27]

The World Health experts, while pointing out that more work is required to determine dieldrin and aldrin's effect on the liver, estimated the acceptable daily intake for aldrin and dieldrin combined in man was 0.0001 mg./kg. per day. It also pointed out that in one study, dieldrin was found in human mother's milk at an average concentration of .006 parts per million.

The danger of pesticides to unborn babies is just beginning to be recognized. Physicians from Baylor University and Texas Children's Hospital, writing in the *Journal of the American Medical Association* on December 18, 1967, on "Maternal Exposures to Potential Teratogens" (causes of birth defect), found that 125 mothers—52 percent of those studied—had been exposed to pesticides during pregnancy. Two infants with major malformations were born to mothers who had first trimester exposures to insecticides and two others to mothers who had later exposures.[28]

The National Cancer Institute is awarding hundreds of thousands of dollars to study the potential cancer-causing properties of old and new pesticides, including fungicides, herbicides, and growth regulators.

"Particular attention is being paid to synergists, compounds that enhance the action of pesticides. The use of synergists could decrease the amount of pesticide needed and thus reduce the problem of pesticide residue in crops," according to the National Advisory Cancer Council. "Synergists appear to act by increasing the toxicity of the pesticides for the insect. However, by a similar process they may also increase the toxicity of pesticides and other suspect cancer-causing chemicals for people. In one study, the effect of synergists, such as piperonyl compounds, on the metabolism of cancer-causing hydrocarbon compound in rats is being studied. Another project is investigating the hazard of the synergist piperonyl butoxide in the diet as associated with the other environmental chemicals— DDT and carcinogenic aromatic amine."[29] These studies are long-term, and no definitive results have been reported.

However, one former government scientist, W. C. Hueper, former Chief of the Environmental Cancer Section, National Cancer Institute, is already convinced of the cancer-causing potential of pesticides. In *Chemical Carcinogenesis and Cancers,* which he wrote with W. D. Conway, he said of chlorinated hydrocarbons such as DDT: "Many of them have distinct hepatotoxic (liver-damaging) properties. Prolonged feeding of rats with DDT and Aramite was followed by the development of hepatomas (liver tumors). While DDT has a minimal tumorigenic effect when given to rats and dogs with the feed in doses highly excessive to those encountered under ordinary exposure conditions, Aramite causes benign and malignant liver tumors in the majority of rats and dogs fed this chemical in the feed at concentrations of 5,000 parts per million. Hepatomas in mice were recently obtained by feeding aldrin and dieldrin, which are chlorinated hydrocarbon pesticides, as well as in rats with methoxychlor.

"The widespread use of aliphatic and aromatic chlorinated hydrocarbons in industry, agriculture and in the home . . . and their distribution as pesticides from airplanes create frequent contacts from various sources with these hepatotoxic agents for members of the general population apart from those associated with the presence of pesticide residues in the foodstuffs of vegetables and animals. Since DDT and other chlorinated pesticides are excreted in the milk, even infants are bound to have some degree of exposure to these agents. They moreover exert a cumulative effect, being stored in various tissue, particularly fat tissue."

The authors pointed out the potential leukemogenic properties, and concluded that the chlorinated hydrocarbons have elicited aplastic anemia and panmyelophthisis (wasting of the bone marrow.)

"Consideration should be given to the possibility that they may have, like other similarly acting agents, such as benzol and ionizing radiation, leukemogenic properties or that such effects are attributable to the solvent vehicles used, which may contain benzol as an impurity."

Since the liver-toxic properties of chlorinated hydrocarbons have been pointed out over and over again, it is not surprising that Dr. D. Coda Martin, President of the American Academy of Nutrition, expressed the opinion that the greater number of hepatitis cases, which have increased so alarmingly in recent years, may be caused by DDT sprayed on the leaves of green vegetables. Another physician, Dr.

Morton S. Biskind, writing in the *American Journal of Digestive Diseases,* pointed out that in a hospital in which technical chlordane was routinely applied for roach control in the kitchen and the food storeroom, an epidemic of hepatitis had persisted among members of the resident staff for more than three years.[30]

The tremendous increase in cirrhosis of the liver has been equated with the increase in alcohol consumption. But alcohol is a solvent, and while it can damage the liver by itself, it may get a great deal of help from the liver-toxic pesticides.

A University of Miami study of pesticide concentrations in fat tissue at human autopsies turned up some startling results. Dr. William B. Deichmann and J. L. Radomski and Alberto Rey, all of the Department of Pharmacology and the Research and Teaching Center of Toxicology at the University of Miami Medical School, found that twice the amount of DDT, DDE, DDD, and dieldrin were in the fat of patients who died of liver or central nervous disease when compared to that in persons who died accidental deaths.

"While there is no evidence that impaired liver function leads to elevated pesticide levels in the body fat, such an eventuality is not remote and indeed would seem metabolically logical," the authors said.

Pesticide levels were essentially "normal" in other diseases of the liver with the exception of one case of amyloidosis (abnormal deposits of protein in organs or tissues) in which all pesticide levels were extremely high—the highest encountered.

In all groups of cancers of the lung, stomach, rectum, pancreas, prostate, and urinary bladder, the level of pesticides was twice as high as normal. Many were complicated by metastatic liver disease, the Miami researchers said.

In all cases of high blood pressure, concentrations of pesticides ranged from two to three times normal, they pointed out.

The authors said they did not believe the high pesticide levels were caused by ingestion, but by household use of pesticides. They said none of the persons autopsied had any occupational connection with pesticides.

Nevertheless, the autopsies did show that there is a relationship between the amount of pesticides in the body and diseases such as cancer, portal cirrhosis, and high blood pressure.[31]

Dr. Kenneth P. DuBois, Professor of Pharmacology at the University of Chicago, also turned up some disquieting results in his laboratory. He found, according to a report in *Medical World News,* August 23, 1968 (a physicians' journal), that pesticides interfere with the effects of medications, nullifying some and making others more toxic. He found, for instance, that barbiturates are counteracted by DDT.

"Such counteraction has generally been written off by physicians as the patient's natural resistance to the drug," Dr. DuBois commented.

DDT and the other chlorinated hydrocarbons, he found, interfere with the actions of drugs by stimulating the production of liver enzymes that ordinarily detoxify chemicals. To assess the enzyme-stimulating effect of a chlorinated hydrocarbon, the Chicago toxicologist gives laboratory rats barbiturates plus the test insecticide. In one study, the amount of sedative that would normally keep a rat asleep for an hour was effective for only ten minutes.

As for the organophosphates that have been proved by other researchers to inhibit cholinesterase, the nerve-impulse-carrying chemical, Dr. DuBois found that even with the permissible levels set by the Food and Drug Administration for food, the organophosphates do indeed inhibit cholinesterase. They also inhibit the nonspecific aliesterases, enzymes that remove drugs and toxic chemicals from the body.

Dr. DuBois found that compounds affected by these enzymes include the muscle relaxant succinylcholine, local anesthetics like procaine, and the insecticide Malathion.

To evaluate the organophosphates' effects on nonspecific esterases in rats and mice, the toxicologist and his staff added varying amounts of insecticide to commercial rodent diet. Then they periodically did autopsies on the rodents during a ninety-day period, and measured enzyme activity in the livers and blood.

The researchers discovered that after the rodents had ingested the permissible levels of insecticide for one week, aliesterase production was inhibited. Two weeks after the researchers substituted an insecticide-free diet, this effect disappeared.

Dr. DuBois did a second set of experiments, and again confirmed his findings. He pointed out that the degree of hazard from the interaction of drugs and pesticides depends upon the margin between the therapeutic dose and the toxic dose of a particular drug. For some drugs, like common headache medications, overexposure would probably do nothing more than prolong the drug's effect, he said. But with drugs like local anesthetics, the pharmacologic and toxic doses are much closer. An ordinary dose of procaine can cause a toxic reaction in a patient with depressed aliesterase activity. The same holds true for the potentially paralyzing succinylcholine.

Man's lethal powers were never more evident than in March of 1968 when sheep began to sicken and die in western Utah. The animals cried red tears, and there was a red discharge from their kidneys. They weakened and lay on the ground, making pathetic efforts to rise but unable to do so. Their attempts gradually grew weaker, and they quivered and died—more than six thousand of them.

Sheepmen accused the Army, which had been testing a nerve gas at its secret Dugway proving grounds in the area. At first an Army spokesman said that the symptoms found in the dying animals "simply do not match those in animals affected by toxic nerve gases."

The head of a Utah State investigating team, Dr. D. A. Osguthorpe, said, "We are reasonably sure these deaths were caused by an organic phosphate compound."

Dr. Mortimer A. Rothenberg, scientific director at Dugway, said that the sheep had suffered symptoms closer to those expected in animals exposed to organic phosphates contained in certain insecticides.

A Washington health official, Dr. B. J. Osheroff, said sheep in Turkey had died after being exposed to a seed-grain preservative that is now outlawed in the United States. He said the sheep in Turkey had similar symptoms.

The sheepmen denied that any spraying had ever been done to their knowledge in some of the areas where the sheep were found dead. The Army said that the nerve gas could not have been released from airplanes over the sheep because the planes had flown in a different direction.[32]

With all the flack flying in both directions, the truth remains that it made little difference whether it was a pesticide or seed-grain preservative or a nerve gas—they may all be made out of organophosphate compounds. In fact, the organophosphate insecticides were first discovered while the Germans were working on a nerve gas.

Organophosphates inhibit the transmission of messages from one nerve to another by interfering with the chemical carrier cholinesterase. That is why it is not surprising that researchers in Melbourne, Australia, reported in the prestigious British medical journal *Lancet* that prolonged exposure to organophosphorus insecticides may cause depressive or schizophrenic reactions, with impairment of memory and of concentration. Measurements of brain waves showed a slowed activity. They concluded: "Organo phosphorous insecticides irreversibly inhibit cholinesterase after lengthy exposure."[33]

Whether the planes carrying the nerve gas flew thirty miles in a different direction to drop their lethal load or whether the farmers had or hadn't sprayed their insecticides for years was also of little relevance. Insecticides in air, water, and earth have traveled hundreds of thousands of miles from the place they were first used, as numerous reports have shown. They may also persist for years in the soil, either in their original form or in broken-down products.

There have not been many measurements of pesticides actually floating in the air. A series of exploratory determinations involving eighteen samples of ambient air collected from four California cities were made in the autumn of 1963. All but two showed measurable amounts of DDT.

According to Dr. Irma West: "It has been postulated that some of the small particles of pesticides released as sprays or dusts when applied to agricultural land may become airborne for some time and distance, eventually producing fall-out.

"There is no known way in which drift of agricultural chemicals can be entirely eliminated, whether applied by ground or aircraft. Drift of tracers used in air pollution studies have been authenticated as far as 22 miles and further distances could be expected depending on the accuracy of the means for sensing tracer chemicals."[34]

The organophosphate insecticides commonly used are: thimet, phosdrin, chlorthion, Malathion, parathion, schradan, TEPP. The list of other bug killers, fungus killers, mite killers, and weed killers is endless and so are their potential dangers—which, unfortunately, are not recognized until too late.

Take the case of the "fire-ant fiasco." A million acres of land were dusted with a concoction of heptachlor designed to remain effective in soil for at least three years. This program continued for over a year before it was revealed that weathering in soil transforms heptachlor into the very persistent and poisonous epoxide. The United

States Food and Drug Administration then banned all use of hepta-chlor on crops.

"It is really frightening," said Lamont C. Cole, Professor of Zoology at Cornell, referring to the "fire-ant fiasco," to realize that ever increasing areas are being treated with new chemicals by persons who do not give a thought for the welfare of—and who are probably unaware of the existence of—the soil organisms on which the very continuation of life depends. . . . I consider it plain irresponsibility to subject the soil biota to hazards like this without intensive pre-liminary research."[35]

But even research for a number of years cannot protect us from agricultural poisoning. Take the case of Captan, used for more than seventeen years to protect seeds against fungus which rots them. Measured by ordinary toxic effects, Captan is mild. The Food and Drug Administration regulations allow a residue of 100 parts per million to be left on raw agricultural products, a limit set in 1958 after experiments with dogs, cattle, and poultry showed no toxic effects from much higher concentrations. In contrast, the residue limit for an insecticide such as chlordane is three-tenths of a part per million.

But Captan, an FDA researcher discovered, has serious genetic effects on animals. Captan's effect on the reproduction of cells is disastrous, according to the experiments of Dr. Marvin Legator of FDA's Cell Biology Research Branch. The chemical inhibits the production of DNA, the basic genetic stuff of life, and breaks up cell chromosomes. Dr. Legator, reporting to a symposium in Wash-ington, said that "Captan is only one of a number of chemicals formerly considered safe that are now suspected of causing genetic damage."[36]

HOW MUCH ARE WE BEING PROTECTED AGAINST HARMFUL AGRICULTURAL CHEMICALS?

Much quoted and reprinted is the work of R. E. Duggan, Deputy Assistant Commissioner for Compliance of the Food and Drug Ad-ministration, and J. E. Weatherwax, on the staff of the FDA Bureau of Science. They studied food from twenty-five different cities during June, 1964, and April, 1966. They selected a diet eaten by American boys sixteen to nineteen years old.[37]

While cautioning about the "limitations of interpreting data from a relatively small number of samples," they said they found that "almost half the lots of raw foods sampled contained pesticide residues, and half of these contained more than one kind." They said that about 3 percent of the samples contained residues in excess of limits or not authorized for use. They rejoiced that most of the food contained residues below the level recommended by law. The study was widely heralded by advocates of greater use of agricultural chemicals. However, the authors said: "Although this conclusion is reassuring, it cannot be said that pesticide residues are not a matter for continued concern."

The World Health Organization points out that "in many cases, the same pesticide is used on a number of different foodstuffs.

"In its evaluation of the available residue data, the FAO Working Party on Pesticide Residues frequently encountered situations where little, if any information, was available on the post-harvest fate of pesticides in many crops.

"For this reason, amongst others, it has been necessary in many instances to take a highly conservative approach and assume that the residues found on the crops at harvest do not undergo any subsequent degradation prior to consumption."

The World Health Organization further states that the organo-chlorine pesticides have been used extensively and have proved efficacious, yet: "Many have been shown to be persistent and cumulative in the animal and human body. In addition, there is evidence that even in low doses they have an effect on the liver.

"The need for a better knowledge of the nature of the terminal residues of some pesticides and for improvement in some of the analytical methods of residues determination . . ." (as set out in the individual monographs).

The joint meeting agreed: "In the course of its work, the FAO Working Party on Pesticide Residues frequently encountered gaps in the information on world patterns of pesticide use, residues resulting from experimental programs, residues found in commerce, and losses of residues during storage and food processing. The results of residue analysis of total diets have also been particularly useful in assessing the probable actual intake of pesticide residues in man."[38]

How is a pesticide approved for use in the United States?

The manufacturers must present their research on the safety of the chemical to the Food and Drug Administration. Pesticide residue tolerances on food are based on the maximum level of pesticide in food that has no discernible effect on test animals, usually rats, during their lifetimes. This "no-effect" level is divided by 100, and sometimes less, to provide a margin of safety. When good agricultural practices allow a lower tolerance, it may be set accordingly. The contribution to the human diet that a particular food makes is also considered in deciding the amount of pesticide residue allowed. Tolerances are therefore reliable to the degree that the test animal and humans react with no more than a hundredfold quantitative difference to the same level of lifelong feeding exposure to the pesticide in question.[39]

Animal-derived foods, which are the major source of pesticides stored in human fat,[40] and fish and game that may contain high levels of pesticides get to our tables without a check anywhere along the line for the chemical.

Dr. John L. Buckley, Chief of the Office of Pesticide Coordination, United States Fish and Wildlife Service, said that of the salmon in Sebago Lake, Maine, more than half of the older fish have stored levels of poisons above that allowed in domestic meat.

Dr. Buckley, who pointed out that the situation was due not to accidental spillage of large amounts of DDT but to the normal and recommended application, questions whether it will be safe for sportsmen to continue to eat fish and other wildlife.

"If there is no choice in using pesticides in agriculture, there is also no choice about adequate monitoring of all our foodstuffs or about setting valid tolerances for pesticides in food," Dr. Irma D. West maintains. She said: "We cannot afford even one mistake which involves all or most of the population."[41]

The American Public Health Association says in its book *Safe Uses of Pesticides,* published in 1968: "What we do not know about pesticides is more important than what we do know. Can pesticides adversely affect the unborn child, the infant or the elderly? What is the effect of insecticides when combined with other so-called inert ingredients? (The term refers only to the effect on the insects.) What is the effect of pesticides on people who are taking prescribed drugs? What is the best way to fight a fire in a warehouse full of pesticides and not have the poisons washed out by water and flushed via storm sewers into nearby streams?"[42]

A corps of 682 FDA inspectors throughout the country does catch pesticide offenses:

• When a terminal manager at Seattle, Washington, observed a pesticide chemical scattered around a shipment of frankfurters, he immediately called the local FDA office. The office called the Washington Department of Agriculture, which sent an inspector out immediately. The residue turned out to be Phorate, an extremely toxic pesticide.[43]

• Squash sent from Pompano Beach, Florida, was picked up in Scranton, Pennsylvania. It contained endrin, which has zero tolerance.[44]

• Corn containing Captan, a pesticide chemical not in conformity with regulations, was picked up in Greenville, New Jersey.[45]

• Celery in Waukesha, Wisconsin, contained parathion and methylparathion in excess of established tolerances.[46]

• Cabbage in Mobile, Alabama, contained Toxaphene, a pesticide.[47]

But what about the food contaminated by pesticides that gets to consumers' tables without detection?

In the spring and summer of 1968, Montana citizens were drinking milk contaminated with the hydrocarbon chlordane. This pesticide is registered only for uses that will not produce residues in milk. It is not supposed to be used on forage for dairy cattle. Yet it was widely used in Montana to kill insects on just such forage.

The recommendation for this use came from an advisory bulletin written by the Assistant State Entomologist and distributed by the Extension Service. When a new monitoring system was instituted in Montana, the contamination was discovered, and hundreds of gallons of contaminated milk were taken off the market.

A staff writer for *Scientist and Citizen,* a publication supported by eminent but worried scientists, Joseph D. Salvia, interviewed Montana farmers, state officials, and scientists. Tracing the problem back from the discovery of the pesticide in milk to the insecticide practices of the previous season, he found that there was no control of materials sprayed by farmers or the commercial applicators they frequently employ. The labels which read "Do not feed treated forage to dairy animals" were ignored, apparently, and the "education" dispensed by presumably expert advisers was contrary to the warnings on the labels.[48]

The chances of discovering high doses of pesticides on food distributed within a state are almost nil. By federal action, according to the FDA Pesticide Residue Program report:

"The FDA's goal was to investigate one percent of the estimated 2,500,000 shipments of raw agricultural commodities in interstate commerce. Twenty-five violative lots were removed from food channels by seizure. Many additional lots bearing illegal residues were destroyed by producers or under state action. Federal actions during the same period included two prosecutions."[49]

Monitoring of pesticides is shared between the Food and Drug Administration and the Department of Agriculture. There have been many instances in which the Department of Agriculture recommended application of a certain chemical, and then the crops were seized by federal Food and Drug inspectors for violations in use of the chemical. Dr. George Kupchik, director of the Environmental Health of the American Public Health Association, said that while division of the duties may be inefficient, he is glad that both the FDA and the Department of Agriculture have the responsibilities. "The FDA favors the consumer and the Department of Agriculture favors the farmer," he said. "If only one department had the power, then either the consumer or the farmer might suffer."[50]

Secretary of Agriculture Orville Freeman told a United States Chamber of Commerce meeting in February, 1968, that he planned to urge Congress to give USDA more authority to deal with water pollution caused by such agricultural operations as pesticide-spraying programs.[51] The Department of Agriculture has reduced its own DDT spraying programs in the past decade about fifty times, from 4.9 million acres in 1957 to just over 100,000 acres. The Agriculture Department and the Food and Drug Administration in February announced that it proposed to reduce the amount of DDT residue it would allow to remain on thirty-six fruits and vegetables.[52]

The congressional watchdog agency's General Accounting Office accused the Agriculture Department of not acting aggressively enough to protect the public from "misbranded, adulterated or unregistered" pesticides in a report sent to Congress in September, 1968. The agency reviewed enforcement actions of the pesticides regulation division of the Agricultural Research Service for the fiscal year that ended June 30, 1967. It also included reports on some cases that were followed into 1968.

The study found that the division had not taken action to prosecute violators of the pesticides control law or to obtain recall of misbranded, adulterated, or unregistered products. Moreover, the agency found the division did not even obtain sufficient data to track defective products to different locations in the country.[53]

In 1965, the FDA realized that it was impossible to maintain zero tolerance for pesticides in milk and some other foods. The advocates of pesticides said that improved testing devices made it possible to show even the most infinitesimal traces of pesticides, and for that reason the zero tolerance was dropped. Opponents of pesticides maintain that the food supply in the United States is so saturated with pesticides that nothing today can remain free of them.

WHAT CAN WE DO ABOUT PROTECTION OF FOODSTUFFS FROM PESTICIDES?

A New Jersey firm was discovered in 1968 to be repacking glycerin, petrolatum, and mineral oil with the same equipment used to manufacture agricultural poisons. Samples of the drugs collected as part of an investigation were found to be adulterated with Malathion, lindane, and DDT. The suspect drug products were being shipped to Veterans Administration facilities.[54] The State of New Jersey and the FDA joined together to prevent such situations again under the "single shield" concept.

We could demand that the state and federal governments produce better testing and monitoring of pesticides and food supplies. But if we do not want to share our food with pests, and if we do not want to pay more for our foods, we must compromise. It takes years to prove a pesticide is absolutely safe.

There are just so many inspectors. Even if we had ten times the number, the chances are that pesticide-contaminated food would still get through.

What is the answer? Better education, of course, but this is not easy. If farmers were to handle pesticides as the government and extension services recommend, they would all have to have college degrees in chemistry and the consciences of saints.

The mixing and handling directions for many pesticides are complicated, especially for farm help, many of whom are illiterate. Such safety precautions as going to a dump and burying the containers are time-consuming, to say the least.

Keeping pesticide-contaminated food, even if one is aware of it, from the market, means a great financial loss, and is much to ask of a man who must scratch a living from the land.

Part of the answer may be found in the suggestion of Dr. George Woodwell, ecologist of the Brookhaven Laboratory, who said on the "Today" show, on television, in 1968, that the great hazards to the future of the human race are still insufficiently recognized. In his opinion, one of the most urgent things that needs to be done is to legislate certain persistent pesticides out of existence and to replace them with pesticides that would effectively control the insect population.

Pyrethrins, for instance, which are produced from a daisylike flower—the pyrethrum—have been effective bug killers for years. They are more expensive than the organochlorine or organophosphate pesticides, but they do not have a residual action. However, they are the only generally available pesticide that can be legally labeled "Nontoxic to Humans and Pets"; and they could be used much more widely.[55]

According to the United States Department of Agriculture, "Pyrethrum is toxic to a wide range of harmful insects, but the toxicity of pyrethrum to man and animals is low. Normally it does not taint materials to which it is applied. These characteristics make pyrethrum an excellent insect deterrent for use around foods and food products."

There are many other nonchemical means of killing insects, from breeding insect-resistant plants to releasing sterile insects that have very effectively cut down the population of their species.

Radiation, light, and harmless-to-man insect viruses have been used with success, and such methods must be developed to replace harmful chemicals.[56]

The fact is that with all our deadly pesticides, we have not destroyed our insect pests. We have just as many bugs today as when we began applying DDT, and the ones we have are rapidly gaining resistance to the chemicals. Furthermore, the Department of Entomology and Economic Zoology at Rutgers reported that "sublethal amounts of certain insecticides will actually increase the rate of reproduction in the female mosquito."[57]

Furthermore, we have succeeded in killing off the natural enemies of these pests. It may be hard to raise sympathy for bats, for instance, but the animals are generally useful and harmless. Insect-eating bats are rapidly being killed off by pesticides. They are among the most susceptible of all animals to the poisons.

Dr. James W. Crow, Professor of Zoology and Genetics at the University of Wisconsin, has listed some serious consequences of the rapid development of resistance:

• The pesticide ceases to be effective . . . larger and larger amounts are needed to control the pest with correspondingly greater upset of the ecological environment and greater risk to man.

• The short useful life of the pesticide means an increasing need for new compounds, so there is less chance for thorough testing and more chance that the compounds will be toxic to man or upsetting to the ecological community.

Dr. Crow suggested that chemical pesticides be applied selectively and used only when really needed. He added that the "hazards to man and to the balance of nature would be made less if a large variety of more selective pesticides could be found. The broader the spectrum of the drug, the greater its risk to other species, including man."[58]

HOW YOU CAN PROTECT YOURSELF FROM IMPROPER USE OF PESTICIDES IN THE HOME[59]

I shudder to think of the many times I sprayed my own kitchen to kill ants, and used insecticide on the rosebushes while my husband watered the lawn, and the children and dog played nearby. So that you won't make the same mistake, or any others with pesticides, here is some advice:

• Read the label and follow the directions. Reread them each time before using. Take the advice seriously. If it says to wear rubber gloves, for instance, do so!

• Use the right pesticide at the right time. Try to pick the least poisonous for the job. Measure accurately. Overdosage seldom kills more insects or diseases.

• Work in a well-ventilated area.

• *Keep pesticides out of reach of the children.* In 1963, for instance, a year-old infant found lindane tablets for a vaporizer under the sink in her home. She ate four to five tablets. She died at the hospital shortly afterward. In the same city, an eighteen-month-old-boy swallowed half a lindane tablet found on the floor of his family car. He died twelve hours later.

• When spraying inside the home to control flying insects, cover all food and utensils; close windows and doors tightly. After spraying, leave the room, close the door. Do not reenter for half an hour or longer. Aquariums, birds, dogs, cats, and other pets must be removed before you spray.

- Outside, remove or cover food and water containers used by pets. Do not contaminate fish ponds or streams.
- *Do not spray with children nearby.*
- Always keep pesticides in their original containers. Make sure they are tightly closed and plainly labeled. Never put a pesticide in an empty food or drink container of any kind.
- Never smoke, drink, or chew gum while handling pesticides.
- Avoid inhaling sprays, dusts, or vapors.
- Have soap, water, and a towel available. Should you spill concentrated pesticide on yourself, wash immediately.
- When you have finished using a pesticide, wash hands and face thoroughly and remove contaminated clothing before smoking or eating. Workclothes should be laundered before they are used again. Watch your shoes. Sometimes they soak up the pesticide, and should be thrown out.
- Store pesticides and pesticide equipment in a locked cabinet or room that is cool, dry, and well ventilated.
- Never store pesticides with or near food, medicine, or cleaning supplies.
- Some pesticides, such as 2, 4-D or Silvex, may have vapors that can be absorbed by nearby containers.
- Be careful in disposing of containers. Do not burn them. Wrap them in several layers of newspaper and place them in a trash can just before the trash is collected. Until then, lock them up.
- Purchase only what you need for one season.
- If you have a special sensitivity to pesticides, consult a physician and, if necessary, avoid further exposure to the offending chemicals.
- If you experience headache, nausea, or blurred vision, or if you accidentally swallow any pesticide, call a physician immediately. Read the label to him. If necessary, go to a doctor's office or hospital, and take the empty container with you.
- Remember to wash all fruits and vegetables—even those that come prewashed in plastic bags—before eating.

2 NOTES

1. Karl H. Kolmeier, Edwin D. Bayrd, "Familial Leukemia: Report of an Instance and Review of the Literature," *Proceedings of the Staff Meetings of the Mayo Clinic,* Vol. 38, Rochester, Minn., Wednesday, November 20, 1963.
2. *New York Times,* November 27, 1967.
3. *Ibid.,* September 28, 1967.
4. *Ibid.,* January 12, 1968.
5. Irma West, M.D., Berkeley, Calif., "Lindane and Hematologic Reactions," *Archives of Environmental Health,* July, 1967, Vol. 15.
6. *Ibid.*
7. Houghton Mifflin, 1962.
8. Jamie L. Whitten, U.S. Congressman (D., Mississippi), November 6, 1967, National Agricultural Chemical Association, Palm Springs, Calif.
9. *Today's Health,* March 1, 1966, special report on pollution.
10. *1968 Outlook Issue of the Farm Cost Situation,* November 22, 1967, a publication of the Economic Research Service, U.S. Department of Agriculture.
11. C. H. Hoffman and L. S. Henderson, "Protecting Our Food," *U.S. Yearbook of Agriculture,* 1966.
12. *Newark Evening News,* March 24, 1968; Association Press report, *New York Times,* March 22, 1968, p. 41.
13. New Jersey Community Pesticide Program release, May 12, 1967. Rachel Carson, *Silent Spring.* Karl H. Kolmeier, Edwin D. Bayrd, *Journal of the American Medical Association,* November 20, 1963; *ibid.,* editorial, December 4, 1967, Vol. 202, No. 10, p. 981.
14. *Science News Letter* 89: 136, February 26, 1966.
15. Irma West, M.D.
16. R. D. O'Brien and F. Matsumara, National Institutes of Health, General Medical Sciences, HEW report, 1964–65.
17. Irma West, M.D., "Pesticides as Contaminants," *Archives of Environmental Health,* November, 1964, Vol. 9, p. 631.
18. *Ibid.*
19. *Ibid.*
20. *Ibid.*
21. Douglas James, Ph.D., American Institute of Biological Sciences meeting, August 20, 1965.
22. David Metcalf, M.D., New York Academy of Sciences Conference, "The Biological Effects of Pesticides in the Mammalian System," May 2–5, 1967.
23. *Medical World News,* June, 1963.
24. World Health Organization, Food and Agriculture Organization, United Nations, meeting in Geneva, November, 1966.
25. Yank Coble, M.D.; Paul Hildebrandt, D.V.M.; James Davis, Ph.D.;

Frank Raasch, M.D.; August Curley, M.S., *Journal of the American Medical Association,* November 6, 1967, Vol. 202, No. 6. Names of patients are fictitious.

26. Frank P. Cleveland, M.D., Cincinnati, "A Summary of Work on Aldrin and Dieldrin Toxicity at the Kettering Laboratory," *Archives of Environmental Health,* 1966.

27. "Evaluation of Some Pesticide Residues in Food," Food and Agriculture Organization of the United Nations, World Health Organization, 1966.

28. James J. Nora, M.D.; Audrey H. Nora, M.D.; Robert J. Sommerville, M.D.; Reba M. Hills, M.D.; and Dan G. McNamara, M.D., "Maternal Exposure to Potential Teratogens," *JAMA,* December 18, 1967, Vol. 202, No. 12.

29. *Progress Against Cancer,* 1966, report by the National Advisory Cancer Council.

30. Booth Mooney, *The Hidden Assassins* (Chicago, Follett, 1966), p. 107.

31. W. B. Deichmann, Ph.D.; J. L. Radomski, Alberto Rey, Department of Pharmacology, University of Miami Medical School, "Retention of Pesticides in Human Adipose Tissue—Preliminary Report," *Industrial Medicine and Surgery,* 37:3, p. 218–219, March, 1968.

32. *New York Times,* March 23, 1968.

33. S. Gerson, M.B., and F. H. Shaw, Ph.D., University of Melbourne and Prince Henry Hospital, Melbourne, Australia, *Lancet,* 1:1371–1374.

34. Irma West, M.D., "Pesticides as Contaminants," *Archives of Environmental Health,* November, 1964, Vol. 9.

35. Lamont Cole, Ph.D., "Pesticides: A Hazard to Nature's Equilibrium," *American Journal of Public Health,* January, 1964, Vol. 54, No. 1, pp. 30–31.

36. *Science News Letter,* June 17, 1967, Vol. 91.

37. R. E. Duggan, J. E. Weatherwax, "Survey of Pesticides in Food," *Science,* September 1, 1967, Vol. 157, No. 379.

38. "Pesticide Residues in Food," Food and Agriculture Organization of the United Nations, Geneva, November, 1966.

39. Irma West, M.D., "Pesticides as Contaminants," *Archives of Environmental Health,* November, 1964, Vol. 9.

40. *Ibid.*

41. *Ibid.*

42. *Safe Uses of Pesticides,* American Public Health Association, 1968.

43. *FDA Papers,* July–August, 1967, p. 37.

44. *Op. cit.,* July–August, 1967, p. 38.

45. *Op. cit.,* October, 1967, p. 29.

46. *Op. cit.,* February, 1967, p. 30.

47. *Op. cit.,* February, 1967, p. 30.

48. Joseph Salvia, *Scientist and Citizen,* October, 1968, St. Louis, Mo.

49. Report: "FDA's Pesticide Residue Program," U.S. Department of Health, Education, and Welfare, Food and Drug Administration, p. 4.
50. Dr. George Kupchik, taped interview, February 26, 1968.
51. Orville Freeman, Secretary of Agriculture, U.S. Chamber of Commerce meeting in Washington, D.C., February, 1968.
52. *Ibid.*
53. *New York Times,* September 17, 1968.
54. *New Jersey Journal of Pharmacy,* August, 1968, p. 10.
55. Tom Bogaard, chemist and General Manager of Kenya Pyrethrum Co., interview with author, January, 1968.
56. "Protecting Our Food," *Yearbook of Agriculture,* 1966, p. 29; *Medical Tribune,* March 7, 1968; p. 23; *Science News Letter,* 85:377, June 13, 1964.
57. *News Views,* College of Agriculture and Environmental Sciences, Rutgers University, New Brunswick, N.J., January, 1968.
58. University of Wisconsin News and Publication Service, February 2, 1966.
59. "Safe Uses of Agricultural and Household Pesticides," U.S. Department of Agriculture Handbook No. 321. William B. Deichmann, Ph.D., *Industrial Medicine and Surgery,* April, 1967. *Safe Uses of Pesticides,* American Public Health Association, prepared by the Subcommittee on Pesticides, 1968. "A Guide to Safe Pest Control Around the Home," New York State College of Agriculture, Cornell Miscellaneous Bulletin 74.

3
Your Food—
Plus What?

A DOCTOR'S DAUGHTER SAT DOWN to breakfast one morning and, without drinking a beverage or eating another food, took a spoonful of crisp cornflakes. She put them in her mouth, and swallowed. Within minutes, her uvula, the piece of flesh that hangs down in the back of the throat, swelled. It took great effort for her to move her limbs, and she felt extremely fatigued.

An allergist tested her skin for sensitivity to corn, cow's milk casein, cow's milk lac albumin, but she showed no allergic reaction.

The source of her sudden spell of illness remained a mystery until, one day, she sat down to supper and took a bite of reconstituted dehydrated potatoes. She suffered the same attack of throat swelling, extreme weakness, and fatigue. Again the allergist tested the patient's skin, this time with potato extract. The results were again negative.

Puzzled by the young woman's symptoms, the doctor examined the labels of the box of cornflakes and the box of potatoes. The cornflakes the doctor's daughter had ingested had been treated with BHA (butylated hydroxyanisole) to preserve freshness. The package of potatoes the young woman ate listed BHT (butylated hydroxytoluene, a relative of BHA) as a preservative and antimold agent. All the girl's symptoms disappeared when she stopped eating foods that contained BHA and BHT.[1]

A middle-aged man came to the Headache Clinic at Montefiore Hospital in the Bronx, New York, because he suffered from severe headaches on Thanksgiving, Christmas, and New Year's Day. The possibility of a psychological cause, of course, was strong because on these occasions he always ate and drank a lot and his mother-in-law always came for dinner. The main dish was inevitably turkey.

It took several years to pinpoint the turkey as the indirect cause of the headaches. It turned out that the patient was allergic to penicillin; and, although he lived in New York, he always ate New Jersey turkeys that had been fed on a mash containing penicillin.[2]

From the fertilizer put on the ground to the preservative listed on the container, there are hidden substances in your food. You may not eat the proverbial "peck of dirt," but remember that every year you eat more than three pounds of *intentional* chemical additives with your meals.[3]

The use of additives in foods made in the United States rose from 419 million pounds in 1955 to 661 million pounds in 1965—a gain of 58 percent in ten years. Experts estimate that the use of food additives will climb to 852 million pounds by 1970 and 1.03 billion pounds in 1975.[4]

Most food additives are believed to be safe in the dosages set by the Food and Drug Administration, although many scientists—including former FDA Commissioner James L. Goddard—say we really don't know.[5]

A number of additives, as shown by the two cases mentioned at the beginning of the chapter, may cause an allergic reaction. In fact, Dr. Orval R. Withers, Clinical Professor of Medicine at the University of Kansas Medical School, estimates that about 10 percent of the population has a tendency to become sensitive, in the course of a lifetime, to some food, drug, or antibiotic found in food.[6]

Chemicals are known to cause cancer. The late Dr. Margaret Kelly, pharmacologist at the National Cancer Institute, proved that newborn mice are as sensitive to chemical carcinogens as they are to viral carcinogens.[7]

The fact that a chemical has been determined "safe" is no assurance. One has only to recall the sleeping pill Thalidomide, considered so safe that it was sold without a prescription in more than forty countries. It was widely used because it had no "hangover effect" the next day. More than seven thousand babies in West Germany alone were born with severe defects as a result of the "safe" sleeping pill.

It may be that all our food additives are perfectly safe, but the odds are against it. Dr. Stephen Lockey, a Pennsylvania allergist, has been collecting hundreds of cases of allergic reactions to hidden drugs in foods and medicines. He has compiled a list of 2,764 intentional food additives.[8]

Chemicals are added to food for a variety of reasons:

AS COLORING AGENTS—The natural coloring materials in foods may be intensified, modified, or stabilized by the addition of natural coloring materials, certified food dyes, or derived colors. These chemicals that enhance the appearance of food are considered important for the "esthetic value they add and the psychological effect they have on our food consumption habits."

AS ANTISPOILANTS—Chemicals may be used to help prevent microbiological spoilage and chemical deterioration. There is a growing preference for these food additives.

AS FLAVORING AGENTS—In number—2,112—flavor additives probably exceed all other intentional chemical food additives combined. Of these, 502 are natural and 1,610 synthetic.

AS AGENTS TO IMPROVE FUNCTIONAL PROPERTIES—Chemicals in this classification act as thickening, firming, and maturing agents, or affect the colloidal properties of foods such as jelling, emulsifying, foaming, and suspension. Calcium salts, for example, help the texture of canned tomatoes.

AS PROCESSING AIDS—Sanitizing agents, metal binding compounds, antifoaming agents, chemicals that prevent fermentation, and chemicals that remove extraneous materials are grouped in this classification. Examples are silicones to prevent foam formation in wine fermentation, and citric acid to combine with metals to prevent oxidative rancidity.

AS MOISTURE CONTENT CONTROLS—Chemicals sometimes are used to increase or decrease the moisture content in food products. For instance, glycerin is approved for use in marshmallows as a humectant to retain soft texture. Calcium silicate is frequently added to table salt to prevent caking due to moisture in the air.

AS ACID-ALKALINE CONTROLS—Various acids, alkalis, and salts may be added to food to establish a desired pH, or acid-alkaline balance. Phosphoric acid in soft drinks and citrate salts in fruit jellies are examples of this chemical control of acid-alkaline balance.

AS PHYSIOLOGIC ACTIVITY CONTROLS—The chemicals in this

group are usually added to fresh foods to serve as ripeners or anti-metabolic agents. Examples of applications for this purpose are ethylene, used to hasten the ripening of bananas; and maleic hydrazide, used to prevent potatoes from sprouting.

AS NUTRITION SUPPLEMENTS—The use of vitamins, minerals, and amino acids has become widespread. The enrichment of cereal foods alone provides 12 to 23 percent of the daily supply of thiamine, niacin, and iron, and 10 percent of riboflavin recommended for human consumption.

The consumer is unaware that these additives are in the products in the supermarket. Take some random examples:

General Mills' Rice Provence contains among its many ingredients, monoglycerides and diglycerides (emulsifiers), monosodium glutamate (flavor enhancer), butylated hydroxyanisole, butylated hydroxtoluene, propyl gallate (antioxidants), propylene glycol (carrier), and citric acid (sequestering agent.)[9]

General Foods' Whip 'n Chill dessert mix contains sodium caseinate (texturizer), propylene glycol monostereate (emulsifier), acetylated monoglycerides (emulsifier), sodium silico aluminate (anticaking agent) and two preservatives, artificial coloring, artificial and natural flavorings, and a number of other ingredients.

Sara Lee's frozen cherry cream cheesecake contains sorbic acid (preservative) and ascorbic acid (antioxidant). General Foods' Awake, a frozen concentrate for imitation orange juice, contains citric acid (acidulant), gum arabic (thickener), carrageenin (stabilizer), vitamins A, B1 and C (nutrient supplements), and calcium phosphate (anticaking compound), in addition to flavors and artificial colors.

Without additives, Rice Provence, Whip 'n Chill, and Awake would be utterly impossible. Without additives, Sara Lee's cherry cream cheesecake, because of limited shelf life, might be commercially unfeasible.[10]

HIDDEN ANTIBIOTICS

In considering the health effects of additives, it is necessary to go back to the beginning—the unintentional additives added to our food when a pesticide, fertilizer, or growth regulator is used, as discussed in the previous chapters.

The next type of additive to be watched for does not come in a factory-processed human food, but in one producing feed and therapeutics for animals.

T. C. Byerly, speaking before a National Academy of Sciences Conference, in 1967, on "The Use of Human Subjects in Safety Evaluation of Food Chemicals," said:

"As an example of the varied chemicals used in livestock production, I checked the advertisements in *Poultry Meat,* September, 1966. Twelve firms advertised the following kinds of products: coccidiostats, histostats (against Histomonads in turkeys), fungistats, prophylactic antibiotics, a tranquilizer stated to prevent aortic rupture, an enzyme preparation to suppress manure odor, a chemical to mask such odor, an anioxidant to protect Vitamin A in feeds. Dips, disinfectants, detergents and sanitizers."[11]

One of the most controversial additives in this category is antibiotics. New data have shown that food animals may retain some antibiotics for as long as forty-seven days and that medication can persist even longer in the kidneys of treated animals. The withdrawal periods established under the Food Additive Amendments of 1958 to ensure that there will be no unsafe residues or no residues of antibiotics have been found impractical.[12]

Why should minute doses of antibiotics in the food we eat bother us? Not only are some persons allergic to the antibiotics used; lavish use of the medications could favor the growth of drug-resistant germs.

As always, we are told we must balance the benefit against the danger.

Since 1950, antibiotics have been widely used at low levels in feeds to stimulate the growth of young chickens and pigs. They are also used to increase egg production. Antibiotics are administered at higher levels in feed or drinking water or by injection in the treatment of various diseases of livestock. In fact, an estimated 2.7 million pounds a year of antibiotic feed additives are used in the United States.[13]

In early experiments, low-level antibiotics usually resulted in at least 10 percent greater weight during early growth and 11 percent greater efficiency in feed utilization. In recent experiments, the response to antibiotics has been less. Untreated growth is as rapid and as efficient as in antibiotic-fed animals.[14]

Many veterinary scientists believe livestock yields would be reduced substantially if antibiotics were withheld, but others contend that, because resistance is engendered, antibiotics in feeds are self-defeating in the long run. C. D. Van Houweling, D.V.M., director of the Bureau of Veterinary Medicine of the Food and Drug Administration, wrote in *FDA Papers,* September, 1967: "It is disquieting to the FDA, among others, that no hard answers are available concerning the use of about 2.7 million pounds of antibiotics annually in medicated feeds. The FDA believes it would be imprudent to persist in such a widespread application without an attempt at systematic understanding of the consequences to the microbial environment of man and animals.

"The seriousness of antibiotic resistance was illustrated several years ago at the very place where antibiotics are so heavily relied on. Hospitals became alarmed over their inability to retain control, with penicillin, over staphylococcal infections. In many cases, overconfidence in penicillin had led to relaxed antiseptic discipline, but it was discovered, in addition, that staphylococcus was manifesting the ability to resist penicillin. The micro-organisms produced an enzyme, penicillinase, which nullified the drug.

"Avoiding unnecessary exposure to antibiotics is prudent not only because of the resistance problem but also because persons and animals can become allergic to antibiotics. Their role in therapy may be precluded if hypersensitivity develops. If used unwittingly in such cases, an antibiotic can elicit a fatal reaction."

Dr. Van Houweling said it is easy to forget that only a sketchy picture exists of the life of the bacteria in the intestines. The normal tract has more than two hundred species, and a balance must exist between them to keep intestinal illness at bay.

"Information is also lacking on the mechanism by which antibiotics encourage growth," Dr. Van Houweling said. "Some observers are uncertain that there is a clear advantage in using medicated feeds. They report an unfavorable effect on natural mechanisms of immunity. One observer asserts that poultry disease, enteric infections in pigs and calves and mastitis in dairy cattle are a greater problem today than they were before the advent of antibiotics."

He concluded, quoting the words of a veterinary journal editorial: "The chance of resistance in human bacterial pathogens having an animal origin is quite good because use and distribution of antibiotics [are] so widespread."

The FDA in 1968 proposed revoking the residue tolerance of chlortetracycline and oxytetracycline in fish and poultry. Chlortetracycline is cleared for application to raw poultry, fish, scallops, and shrimps to retard spoilage with tolerances of seven parts per million on uncooked poultry and five parts per million on raw marine products.

Certain antibiotics of the tetracycline class have been found to stain baby teeth, cause sensitivity to light, skin rash, and liver toxicity,[15] as well as interference with kidney function.[16] The residue tolerances for tetracyclines in raw poultry and fish were established on the basis that residue in poultry would be destroyed in cooking and residue in raw seafood would not constitute a danger. However, after years of use, it was discovered this was not true.

Penicillin reactions have produced more than one thousand deaths in the United States. According to Dr. Murray C. Zimmerman of Whittier, California, writing in the *Archives of Dermatology:* "The reactions are increasing steadily in both frequency and severity. Part of this increase may be due to allergies developed by the daily exposure of millions of Americans to penicillin-contaminated dairy products."[17]

Penicillin is widely used to treat mastitis, an inflammation of the udder in cows. At any given time, more than 25 percent of the 26 million cattle in the United States have mastitis. Ironically, although antibiotic treatment has been shown to eliminate one kind of mastitis, in frequent cases it is replaced by another kind of infection.[18]

There is no doubt that penicillin used to treat sick cows can affect the users of dairy products. Two cases of Dr. Zimmerman's prove that.

One, a young man who had an injection of penicillin, developed severe hives, arthritis, arthralgia, and fever. For sixty days, his symptoms were partially suppressed by massive doses of corticotrophin, prednisolone, antihistamines, epinephrine, calcium, and various other medicines. He continued to have hives for nine weeks until he was given Neutrapen, a drug that neutralizes penicillin. He cleared up almost completely within forty-eight hours.

However, every time he ate dairy products, he had mild, repeated attacks of his symptoms. At the request of Dr. Zimmerman and another physician, the patient ate dairy products in their presence, and the hives soon followed. At little as eight ounces of milk brought on the attack.

If the patient was given Neutrapen in advance, he was able to eat dairy products without symptoms. One time, the doctors gave the patient an injection of plain salt water which the patient thought was Neutrapen. Upon eating dairy products, the patient again had the hives, confirming the presence of penicillin allergy connected with dairy products.

Another of Dr. Zimmerman's patients, a thirty-five-year-old woman, received a penicillin injection for an industrial injury. She had hives, although she had no previous allergic history. She was given Neutrapen and her hives cleared. She was told to avoid dairy products. A short time later, she had a severe outbreak of hives but denied all penicillin exposure. She finally admitted eating roquefort cheese three hours before the hives began, saying: "I didn't think you could find out so easily that I cheated a little bit."

Government scientists and dairymen, of course, have been aware of the problem of penicillin in dairy products and they have taken steps to cut the amount. Milk is supposed to be thrown out for seventy-two hours after a cow receives penicillin. In 1957, the estimate was that 11 percent of the milk had penicillin in it. In 1966, it was down to 3 percent.[19]

In addition, Dr. Frank Rosen, a Maplewood, New Jersey, allergist, and former president of the New Jersey Allergy Foundation, said that as much as three hundred units of antibiotics per gram of tissue have been found in beef. He said that one or two units per gram is enough to cause a reaction and that ten units par gram can cause death in a person "exquisitely sensitive."

The United States does not require antibiotics to be sold to farmers on a prescription basis. The drugs are brought directly from salesmen, and then are administered by the farmer either in the feed or by injection.

About the same time that antibiotics came into use in animal feed, two arsenicals also appeared as feed additives. They are 3-nitro-4-hydroxyphenylarsonic acid and arsanilic acid. When fed without an antibiotic to young, growing animals, either of these compounds affects the growth and efficiency of feed utilization in the same manner as an antibiotic.

Quoting from the statement of Dr. H. R. Bird, of the Department of Poultry Husbandry, University of Wisconsin, in the *American Journal of Clinical Nutrition,* May–June, 1961:

"There is no evidence that organic arsenicals are carcinogenic in any species. But because their use in feeds adds a fraction of a part per million of arsenic to food materials which already contain a trace of arsenic and because a proportion of the fraction of a part per million is presumably inorganic arsenic, and because large quantities of inorganic arsenic applied to the skin for long periods are believed to cause cancer, the Delaney Amendment (1958) prohibits the organic arsenicals in feeds. However, users having prior sanctions can continue to use it by virtue of the 'grandfather clause' [that legal exception exempting violators accustomed to procedures not previously forbidden]. Thus the users with prior sanctions have a sort of monopoly on this alleged method of undermining the public health."[20]

Incidentally, Dr. W. C. Hueper, former Chief of the Environmental Cancer Division, National Cancer Institute, said: "Arsenicals in foods have been responsible for a considerable number of chronic arsenic poisonings among consumers of contaminated foodstuff—especially wine. Recent reports from Germany indicate that vineyard workers who drank wine contaminated with considerable amounts of arsenical pesticides developed, more than ten years after cessation of exposure to these agents, cancer of the skin, lung and liver. These observations on dietary arsenic cancer parallel those previously recorded from Germany and Argentina where [there was] consumption of drinking water polluted with arsenicals. Such neoplastic sequelae have repeatedly been observed after a medicinal consumption of arsenicals. Airborne arsenic in urban atmospheres and arsenical residues in tobacco smoke are among frequent contributors to human exposure."[21]

HIDDEN HORMONES

Ranking in controversy with antibiotics, in animal feed and production, are the female estrogen hormones. The practice of injecting pellets of diethylstilbestrol under the skin of chickens and turkeys was permitted by the FDA from 1947 to 1959. Because it was found that human consumers were getting the residue of the hormone in their poultry, this practice was stopped.

However, permission was given to use diethylstilbestrol as a feed additive for cattle and dienestrol diacetate as a feed additive for chickens. Conflicting reports of whether there is a residue in edible tissues of poultry and beef have been made,[22] as well as conflicting reports about the constant ability of the hormone to affect growth.[23]

From *Agricultural Research,* a publication of the United States Department of Agriculture, March, 1968: "Scientists are attempting to find why growth stimulants markedly improve the performance of yearling steers so they gain weight as rapidly as young calves."

That the growth stimulants save cattle producers money is well established. Research dating back fifteen years has shown repeatedly that gains go up about 15 percent and feed efficiency is improved 12 percent, if steers are properly treated with diethylstilbestrol—stilbestrol for short. Treated cattle also produce meat with more protein and less fat.

"Today, about 80 percent of the fed cattle marketed have been treated with stilbestrol. Despite the clear benefits from treatment, scientists have known very little about how the growth stimulants work."

They do know that even minute amounts of estrogen are powerful. Four small children, three boys and one girl, showed signs of marked pigmentation of the nipples and areolas of the breast. The girl also developed pubic hair and vaginal bleeding. In three cases, the substance containing estrogen was a hair lotion; in one case, an ointment.

The report, which appeared in a Swiss medical journal and the *Journal of the American Medical Association,* said that forty cases described in the literature showed wide variations in the amount and mode of application of estrogen-containing substances. The month after discontinuation of the substances, all symptoms gradually receded in the children. The article firmly stated: "Administration of estrogen-containing substances to children should be avoided.[24]

Cancer of the kidneys in male hamsters and castrated female hamsters has been produced with implants of diethylstilbestrol.[25]

Here is what Dr. Hueper has to say on the use of diethylstilbestrol for accelerated fattening of food animals:

"Practical experience has shown that farmers and poultry men do not always insert the estrogen pellets in parts [neck] of animals which usually are discarded, but in parts which are eaten; they implant more than one pellet of 15 mg. of estrogenic chemical, and they sell their animals for human consumption before the safety period of six weeks after implantation has elapsed, while cattle estrogenized by both routes are slaughtered, as a rule, without observing a 60-hour estrogen-free waiting period. It is noteworthy, moreover, that at least one synthetic estrogen, tri-p-anisolcholeroethylene, is stored in the human fat tissue after oral administration and thus appears to be most objectionable from a carcinogenic viewpoint because of its prolonged effect.

"Since members of the general population may have appreciable contacts with exogenous estrogens from other sources (medicines, cosmetics, production of estrogens, handling of estrogenic preparations, preparation and handling of estrogenic feed), such exposures or the possibility of such exposures, especially when they are avoidable and not essential or justified, appear to be objectionable even if it is still controversial whether or not estrogens cause cancers in man.

"It is rather remarkable that biologically potent chemicals which are obtainable for medicinal reasons only on prescription by a licensed physician can be used freely in large quantities by persons without any proper training concerning the potential health hazards associated with the handling and consumption of large quantities of these hormonal substances. Such practices are difficult to control adequately on a nationwide basis in foodstuffs handled in interstate and intrastate commerce by thousands of individual producers in quantities of several million animals."[26]

ADDITIVES IN FOOD PROCESSING

When food processors are criticized about adding chemicals to their products, they always point with pride to the vitamins they put in food. Indeed, the addition to milk of vitamin D has practically wiped out rickets.

Furthermore, it now appears that too much of a good thing can be harmful, which is the phrase defenders of food chemicals always use in defense. Dr. Helen Taussig, former president of the American Heart Association, says there is strong evidence suggesting that prolonged intake of excess vitamin D can lead to heart disease, blood-vessel damage, and even birth defects.

The common feature of these disorders is calcification of the heart valves, sometimes accompanied by narrowing of the aorta, the major artery leading from the heart. Vitamin D has long been known to speed the body's production of calcium, and may sometimes overdo it. Many children who are born with defective hearts—as opposed to those who develop them later—also suffer from mental retardation.

In a report to the American College of Physicians, Dr. Helen Taussig said that early evidence implicating vitamin D came from England in the early 1950's. The British were then supplementing each quart of milk with 1,000 units of vitamin D, and were also adding it to cereals, bread, and flour. Children born of mothers nourished on this food often had unhealthy calcium deposits and a peculiar facial expression indicative of subnormal IQ.

When the extra vitamin D was taken out of the foodstuffs and reduced by about half in the milk, the number of babies born with these defects fell sharply. They are still born frequently in this country with such defects.

In 1966, National Institutes of Health scientists first showed that vitamin D crosses the placental barrier.

Scientists at the National Heart Institute and the National Dental Institute are now collaborating on studies of the effects of vitamin D. The dentists have noticed that malocclusion is more common today than formerly, and seems to be increasing in frequency. They believe the increase may be due to too much vitamin D.[27]

Nutritionists recommend 400 units of vitamin D per day during pregnancy. But some pregnant women taking vitamin pills and vitamin-enriched milk often consume 2,000 to 3,000 units daily.

Dr. Robert E. Cooke of Johns Hopkins University reported finding fourteen to sixteen cases of children with serious arterial lesions from overcalcification of the blood vessels related to excess vitamin D in their mothers' diets.

Dr. Taussig believes that some people inherit a natural resistance to rickets and that it is these people who are made sick when extra doses of the vitamin are added to their diets. Her suspicion is the stronger because the disorder often seems to run in families.

"With our present state of knowledge," Dr. Taussig warned, "this is a good time to remember that some is good but more is not necessarily better. People who need vitamin D should, of course, have it, but there is no need to make it part of everyone's routine."

If too much vitamin D is bad, too little vitamin A is unhealthy.

An unexplained and "shocking" incidence of probable vitamin-A deficiency has been discovered in Canada, one of the better-fed nations in the world, according to a Canadian nutrition scientist in a report made at the Western Hemisphere Nutrition Congress in Puerto Rico, in August, 1968. The evidence was gathered in autopsy examinations of livers, said T. Keith Murray, Ph.D., Chief of the Nutrition Division, Canadian Food and Drug Directorate. Liver is a storage organ for vitamin A; and a liver seriously depleted of vitamin-A stores is taken as a sign of vitamin-A deficiency.

Postmortem examination of more than a hundred persons ten years of age or older revealed that more than 30 percent of them had no more vitamin A in liver storage than is customarily found in newborn infants.

"Clearly a high proportion of Canadians were in unsatisfactory vitamin-A status at the time of death," he said.

"It is hard to believe that this is entirely a dietary problem. The 'apparent' per capita consumption of vitamin A in Canada is 6800 International Units per day, well above minimum requirements. Even allowing for wastage, cooking losses and uneven distribution it does not seem likely that so many of our population do not get enough vitamin A to maintain their reserves.

"No clear pattern relating low stores to a particular disease has emerged, however, and we suspect that some environmental factor— drugs, pesticides, food additives, etc.—may be reducing the utilization or increasing the metabolism of vitamin A."[28]

BABY FOODS

If any food should be pure and without potentially harmful additives, it should be food that is intended for infants. The World Health Organization has cautioned that baby foods "require separate consideration from all other foods as regards the use of food additives and toxicological risks."

The WHO committee pointed out that infants don't have fully developed systems and cannot eliminate poisons from the body as adults do. In addition, if a baby eats the same concentration of an additive in his food that an adult does, it will result in a higher concentration in his body.

One additive commonly found today in baby foods is sodium nitrite, used to preserve and produce the pink color in cured meats. Nitrites reduce the blood's ability to carry oxygen from the lungs to the body tissues. Nitrates, which are unintentional additives to baby foods (although not to adult foods), become nitrites when intestinal bacteria convert them to nitrites.

An editorial in *The Lancet,* highly respected British medical journal of May 18, 1968, warned of a possibility that under certain circumstances foods preserved with nitrites may combine with amines in the intestinal tract during the process of digestion and with nitro-samines and N-nitroso compounds, most of which have been proved to be strong carcinogens.

A highly respected scientist, Dr. Barry Commoner, Director of the Center for the Biology of the Natural Systems, University of Washington, St. Louis, Missouri, said: "Sufficiently concentrated die-tary nitrate can lead to respiratory failure, and even death." He cau-tioned that infants are particularly susceptible to this hazard because their intestinal bacteria are more likely to include types that convert nitrate to nitrite.

Dr. Commoner, who sounded some of the earliest warnings about the danger from nuclear fallout, said a study of commercial baby food conducted by the Missouri Agricultural Experiment Station showed that certain vegetables—beets and spinach—contained as much as 0.8 percent nitrate.

"At this rate," the biologist calculates, "an infant fed a two-ounce jar of baby food would receive about 40 milligrams of nitro-gen as nitrate." But, he added, "public health officials recommend that infants take in [in] their food and water no more than 12 milli-grams of nitrate nitrogen daily."

Research by European scientists, Dr. Commoner said, places the blame for the excess of nitrates in the food directly on chemical fertilizers. Spinach grown without chemical fertilizer contains less nitrates than spinach grown with it.[29]

Dr. Commoner did not mention the sodium nitrite deliberately added to baby food.

In one brand of meat for infants, the author found ascorbic acid listed as well as sodium nitrite. *The Merck Index,* an encyclopedia of chemicals and drugs, states in the Eighth Edition (1968) that ascor-bic acid should not be formulated with sodium nitrite. The reference is based on Russian scientific work done in 1952 which showed that ascorbic acid makes sodium nitrite more potent. (In some packaged meat for adults, the author has seen ascorbic acid, sodium nitrite, and sodium nitrate listed among the numerous additives.)

Although this author is not aware of any current studies going on, the possibility that nitrates and nitrites may be the indirect cause of "crib deaths" certainly should be investigated. More than 20,000 crib deaths occur annually in the United States, when parents put an apparently healthy child to bed and then find the baby dead some time later. Theories of causes range from undetected heart disease or self-inflicted whiplash injury to infanticide, smothering, and allergy. No one, as yet, has proved a cause.

Too much of another common substance is evidently blithely being added to baby foods. Here is a direct quote from Philip L. White, Secretary of the Council on Foods and Nutrition of the American Medical Association, from the AMA publication *Today's Health,* July, 1968:

"It has been suspected for some time that the sodium content of baby foods is higher than necessary. Salt is added to most baby foods to enhance their flavor. Whether this is done for the benefit of the child or the mother is debatable. Most likely, it is for the mother's benefit, since the baby's taste perception is slow to develop.

"Baby-food manufacturers design their products to be attractive to mothers. If a food item is not acceptable to the mother, she will not use it or will over-react to apparent rejection by the baby and will not buy it again. Therefore, salt is added in fairly heavy amounts to most baby foods. The taste and color are developed to attract the mother while the consistency is developed to accommodate the baby.

"A study of the sodium intake of infants found that infants two months of age received essentially all of their sodium from milk. Infants from five to seven months received about 50 percent of their sodium from milk and 40 percent from vegetables and meat, and eggs (chiefly in prepared baby foods). The average daily sodium intake was just under one gram. Youngsters about one year old derived 60 percent of their sodium from vegetables, meat and eggs and 30 percent from milk. At this age, the usual daily intake of sodium was 1.4 grams. This would seem to be a large amount of sodium.

"Evidence is beginning to accumulate suggesting a relationship between high sodium intake and early development of hypertension (high blood pressure). Studies have demonstrated that high intakes of sodium will hasten the onset of hypertension in strains of animals susceptible to the disease.

"Pediatricians, while not unconcerned about the rather large amount of sodium in the diets of infants, feel that until more convincing evidence of hazard is available, there is little reason to criticize current manufacturing procedures. The infant can excrete the sodium not required in metabolism without apparent difficulty so long as his kidney function is adequate and his water intake is ample. On the other hand, there is little to be gained by giving the infant sodium far in excess of his requirements. This is particularly pertinent since salt is added for flavor only."

Another additive to which young children may be exposed in ice cream, jellies, chocolate drinks, icings, and certain candies is carboxymethyl cellulose. Made from a cotton by-product, it is added as stabilizer. It was in every one of the highly advertised mixes for children to put in their milk that the author found on the supermarket shelves. Carboxymethyl cellulose has been shown to cause cancer in animals.[30]

Fredrick J. Stare, M.D., Professor of Nutrition and head of the Department of Nutrition at Harvard School of Public Health, and Dr. Charles A. Janeway, Professor of Pediatrics at Harvard Medical School, wrote an indignant article that appeared in the prestigious *New England Journal of Medicine,* on September 7, 1967, entitled: "Are All Baby Foods Special Dietary Foods?" They referred to the pending revision of regulations for food of special use by the Food and Drug Administration.

"We are disturbed . . . by the interpretation that may be given those responsible for the enforcement to the definition of Special Dietary Foods which would place ordinary baby foods in this classification.

"There are few cases in which infant tolerances for certain food additives—for example, calcium silicate—are considered to be lower than adult tolerance. These differences do not appear to be valid reasons for classifying all baby foods as special dietary foods, particularly since these situations have been handled quite satisfactorily by the setting of specific tolerances for their use in baby foods under the food additive regulations.

"Those whom we have consulted in the 'baby food' industry contend that the reclassification of baby foods as special dietary-purpose foods would work a hardship on current business practices and serve no advantage to the consumer. Reclassification would probably make necessary certain changes in labeling (for example, it would be necessary to note the source of all ingredients and to specify all flavoring ingredients by their generic names). This would add more copy to labels that are already too small to be read with ease."

To that last statement, as a mother of allergic children, I am distressed that a nutritionist of international renown and a respected pediatrician could make that statement. Certainly, everything that is put into baby-food jars should be described on the label. If necessary, make a bigger label or even a bigger jar.

As for baby foods being under a special dietary protection, a government official answered the article in the *New England Journal* for the following month by pointing out that strained and chopped fruits and vegetables marketed as foods for infants are, in fact, classified as foods for special dietary use and have been so since 1941.

I don't know whether many other doctors agree with the two Harvard physicians, but few mothers would like to see baby foods exempt from the special attention given dietary foods—imperfect as it is—by the Food and Drug Administration.

ARTIFICIAL SWEETENERS

Another additive that affects older children and adults is the artificial sweetener. The use of such chemicals in the United States has climbed from 0.25 million pounds in 1955 to 13 million pounds in 1965, a spectacular gain of 3,900 percent.[31]

About 60 million Americans have taken avidly to low-calorie foods. These include soft drinks, canned fruit, frozen desserts, jellies, salad dressings, and others. Almost all these products contain artificial sweeteners. Liquid diet food also contains such substances.

More than 250 million cases of soft drinks—equivalent to more than six billion 8-ounce bottles of low-calorie beverages—were sold in the United States in 1965. A 6-ounce serving of Coca-Cola contains about 70 calories. Tab, its noncaloric counterpart, contains one calorie.

The first of the artificial sweeteners, discovered in 1879, was saccharin. Pound for pound, it has about three hundred times the sweetness of natural sugar. The newer cyclamates have about thirty times the sweetness of sucrose. Although the cyclamates are much less sweet than saccharin, they have less of the bitter aftertaste.

To make the soft drinks sweetened with artificial flavorings taste less watery compared to those flavored with sugar, many manufacturers add gums as bodying agents, including carboxymethyl cellulose.[32]

How safe, really, are artificial sweeteners?

The National Academy of Sciences, at the request of the Food and Drug Administration, has now appointed a committee to find out.

In 1955, a study, "The Safety of Artificial Sweeteners," conducted by members of the Academy, concluded that there was no evidence to insinuate the "use of nonnutritive sweeteners, saccharin and cyclamate, for special dietary purposes, is hazardous." The report noted that "ingestion of more than 5 grams a day of the cyclamates is capable in some adults of inducing the formation of soft stools."

In the fall of 1964, the *Medical Letter,* published by a group of prominent United States physicians, asserted that excessive use of these sweeteners is against the public interest.

In 1965, Wisconsin Alumni Research Foundation reported after a diet of 5 percent calcium cyclamate for nine months and 95 percent normal nutrition, laboratory rats grew 12 percent less than a control group not receiving the sweetener. When the diet was changed to include 10 percent cyclamate, the rats suffered a growth impairment of 50 percent.

In 1966, FDA researchers studied the sweeteners after Japanese scientists said that birth defects associated with artificial sweeteners were found in experimental animals. Tests to verify this finding, which are expected to take years, are being done at Albany Medical College.

The National Academy of Sciences announced that the new study is "appropriate in the light of the new toxicological information on the increased use of artificial sweeteners."

Research at Albany has already shown that cyclamates may cause symptoms imitating hyperthyroidism, and result in patients being treated for the hormone disorder erroneously. Furthermore, the Albany researchers found that some people convert cyclamates into cyclohexylamine, a substance that raises blood pressure.[33]

Some 50 million adults today are on some form of diet. Surveys estimate that 75 percent of all families in the United States in 1967 used a calorie-controlled food of some sort.[34]

In the meantime, a substance being considered as a replacement for the cyclamates is hesperidin, one of the bioflavonoids. United States Department of Agriculture researchers who developed the process said it appears preferable to currently marketed artificial sweeteners because it is a natural ingredient in all citrus fruits.[35]

CHEMICALS IN COMBINATION

During 1965 and 1966, there appeared to be an "epidemic" among apparently healthy Canadians, Americans, and Belgian men in their mid-forties who suddenly dropped dead. The only thing they had in common was a love of drinking beer. Autopsies showed that the beer drinkers had a peculiar destruction of their heart muscle.

Detective work by physicians and government scientists turned up the fact that a month before the beer drinkers began to die, some beer manufacturers began to add cobalt, a metal, to their product to improve the quality of the foam.

University of Michigan researchers sought to determine whether cobalt additives could, indeed, cause heart disease. James L. Hall and Dr. Edward B. Smith, who conducted these studies in animals, presented their findings to the annual meeting of the American Association of Pathologists and Bacteriologists in Chicago in 1968.

When rabbits were given cobalt in beer, they said, the animals' hearts took on a "moth-eaten" appearance, "with focal areas of non-inflammatory degeneration marked by interstitial edema, separation of fibers, vacuolation and fibrillar degneration. Loss of cross-striations was also a prominent finding."

These lesions were the same as those described in the hearts of the unlucky beer drinkers.

When the cobalt was given without the beer, there were no such changes in the animals' hearts, leading the researchers to conclude that the combination of cobalt and alcohol caused the damage.[36]

One of the dangers that are becoming more and more a matter of concern among eminent scientists is the effects of chemicals that singly may be harmless but in combination may be extremely toxic.

It is known that a sensitive balance exists among the microbes that normally reside in the human gastrointestinal tract. Dr. R. E. Eckhardt, of Esso Research, a physician, questions whether a hangover is really due to the fact that the alcohol consumed produces cerebral edema or whether it is a result of toxins liberated from micro-organisms that become more active because they may not be as sensitive to the alcohol as other organisms. He questions what effect the ingestion of perhaps unknown toxins in other foods we eat may have on this sensitive balance within our gastrointestinal tract.[37]

This chemical interaction in food has been dramatically demonstrated in the more than thirty-one court cases of the "depressed cheese eaters." After taking Parnate, a medicine for combating mental depression, and then eating cheese, these people suffered severe high blood pressure that resulted in symptoms ranging from convulsions to strokes. Parnate inhibits the brain chemical monoamine oxidase (MAO). Cheese and other foods, such as beers, wines, yogurt, and beans, contain the natural chemical tyramine. Together, Parnate and tyramine combine to explode the blood pressure.

Another result of the strange effects of chemical combinations is now being called the "Chinese food syndrome."

A Cantonese doctor, Robert Ho Man Kwok, enjoyed Chinese food in the Far East and Europe. But when he came to the United States in 1960, he had an odd reaction. He reported in the *New England Journal of Medicine* that every time he eats in a Chinese-American restaurant he develops a strange numbness of the neck, back, and arms that lasts for about two hours, with no hangover effect.

In the following issue of the *New England Journal,* ten other letters, including seven from physicians, agreed that some people were indeed affected by a "Chinese food syndrome." Among the symptoms the writers described were headaches, heavy sweating, weakness, and numbness.

Richard Lyons, a science writer for the *New York Times,* interviewed Chinese restaurant owners in New York, and asked them about the phenomena described in the medical journal.

One restaurant owner commented, "The only headaches I get are from running this place and paying taxes." Only one owner admitted that he had heard of three or four cases of a strange reaction to Chinese food among thousands.[38]

Dr. Kwok, who is a senior investigator with the National Biomedical Research Foundation, said he had discussed the "Chinese food syndrome" with some Chinese friends who had also been affected by it. They speculated that monosodium glutamate seasoning or soy sauce or cooking wine might be the cause. Another possibility, he said, is that the high salt content of Chinese food may produce a temporary excess of sodium in the blood that reduces the potassium levels of the body. This, in turn, can cause a numbness of the muscles, generalized weakness and throbbing. The condition is termed "hypokalemia."

Another letter writer to the *New England Journal,* Dr. Herbert

H. Schaumburg, of the Bronx, New York, agreed that an excess of sodium "sounds reasonable." He said that three times he had experienced a tightening of the face and temple muscles, numbness, weeping, and even fainting after eating "in my favorite Chinese restaurant." (One wonders why he doesn't give up eating Chinese food, especially in that restaurant.)

MUTAGENS

The effects of chemicals in our food singly and in combination is far from a laughing matter. The effects may irreparably damage human beings for generations to come.

Dr. James Crow, of the University of Wisconsin, Chief of the National Institutes of Health's Genetic Study Section, said that exposure of large numbers of people to a chemical mutagen could cause a "genetic emergency" or even a "genetic disaster."[39]

Unlike teratogens, which damage an already conceived infant, and afflict only a single generation, mutations occur in the heart of the heredity cells. The damage could lie dormant for several generations, then affect many generations thereafter. The first warning of such an illness, Dr. Crow said, could be an increase in the number and incidence of severity of genetic illness; a marked change in the birth ratio of men to women, or an almost inperceptible loss of vigor and vitality, progressing from generation to generation.[40]

Recent United States and Canadian studies of human conception indicate that at least 25 percent of human conceptions end in intrauterine deaths. Among these spontaneous abortions, chromosomal anomalies can be found in 30 percent, and in 8 percent of all conceptions.[41]

Mongolism and other chromosomal abnormalities are found in at least 1 percent of live births. Another 5 percent of live-born infants have genetic diseases of yet undetermined origin, including diabetes and cystic fibrosis—thus, about one conception out of every six conceptions results in a dead or defective child due to genetic causes.[42] About 50 percent of the dead or defective babies can be shown to carry a "bad" gene the origin of which is unknown. Another 5 percent have known causes such as X ray or viruses. What causes the balance of defective babies is unknown, but researchers suspect that much of this fetal wastage is due to new mutagens. No one knows what, if any, part of these mutations is caused by chemicals.

However, Dr. Crow and a number of other scientists interested in genetics held a meeting at Jackson Laboratories, Bar Harbor, Maine, in 1967, to discuss chemical mutagens. At the request of the National Institutes of Health, the report was held back from publication, reportedly because the federal government wanted to have some corrective measures ready before it was released. Here are some of the points the scientists made:

• A number of chemicals—some with widespread use—are known to induce genetic damage in various organisms.

• Identity of the genetic material in all organisms implies that a chemical that is mutagenic to one species is likely to be so in others, and must be viewed with suspicion.

• Some compounds are highly mutagenic in experimental organisms in concentrations that are not toxic and that have no direct effect on fertility, so that no natural barrier prevents mutations from being passed on to future generations.

• Perhaps most insidious are compounds that induce gene mutations without chromosome breakage, and thus cannot be detected microscopically.

The chemicals that most concerned the Bar Harbor conferees as potential mutagens included chemosterilants and other pesticides, food additives, cosmetics, air pollutants, herbicides, known carcinogens, industrial chemicals, drugs, vaccines, and contraceptives.

For a long time it has been known that caffeine breaks chromosomes in lower animals and mammalian cells when given in large amounts. Americans over the age of fourteen years consume caffeine in coffee, tea, cola, and drugs at an average rate of 500 milligrams a day.[43] Caffeine may be residually present in the body and appears to retard the natural repair mechanism for broken chromosomes. Its destructive effect may be synergistic with other chromosome breakers, such as X rays.

Captan, as mentioned in the first chapter of this book, is one of the most popular and supposedly least toxic fungicides. For more than seventeen years, it has been used freely on gardens and in orchards. Yet FDA researchers found that it inhibits cell division and is extremely teratogenic in chickens. It pops the eyes out of one kind of fish. At last report, the FDA was studying the matter.

Ironically, information on the mutagenicity of drugs and food additives had not in the past been part of the requirements for approval by the FDA.

A Dow Chemical Company biological researcher said that the cost of testing two or three highly suspicious chemicals for mutagenicity could reach $500,000 per chemical, even in the animal stage and with the use of computers.[44]

CANCER

If chemicals can cause genetic damage, they can also cause cancer, because both have to do with the abnormal growth of the cell.

Dr. Philippe Shubik, formerly Professor and Director of the Division of Oncology at the Chicago Medical School Institute for Medical Research, and now Director of the Eppley Institute for Cancer Research, University of Nebraska, said: "Within the past decade, particularly, it has become apparent that chemical carcinogenic factors may well be responsible for a large number of cancers in man. An expert committee for the World Health Organization, writing on cancer, concluded that at least 50 percent of all cancers in human beings could be considered to be caused by extrinsic environmental agents.

"It is our belief that many, if not all the majority of cancers in human beings will eventually be shown to be caused by defined agents, and that many of these will be preventable."[45]

Dr. Shubik's colleague in the Division of Oncology, Dr. William Lijinsky, said that the "idea that some cancer in human beings is caused by exposure to chemicals is difficult to deny."[46]

Seventeen years ago, the cancer incidence rate was a little over 250 per 100,000 per year. Projecting the rates into 1985, the insurance companies expect the ratio to reach about 375 per 100,000.[47]

Dr. Morton L. Levin, Director and Assistant Commissioner for Medical Services, State Department of Health, Albany, New York, when testifying before a congressional committee studying food additives in the late 1950's, said: "We must remember that cancer in the human population today, particularly in the United States, will affect one out of four individuals *at some time during life*. We cannot rule out the possibility that substances which we do not today suspect may actually be causative of cancer.[48]

After the hearings, which were conducted by Congressman James Delaney, the Food Additives Amendment, Public Law 85-929, was passed on December 6, 1958. The law specifically states that no additive may be permitted in any amount if the tests show that it produces cancer when fed to man or animals or by other appropriate test.[49]

This part of the law has been severely attacked by food and chemical manufacturers and even by the Nutrition Council of the American Medical Association. The AMA Council on Nutrition "urged either repeal or revision of certain clauses in the Food Additives Amendments and the 1960 Color Additives Amendments. Both clauses prohibit the setting of tolerances for the use of cancer-causing agents in food.

"These clauses could prohibit the addition of certain essential nutrients to foods if 'any amount' of the substance was shown to cause cancer. Technically, these clauses contribute nothing to the safe use of food additives since any hazardous use of an additive is already prohibited in the general provision of the food additives amendment."[50]

Fortunately, the FDA has withstood the attacks against the "no cancer" clause. The Secretary of Health, in defending the clause, said: "No one really knows how to set a safe tolerance for substances in given foods when those substances are known to cause cancer when added to the diet of animals."

Eminent scientists, including those on the National Academy of Sciences Food Protection Committee, state that no one, at this time, can tell how much or how little of a carcinogen would be required to produce cancer in a human being or how long it would take the cancer to develop.[51]

The National Academy of Sciences' Food Protection Committee, while agreeing that low doses of a known carcinogen have been applied in small amounts to mouse skin without cancer developing, stated:

"The possibility exists that doses at 'no effect' levels do in fact exert carcinogenic effects but that the effects are too weak to detect with the numbers of animals feasible for routine testing. Such a possible effect, though extremely weak, might become evident in a large population such as, for example, the population potentially exposed to food additives in our culture. There is also the possibility of synergistic effects among substances present in the diet and of an individual susceptibility to carcinogens, although little is known about these factors.[52]

It would be wonderful if the Delaney Amendment had protected our food against even known carcinogens. Unfortunately, potentially cancer-causing chemicals are still being added to our food.

Dr. William Hueper, that voice crying in the wilderness, said: "Several thousand different chemicals and chemical mixtures used as additives and pesticides for a great variety of purposes are now incorporated into foods. Many of these have not been adequately tested for carcinogenic properties. There is practically no feasible escape route left for the captive population to avoid continued contact with unintentional food additives."

He said the evidence at hand indicates that several food and cosmetic dyes are probably human carcinogens and that others are potential carcinogens. He added that many additional ones have not been adequately tested. Here are some of the food additives and their carcinogenic properties that Dr. Hueper lists in his book *Chemical Carcinogenesis and Cancers,* written in collaboration with W. D. Conway:

"EMULSIFYING AGENTS AND SHORTENINGS—An emulsifying agent prepared from a vegetable oil by the application of heat and oxygen, containing highly oxidized and highly polymerized aliphatic compounds and used for the processing of vegetables and animal fats used in the manufacture of margarine, was shown to produce sarcomas in rats at the site of subcutaneous introduction. Distinct caution, therefore, is indicated in the incorporation of highly oxidized oils such as those probably formed in the deep-fat frying process into products of human consumption. Liver tumors were produced in 40 percent of mice fed a commonly used shortening and in 65 percent of mice given orally a specific solvent fraction of this foodstuff.

"One experiment using polyoxyethylene stereate proposed for use in bread and rolls produced, when fed at 26 percent level in the diet, not only bladder stones in 25 out of 150 rats, but in 13, bladder tumors.

"SYNTHETIC MUCILAGES, THICKENERS AND STABILIZERS—The recent demonstration of various cancerous responses in rats by the parental introduction of water soluble, highly polymerized compounds such as polyvinyl pyrrolidone, carboxymethol cellulose and dextran should provide an indication for an intensive and competent investigation into potential similar responses by some of the similar synthetic polyglucoses. Since such products have no nutrient value, it would be wise to eliminate them for the time being from the list of permitted food additives. [They are still on the list.]

"FLAVORING AGENTS—No comprehensive information is available concerning potential carcinogenic properties of the approximately [2,112] flavoring agents employed. Lemon oil, however, has recently been reported to be a co-carcinogen. Safrole, which served for many years as a flavoring agent of soft drinks, especially root beer, was shown to cause cancer of the liver when fed to rats kept on a normal diet.

"SURFACANTS—Employed in food as antifoaming agents, emulsifiers and dispersants or may be introduced unintentionally into them as a residue of detergents or used for cleaning cooking utensils and dinner ware. In experiments on animals, it has been shown that some chemicals of this type exert carcinogenic or weakly carcinogenic effects on the action of known polycyclic aromatic hydrocarbons given by mouth and facilitate the penetration of these agents through the mucosa of the alimentary tract and skin. Candies, soft drinks, dill pickles, vitamins, ice cream, cream whip, cakes, bread and rolls."

Dr. R. E. Eckardt, of Esso Research, said in 1966 that nitrosamines produced a variety of tumors at different sites. Some of them produced tumors after a single dose in animals. He said it is believed that certain nitrosamines may occur in tobacco smoke but that more recently they have been demonstrated in "herring meal preserved with nitrite."

He noted that "nitrites have been used as food preservatives for centuries."[53]

He also noted that aflatoxins may cause liver tumors.

"These compounds came to light," he said, "when thousands of turkeys died in England. Investigation showed they died of liver damage and that this liver damage resulted from toxins developed by a mold which grew on the ground nuts (peanuts to a large extent) which constituted a major portion of their diet. Wheat aflatoxin fed to trout produced liver tumors.

"Whether these aflatoxins are important to the human is as yet unestablished," he continued. "They have been detected in trace quantities in certain batches of peanut butter. Additionally, it is known that liver cancers have a peculiar distribution around the world, being rare in the United States but prevalent in the Chinese and certain African tribes."

One of the National Cancer Institutes research projects is the study of toxic products synthesized by molds that are intentionally added to the food for the purpose of fermentation. Moldy rice, prepared by growing certain strains of *Aspergillus* on rice kernels, and used in the Orient as a starter for fermentation of cereals and beans, has been shown to damage the livers of experimental animals.[54]

Even when cancer has been definitely linked to an additive, it takes a long time for that additive to be taken off the market. Red Number 4, used in maraschino cherries, was shown to be carcinogenic in animals, but is still on the market.

Proving a relationship between a chemical and cancer is extremely difficult today. Many people still do not believe the statistical evidence linking cigarette smoking and lung cancer. The problem is that cancer may take as long as twenty years to develop.

As Dr. Lijinsky said, "We are swimming in a sea of carcinogens."

Certainly, every additive to food should be studied for its cancer-causing potential. Since most are added for economic purposes only, the consequences may not be worth it for one out of four of us.

ALLERGY

Allergy may not be as frightening as cancer or birth defects to most people, but to some who suffer from it, it can be just as deadly as any malady of man.

Take the case of a young man who had a stuffy nose and recurrent asthma attacks because of allergies. It was known that he was allergic to iodine and peanuts. One day, he took his wife out for ice cream. He ordered a banana split with chocolate and strawberry ice cream. He took a few delicious bites, gasped, grabbed his throat, and turned blue. Without speedy medical attention, he might have died.

The young man, it turned out, was "violently sensitive to artificial Chocolatin and Strawberrin, the two flavoring agents in the ice cream."[55]

This was a true case reported by Dr. Stephen Lockey, of Lancaster, Pennsylvania, an allergist who has been calling for recognition of allergic reaction to hidden drugs for years. He often quotes an Englishman, Dr. A. Kewick, who wrote: "The world is short of food, and any substance which can be added to preserve food and yet be harmless to the consumer should be encouraged. Unfortunately, for all concerned, many additives considered harmless have proven otherwise."

Dr. Eugene Cowen, another allergist, wrote in the *Annals of Allergy:* "The attention to date on the problem of additives has been focused primarily upon the carcinogenic potentials, hematopoietic effects, intestinal bacterial flora changes and other physiological alterations. Except in a few cases, search of the literature has revealed no interest in the potential allergenic effect of excipient vehicles and additives."[56]

Unlike Dr. Lockey and Dr. Cowen, many scientists feel that you cannot abstain from using a food additive just because some people are allergic to it.

However, Dr. Howard G. Rapport, writing in the *Journal of Asthma Research,* September, 1967, said: "Allergy is the most important chronic disease of childhood. Allergic illness is responsible for more days of school absence than any other chronic condition. It is the cause of loss of school, play time and growth time. It destroys healthy family life.

The problem of allergic disease in childhood is unfortunately growing more significant each year. The question of what we are able to do about it does not have an easy answer. Every day we are exposed to new types of plastics, synthetic detergents, food additives, insecticides, weed killers and dozens of new chemical compounds which frequently end up in our rivers and reservoirs and the very air we breath.

"Allergic illness kills more children each year than poliomyelitis, rheumatic fever or pneumonia.

"Each new compound is, of course, a potential invitation to allergy. New techniques in the production and storage of food have also taken their toll, permitting and even promoting early weaning and total dependence on manufactured formulas and introduction of solid foods as early as the first or second month of life. Allergically, this has created many problems."[57]

Dr. Cowen emphasized in his article: "Elimination of allergenic agents, where possible, has always been the cornerstone of the therapy for the allergic patient with the increasing complexities of today's environment, the ability to adequately eliminate proved ingestant allergens is being seriously impaired. Much of this is the result of astronomical numbers of additives to our foods and drugs, and it is further complicated by the inadequate labeling of these additives, vehicles and excipients as to their exact nature and source."

Take the case of the "yellow peril." Sensitivity to aspirin has been known for more than half a century. It can cause fatal swelling of the tissues, stuffy nose, or asthma.[58]

Max Samter, M.D., of the University of Illinois College of Medicine, and Ray F. Beers, Jr., M.D., from the same institution, reported their findings in "Intolerance to Aspirin" in the May, 1968, issue of the *Annals of Internal Medicine*. They found certain patients showed symptoms of aspirin allergy after eating fresh pork, sweet corn, soft drinks, and cheese crackers.

"None of the patients who reported reactions after ingestion of food gave positive skin reactions to the food under suspicion," they wrote. "Analysis of the suspected foods established the presence of multiple additives in all but two of the samples. Of the preservatives, sodium benzoate was used most commonly; of coloring matter, hydrazine yellow 'tartrazine' [yellow # 5] turned out to be a component of all but one of the yellows in orange foods. The ability of hydrazine yellow to induce angioedema [tissue swelling] and respiratory symptoms in susceptible patients has been previously described but it had not been shown that reactions to hydrazine yellow and to aspirin co-exist in the same patients."

Since tartrazine and aspirin are chemically not alike but produce the same symptoms in aspirin-sensitive patients, the Illinois Medical College researchers conclude that the only thing they have in common is that they are minor analgesics. Whatever it is in the body that makes an aspirin-sensitive person react to the drug the way he does also makes him react to tartrazine, a hidden additive in food.

As a result, an aspirin-sensitive person who carefully avoids aspirin-containing products could have an asthma attack or serious edema after eating a food containing yellow coloring, and never know why.

PACKAGING

Allergy, cancer, and mutagenicity may occur not only from unintentional additives like pesticides and intentional additives like flavoring, colors, and surfacants, but also from packaging.

Paul E. Johnson, writing on the "Health Aspects of Food Additives" in the *American Journal of Public Health,* said: "There are several hundred chemicals used in formulating food packaging materials which might become additives; the basic glass, film paper, metal, cloth or wood plus the sizing and coating material; the plasticizers, the adhesives, the dyes and printing inks and the solvents, germicides, antioxidants and other miscellaneous chemicals associated with them."[59]

The Food Additives Amendment of 1958 gave the Food and Drug Administration the responsibility of making sure that indirect additives in foods, including those that migrate into them from packaging materials, be regulated to assure human safety. FDA Bureau of Science Director William H. Summerson told the National Conference on Indirect Food Additives in February, 1968, that his agency must be told for each new packaging material:

1. Whether or not it gets into the food.
2. How much may get in.
3. Whether that amount is safe for people.

Summerson noted that there has been great demand for using organo-tin compounds in packaging material. He said that the compounds have been shown to be extremely toxic and that only the FDA requirement of proof of safety prevented them from being used by the manufacturers. Unfortunately, the FDA and the food manufacturers cannot always predict what the consumer is going to do on his own.

Take the case of a fifty-five-year-old physician. He was hospitalized with an enlarged liver, progressive erythropenia (loss of red blood cells). He told his doctors that he had been feeling generally fatigued for quite a while with a sensation of heaviness in both arms, insomnia, headaches, loss of appetite, nausea, and occasional diarrhea. He had lost ten pounds in one month, and also had stomach cramps. This successful, wise, middle-aged physician presented a typical picture of lead poisoning. But how was he being poisoned?

In discussing his habits, his physicians learned that every evening the doctor sipped chilled soda from a mug made by his son. He usually drank two bottles of cola over several hours. He had been continuing this ritual for two years. The son had made the mug at college, glazing it with lead oxide. He had intended the piece for a vase, but his father preferred it as a mug. The soda leached enough lead from the mug's inner surface to poison the physician.

The doctors who made the connection between the mug and

the lead poisoning also discovered that the ceramics industry uses some 25,000 to 30,000 tons of lead a year "and [that] there is a lack of government regulation for what could be a potentially dangerous situation."[60]

Another unexpected food additive may be from plastic dishes. Dorothy C. Smith, of the National Health and Welfare Service, Ontario, Canada, was asked whether formaldehyde might mix in with hot food when it is served on plastic dishes made from urea or melamine resins. She answered: "These tests show that hot liquids do, in fact, extract free formaldehyde from these plastics. Trace quantities were found in new, glossy dishes, but appreciable quantities were obtained when broken pieces were exposed to solvents at 57 degrees over a period of 24 hours. Under normal conditions of use, no significant amounts of formaldehyde would be released in food or drink from this type of plastic ware."

This is one woman's opinion, of course, and certainly the effects of formaldehyde released from plastic dishes mixed with certain foods and their additives should be studied further.

THE LAW

The practice of adding chemicals to food is a very old one, says the Food and Drug Administration publication "What the Consumer Should Know About Food Additives": "No doubt it began when man first learned to preserve meat by putting salt on it." The booklet goes on to say that during the early days of the Industrial Revolution in England and America, there was much trial-and-error experimentation with material used to preserve foods or to conceal inferiority by coloring them with dyes that were sometimes highly poisonous. Dr. Harvey W. Wiley's battle for the original pure-food law was to a large extent a fight against chemical preservatives such as boric acid, formaldehyde and salicylic acid.

"Food and Drug Administration scientists, appraising the situation in the mid-1950s, knew that several hundred of those additives were being used. They knew also that some of those in use had not been thoroughly tested for safety. Hearings were held by Congressman James Delaney which led to the amendments named after him. Under the law, prior to September 1958, the FDA could not prevent the use of a chemical simply because it was questionable or had not been adequately tested. It was necessary to be able to prove in court that the chemical was poisonous or deleterious. This is not difficult for chemicals which cause immediate or acute illness.

"But today, the big problem which concerns modern scientists is the long-term effect—what may happen in the body as the result of years or even a lifetime of exposure," the booklet said.[61]

Now the law reads that the food and chemical manufacturers are required to run extensive animal feeding tests on these additives before they are marketed. Results of these tests must be submitted to the FDA. If the FDA scientists are satisfied that the additive may be used safely, a regulation will be issued permitting its use.

The situation is certainly better than it was before the 1958 amendments. But are we really protected?

The American Medical Association's Council on Foods and Nutrition pointed out in 1961: "The new Food Additives Amendment gives special consideration to additives used in food prior to Jan. 1, 1958. Continued use of these additives is now permitted without toxicity tests if qualified experts generally recognize them as having been shown safe through either toxicologic tests or experience based on common use in food.

"Some chemicals used in foods had been evaluated prior to the enactment of the Food Additives Amendment and found to be safe. These are allowed at the present time by virtue of this prior sanction. However, experience based on common use in food will not prove the absence of chronic harmful effects. Both animal test and experience with use are needed for evaluating safety. The Council on Foods and Nutrition believes that decisions to continue the use of additives should be based on demonstrations of their safety through scientific methods. Furthermore, the food industry should be allowed adequate time to demonstrate the safety of new chemicals used in foods."

The Council goes on to say: "The formulation of state laws for food additives should be encouraged to provide adequate regulations for all foods, whether or not they enter interstate commerce. Federal agencies do not have jurisdiction over foods that are produced and sold locally. . . .

"At present, not only the laws but also the laboratories and inspection services in most states are inadequate to conduct a food control program comparable to that of federal agencies. Sufficient state funds should be appropriated to support research and testing on present food additives.

"Public and private funds should be appropriated to support research and toxicological testing of food additives. Only when sufficient scientific knowledge is obtained will we be able to make progress in the expanded use of safe food additives."[62]

But recognition of the dangers of a food additive is very slow. When the Federal Food and Drug Act was passed in 1906, seven synthetic colors were approved for use in foods. By 1950, that number had grown to nineteen. In 1956, the government banned Food and Drug Certified Yellows numbers 1, 2, 3, and 4 and Red Number 1. In early 1965, it prohibited Red Number 4, but a few months later relaxed its ruling on Number 4 at the request of food and chemical companies. It is still in use.[63]

Coumarin, a component of vanilla-like flavoring preparations, was also banned after years of use. Coumarin has been shown to cause marked growth retardation, testicular atrophy, liver damage, and death in animals.[64] Safrole, a flavoring material, was also banned after years of use. It was found to cause testicular atrophy, cirrhosis, necrosis, and cancer of the liver in animals.[65]

The list is long—and growing longer all the time—concerning additives that have been used for years and then found to be harmful.

The Canadian Food and Drug Directorate in October, 1967, banned the use of noridhydroguaiaretic acid (NDGA), a food additive used to keep fat from going rancid. The move was made after animal studies showed that the antioxidant "may result in hazards to health."

NDGA is still being used in the United States in shortenings, cake mixes, and soft drinks, including Tang. The FDA has taken NDGA off the "generally recognized as safe list."[66]

Another problem, of course, is the illegal use of additives. Cakes seized in one of New York City's largest bakeries contained toxic dyes. Food and Drug inspectors seized seventy specialty cakes from the establishment, which did a huge catering business. The laboratory report showed that the cake and its decorative roses contained titanium dioxide, lead chromate, and dinitroaniline, ingredients of floral paint sprays.[67]

The FDA inspectors seized a shipment of cottage cheese in New Mexico containing coumarin, the liver-damaging, testicular-atrophying component of vanilla previously mentioned.[68]

With the limited number of Food and Drug inspectors who have to police millions and millions of shipments of food and drugs, chances of catching illegal additives are slim. Fortunately, most food and chemical manufacturers are honorable.

Former Food and Drug Commissioner James L. Goddard said: "In a society where we use three and a half pounds of food additives [per person] per year, we have to be re-evaluating constantly. We need more sophisticated testing programs; ones which give the consumer the assurance of safety he wants. We also have a growing awareness of the interaction of drugs."[69]

In the publication "Some Considerations in the Use of Human Subjects in Safety Evaluation of Pesticides and Food Chemicals," members of the National Academy of Sciences and the National Research Council showed they were well aware of the problem of food additive safety:

"A continuing problem facing industry and the public is that of establishing that a particular use of a chemical in food production, processing, packaging or storage will not be harmful to the consumer. It is generally recognized that absolute assurance that a usage will not prove harmful in any degree is unattainable. Therefore, effort is directed toward assuring that the hazard associated with the use is very small in relation to the health, agricultural and economic benefits to be derived."[70]

When they say "economic benefit," of course, it must be decided whether they are talking about the producer or the consumer. For instance, at the American Chemical Society meeting in April, 1968, a paper was presented on the properties of 1, 4, 5, 6-tetrahydro-2-acetopyridine. What is 1, 4, 5, 6-tetrahydro-2-acetopyridine? It is "A Cracker Odor Constituent of Bread Aroma." The authors of the paper said that, unfortunately, the flavor aroma of bread, which has universal appeal, fades within twenty-four hours after baking. They felt that the chemicals that smelled like bread could be used to spray a loaf and keep it smelling fresh.[71]

If the sixteen additives now added to bread makes it look and feel soft and fresh, and if 1, 4, 5, 6-tetrahydro-2-acetopyridine makes it smell fresh, is the bread fresh?

A&P is now advertising Jane Parker White Bread: "We date our Jane Parker White Bread. It's the only absolute guarantee of freshness you have . . . unless you bake your own."[72]

How right they are! And we must ask if it is necessary to add chemicals to something to make us think it is fresh.

The National Academy of Sciences says: "As methods of investigation improve, it should be possible to improve the assurance of safety. Usually this assurance has rested on the interpretation of the results of exposure of experimental animals to the chemicals in question. While this approach has generally served admirably for assurance of safety of pesticides and food chemicals, its weakness is that the result obtained with laboratory animals may not always make it possible to predict what will occur in man.

"Once a chemical is released to the general environment, it would probably not be possible to identify exposed and non-exposed segments of the population or to classify persons by degrees of exposure, except to the extent that special groups might be identified whose dietary or other habits result in exposure different from that of the population.

"The possibility of carcinogenicity is particularly important, since the period of induction of cancer may be a considerable portion of the lifespan."

The Academy confesses that there is, as yet, no solution to the problem of translating toxicological data derived from animal studies into levels that provide an adequate margin of safety in human use. They also recognize that certain common disorders, particularly those affecting the kidneys, liver, and lungs, as well as chronic alcoholism, may greatly modify the response to and excretion pattern of many agents.

They suggest that if there is sufficient reason, once studies in normal volunteers have been completed and the safety limits for an agent established, similar studies might be carried out in selected groups of volunteer patients with disorders that may affect their responses. Whether manufacturers would take the trouble or whether patients with liver disease or chronic alcoholism would submit to the studies might be a problem. At least, an attempt should be made.

Besides patients with ailments, many scientists—including Dr. Walter A. Compton, President of Miles Laboratories, believes that the FDA fails to take into account personal likes and dislikes and eating habits. Dr. Compton made the statement in defending vitamin supplements, but it is just as true for other chemical additives.

Until we have better methods of testing, there are commonsense rules that would give us better protection from potentially harmful—even deadly—chemical additives. Alastair C. Frazer, speaking on "Unexpected Toxic Effects" in "Some Considerations in the Use of Human Subjects in Safety Evaluation of Pesticides and Food Chemicals," the National Academy of Sciences publication, suggests:

1. Epidemiological studies in those occupationally exposed. Any chemical substance proposed for introduction into the environment has to be manufactured, prepared, packed, or otherwise distributed. Those handling the substances are commonly exposed to it in quantities considerably in excess of those likely to reach the public at large. Possible toxic effects should be readily detected in such groups if appropriate studies are made.

2. Detailed investigation of accidental poisoning can also provide valuable toxicological information. This may be particularly useful in the case of substances with relatively high toxicity for which special handling precautions are normally used. Accidents may occur either during manufacturing, distribution, or application. The use of trained combat teams to make an effective study of such incidents has been suggested.

3. With substances of low toxic potential, such as a new food additive, some control of unexpected effects might be afforded by restricting the initial marketing to a particular zone. Since this is not infrequently done for sales purposes, for example, to link television advertising with the distribution and display of new products, there might be some possibility of zoning distribution for safety purposes.

3 NOTES

1. Case of Rita L. Don, M.D., 102 University Towers, 1900 N. Oregon St., El Paso, Texas. Given to author by Steven S. Lockey, M.D., 60 N. West End Ave., Lancaster, Pa. 17603.
2. *New York Times,* March 4, 1968.
3. James L. Goddard, M.D., Food and Drug Commissioner, tape-recorded interview with author, May, 1968.
4. Howard J. Sanders, Associate Editor, "Food Additives," *Chemical and Engineering News,* October 10, 1966.
5. James L. Goddard, M.D., Food and Drug Commissioner, *Science News Letter,* December 10, 1966.
6. Orville Withers, M.D., *The New Physician,* July, 1968; correspondence with author, March, 1968.

7. *National Institutes of Health News Record,* May 28, 1968.
8. Stephen Lockey, M.D., 60 N. West End Ave., Lancaster, Pa., correspondence with author, March, 1968.
9. Howard J. Sanders, *op. cit.*
10. *Ibid.*
11. T. C. Byerly, "Use of Human Subjects in Safety Evaluation of Food Chemicals," National Academy of Sciences, 1967.
12. *Federal Register,* April 11, 1968.
13. H. R. Bird, Ph.D., Department of Poultry Husbandry, University of Wisconsin, *American Journal of Clinical Nutrition,* May–June, 1961, Vol. 9.
14. *Federal Register,* April 11, 1968.
15. *Physicians Desk Reference 1968,* Medical Economics, 22nd edition, p. 1015.
16. Bernard Robins, M.D., "Deterioration of Renal Function Due to Tetracycline," *Beth Israel Hospital Journal,* 1964.
17. Murray C. Zimmerman, *Archives of Dermatology,* January, 1959, Vol. 79.
18. T. C. Byerly, *op. cit.*
19. Frank Rosen, allergist and former president of the New Jersey Allergy Foundation. Correspondence with author.
20. *Medical World News,* May 17, 1968.
21. W. C. Hueper and W. D. Conway, *Chemical Carcinogensis and Cancers* (Springfield, Ill., C. C. Thomas, 1964), p. 654.
22. H. R. Bird, *op. cit.*
23. *Ibid.*
24. R. Landolt, "Premature Signs of Puberty Following Unintentional Estrogen Administration," *Schweiz Med. Wsch.,* 98:638–640, April 27, 1968.
25. J. C. Roe, *Current Concepts in Cancer, JAMA,* May 13, 1968, Vol. 204, No. 7, p. 142.
26. Hueper and Conway, *op. cit.*
27. News from the National Institutes of Health, December 15, 1967.
28. American Medical Association release, August 28, 1968.
29. Barry Commoner, speech before the American Association for the Advancement of Sciences, New York, December 27, 1967, and speech before the National Parks Association, Washington, D.C., March 16, 1968.
30. Hueper and Conway, *op. cit.*
31. Howard J. Sanders, *op. cit.*
32. *Ibid.*
33. W. David Gardner, in *The New Republic,* September 14, 1968.
34. "Cyclamate Sweeteners in the Human Diet," Calorie Control Council, Abbott Laboratories, news conference transcript, Chicago, September 17, 1968.
35. *Agricultural Research,* March 16, 1968.

36. *Modern Medicine,* January 1, 1968.
37. R. E. Eckhardt, M.D., Ph.D., Esso (New Jersey) Research Medical Bulletin, 26:142, July, 1966.
38. *New York Times,* May 19, 1968.
39. "Do Chemicals Sow the Seeds of Genetic Change?" *Medical World News,* April 26, 1968.
40. *Ibid.*
41. *Medical World News,* May 17, 1968.
42. *Ibid.*
43. *Ibid.*
44. *Ibid.*
45. Dr. Philippe Shubik, "The Cancer Bulletin" of the Chicago Medical School, August, 1967. Dr. Shubik has moved to the University of Nebraska.
46. William Lijinsky, M.D., Division of Oncology, Chicago Medical School, "The Cancer Bulletin," August, 1967.
47. *Health Insurance News,* March, 1968.
48. Morton Levin, M.D., Assistant Commissioner for Medical Services, New York State Congressional Hearings on Food Additives, 1957.
49. Law 85–929, December 6, 1958.
50. *Journal of the American Medical Association,* November 18, 1961.
51. Color Additives Amendment, p. 17.
52. "Problems in the Evaluation of Carcinogenic Hazards from the Use of Food Additives," Food Protection Committee, Food and Nutrition Board, National Academy of Sciences, December, 1959.
53. R. E. Eckhardt, M.D., *op. cit.*
54. *Progress Against Cancer* (National Institutes of Health, 1966).
55. Case of Stephen D. Lockey, Lancaster, Pa.
56. Eugene Cowen, M.D., Assistant Clinical Professor of Medicine, University of Colorado Medical Center, *Annals of Allergy,* March, 1967, Vol. 25.
57. Howard Rapport, M.D., *Journal of Asthma Research,* September, 1967, Vol. 5.
58. Max Samter, M.D., and Ray Beers, Jr., M.D., "Intolerance to Aspirin: Clinical Studies and Consideration of Its Pathogenesis," Annals of Internal Medicine, May, 1968, Vol. 68, No. 5.
59. Paul E. Johnson, "Health Aspects of Food Additives," *American Journal of Public Health,* 56:6, June, 1966.
60. Robert W. Harris, M.D., and William R. Elsea, M.D., "Ceramics Glaze as a Source of Lead Poisoning," *Journal of the American Medical Association,* November 6, 1967, Vol. 202, No. 6.
61. "What Consumers Should Know About Food Additives," FDA publication 10, revised in June, 1962.
62. "Safe Use of Chemicals in Foods: A Council Statement," *Journal of the American Medical Association,* November 18, 1961, Vol. 178, No. 7, p. 749.

63. Howard J. Sanders, "Food Additives," *Chemical and Engineering News*, October 10 and 17, 1966.
64. W. H. Hagan, *et. al.*, Division of Toxicological Evaluation, FDA, *Food and Cosmetics Toxicology*, April, 1967, Vol. 5, No. 2.
65. *Ibid.*
66. Paul Schvette, Deputy Assistant Commissioner for Education and Information, FDA, HEW, personal correspondence June 5, 1968.
67. Abraham Goodman, Assistant to the Council President of New York City, personal communication with author, November 21, 1968.
68. *FDA Papers*, February, 1967, p. 35.
69. Tape-recorded interview, May, 1968.
70. "Some Considerations in the Use of Human Subjects in the Safety Evaluation of Pesticides and Food Chemicals," Food Committee, National Academy of Sciences, 1965.
71. Irving R. Hunter, *et. al.*, "Preparation and Properties of 1, 4, 5, 6 -tetrahydro-2-acetopyridine, a Cracker Odor Constituent of Bread Aroma," American Chemical Society meeting, San Francisco, April, 1968.
72. A&P advertisement for Jane Parker Bread, 1968.

4

Meat and Poultry Hazards

As all good shoppers know, when buying meat you should consider its color—a bright red means freshness. However, sodium nicotinate and related substances act to preserve the bright red color of meat. In many states it is legal to use these additives. One company that produces the additive purportedly produces enough to doctor 320 million pounds of meat a year solely for cosmetic and therefore for economic purposes.

The Council on Drugs of the American Medical Association in 1960 recommended that the intake of nicotinic acid be 4 milligrams daily for infants, 13 to 17 milligrams daily for those between thirteen and twenty years of age, and 12 to 18 milligrams for adults.

When a doctor's wife became ill after eating hamburger meat, the irate physician investigated and found that their butcher had added a handful of sodium nicotinate to their hamburger despite the fact that instructions on the chemical container said to add only two ounces to one hundred pounds of meat.

One evening, members of a sorority house at Northwestern University sat down to a dinner that consisted of Swedish meatballs, noodles, broccoli, butter, rolls, green olives, celery, chocolate roll, coffee and sugar and cream. There were glasses of iced water at each place setting. The boys hired to wait on the tables carried in the heavy trays, laden with food for 121 persons. It was an ordinary meal on an ordinary school night until ten minutes after it began. Then one of the girls stood up and yelled, "I'm burning up! I feel like

I'm in an oven." A blond-haired girl with a light complexion, she looked as if someone had splashed red paint over her face. Her skin burned and itched, and her ears tingled. She complained of a pain in her stomach, and began to shake with chills.

Within seconds, thirty-nine of the girls and five of the male student waiters developed the symptoms. They had extreme flushing, tingling, itching, dry mouth, stomach pains, and swelling of the face and knees. Oddly, the worst symptoms were among the fair-haired members of the group.

Doctors summoned to the sorority house found blood pressures ranged from 80 to 160 systolic and 58 to 80 diastolic, and pulses varied from 64 to 96. Something the students had eaten had caused dilatation of their blood vessels and a severe allergic-like reaction.

The doctors began administering Benadryl to the students, an antihistamine, at 25 to 50 milligrams a shot. Either the Benadryl ran out or some students refused to take it, but within twenty to forty minutes the symptoms began to subside in students whether they had received the medication or not. That is, the symptoms eased in all but two students. They had to be hospitalized.

What was it that had caused the sudden illness? Why did only forty-four out of the 121 persons eating the same food become ill? Why were some more severely affected than others? Doctors had to check food storage, preparation, food service, pesticides, rodenticides, utensils (were they galvanized or cadmium lined?) and disinfectants. Nothing was found to account for the poisoning.

The following morning, despite initial denial, it was discovered that at the meat-purveying firm sodium nicotinate had been added to the ground beef before it was delivered to the sorority house. Ironically, chemical tests that were performed at the Chicago Board of Health on some of the ground meat proved negative. Later, however, microbiological tests showed as much as 225 milligrams of sodium nicotinate per 100 grams of meat.

The officials of the meat firm confessed that two ounces of powdered sodium nicotinate had been sprinkled on the ground meat directly following the first coarse grind and prior to the second fine grind. Because of the uneven distribution of the chemical and because of the varying susceptibility, only forty-four out of the 121 became ill.

Similar stories could be told about incidents concerning sodium nicotinate around the country. Eighty-eight persons in 38 families became ill over a thirteen-day period when the butcher from whom they purchased meat began using the chemical.

The doctors who described these cases in "Food Poisoning Due to Sodium Nicotinate" in the *American Journal of Public Health,* October, 1962, were Dr. Edward Press and Dr. Leona Yeager. They said: "In the opinion of the authors, the use of such additives should be properly controlled and regulated in order to avoid misuse. The product in which it has been used should be properly labeled or some other method of making the consumer aware an additive has been added should be utilized."[1]

The above cases concern a relatively mild illness with a legally, if improperly, used additive.

But the truth of the matter is that even with the new meat legislation in 1968, you can still literally buy a pig's eye in your frankfurter. In other words, there may be a lot more in your meat than you bargained for.

Rodney E. Leonard, Deputy Assistant Secretary of the Consumer and Marketing Service, United States Department of Agriculture, said in testimony before Congress in 1967:

"There exists considerable disparity between statutory provisions of federal, state and local laws which creates a form of economic separation that carries with it significant advantage for the unregulated. . . .

"To be more specific, excessive water can be used in the processing of hams and other pork cuts; cereal, flour and dry milk can be substituted in the manufacture of sausage. Such chemicals as niacin and sodium sulfite can be used to prevent color fading and mask spoilage. Products such as frankfurters and bologna can be labeled 'all meat' when in fact they contain all types of meat by-products, extenders, excessive water and fat.

"Seven states do not have any laws specifically covering the inspection of meat, although they have a general-type food law which partially regulates meatpacking from the standpoint of specified sanitation and/or labeling requirements. These states are Alabama, Alaska, Delaware, Maryland, Minnesota, New Hampshire and South Dakota.

"There are 42 states with some form of a meat inspection statute—two require only mandatory licensing of packers with no provision for actual inspection of meat: 11 provide for only voluntary programs and 29 have mandatory inspection laws.

"Administrators of state meat inspection programs generally admit that they have neither the money nor the manpower to conduct an intensive, continuous inspection service for both slaughtering and processing operations. State legislators, veterinary associations, industry groups and others have tried repeatedly to obtain meaningful legislation and enforcement."[2]

Although federal inspection of interstate meat by the United States Department of Agriculture has been in force since 1906, and although twenty-seven states have mandatory inspection of intrastate meats, the reports of USDA inspectors, factory workers, and scientists about some of the meat being eaten by unsuspecting Americans today is enough to make a person a vegetarian.

Take the testimony of Stephen Kota, Compliance and Evaluation Staff Officer, Consumer and Marketing Service, United States Department of Agriculture, Norfolk, Virginia. He said:

"In one establishment, I found abscessed beef and beef livers, abscessed pork livers, parasitic livers mixed with edible product and beef head meat, cheek meat, a battered rusty lard-type drum with hair floating on top. . . .

"The owner was with me at the time. On questioning him on the mixture, he said, 'These will be re-checked later.'

"This state has a mandatory law, not fully implemented . . . the antemortem and postmortem inspection is done on the spot. Some inspectors cover as many as 10 counties.

"In the cooler, I found a rusty, battered drum half full of water and beef head meat with hair floating on top, and a stick used to stir this to wash it. Beef heads untrimmed on the floor with meat . . . they would be trimmed later.

"[There were] rodent harbors, unscreened windows, vermin droppings . . .

"In another plant I found the killing floor rails to hold the cattle were not high enough. Approximately one foot of the average size side of beef would drag on the floor, and the holding cooler was also short in this respect. And there was a box where the slaughtered cattle were to go. The kill floor in both instances was very primitive, inadequate drains, one three-inch drain for a killing floor.

"This particular plant is the boneless beef king of this State."

Kota said some of the meat from these plants was put into frankfurters.

"I picked this [frankfurter] up in a retail store outlet. It was obviously colored. It was not noted on the label that it was artificially colored. Hamburger the same way. It was obviously colored and it was not noted on the label that it was colored. . . ."

He said he found situations where "all meat frankfurters had lungs and almost every other part of the cow in it."[3]

Leslie Orear, Director of Publications, United Packinghouse Food and Allied Workers, AFL-CIO, told the congressional hearings:

"Congress and the American housewife both remain serenely unaware of the dimensions of the problem.

"Even those somewhat inured to the run-of-the-mill stories of cockroaches and rats were deeply shocked to examine a series of affidavits from employees of a North Carolina packing house, a large one for that state, which recounted instances of 'snuff spit' on the floor, sausage meat fallen on the same floor which was then picked up and shoved into the stuffer, and so on.

"One woman swore that she had seen 'condemned meat' reworked and put in smoked sausage. 'I have seen large cartons packed with lard after rat leaving had been emptied from them,' she said. There were several such statements."[4]

If you think that is about as bad as things can get, there was much testimony at the congressional hearings about people who specialize in buying diseased meat. They are called "cripple buyers," and the meat is referred to as "4-D" (dead, diseased, dying, or disabled).

Reuben A. Baumgart, Compliance and Evaluation Staff, Consumer and Marketing Service, United States Department of Agriculture, Milwaukee, Wisconsin, said that "cripple buyers" advertise rather heavily in newspapers. They will pay up to $100 per animal for 4-D meat.

"If they feel it is a real good animal, it might go to a federal plant, if they think it will pass—if they don't think so, it might go to some other plant where it might get some sort of inspection, and if it is really bad, it will go to one without any inspection."

Senator Joseph M. Montoya, of New Mexico, said, "I happen to know that there are many pink-eyed cattle which have been taken to the cattle sales rings and sold for slaughter, and the same is true of

cancerous cattle, cancer-infected cattle." He said also that injured
cattle and cattle with gangrene are taken to cattle sales rings and sold
for slaughter, that the extent of the gangrene infection is not subject
to any federal inspection, and that in many cases there is no local
inspection, either antemortem or postmortem.

In 1962 and in 1967, United States Department of Agriculture
inspectors surveyed hundreds of meat plants. According to Senator
Walter F. Mondale, of Minnesota, they found "in virtually every
jurisdiction instances of unsanitary meat, unwholesome meat, unsanitary packing conditions, or processing conditions, the introduction of
additives such as water and other fillers, and the misleading labeling
requirements were widely found in all jurisdictions to be beneath the
standards of Federal inspection."

Here are some reports of USDA inspectors quoted in the hearings of the Meat Inspection bill and in the *Congressional Record:*[5]

MISSISSIPPI—*Voluntary Inspection*

"Carcasses of hogs and cattle still had hair and pieces of hide
on them and were contaminated with filings, floor dirt, feces and
grease.

"Emaciated-appearing carcass that had the inspection was observed to have a well-marked inflammation of pleural and peritoneal
surfaces.

"Hogs which carried the state inspection stamp were observed
in one of the coolers with a great deal of hair, bruises, scuff and
toenails on the carcasses and with the livers still hanging by their
natural attachments. Cattle were observed being slaughtered without
even the most cursory examination. . . .

"A large amount of extensively moldy product [was] observed
on the racks. Smoked sausage with the appearance of a ready-to-eat
product was being smoked at a temperature of 120 degrees or less.

"Walls in the killing area and others were deeply coated with
dried blood, tissue scraps and cobwebs. Cooler floors were covered
with trash, meat scraps and dirty water. . . ."

VIRGINIA—*Mandatory Inspection, nationally known firm*

"It was noted the meat-grinder bearings had much encrusted
putrid material which would readily result in bacterial contamination
of the ground meat. Sausage was hung on unclean aluminum smoke

sticks, and no attempt had been made to clean the sausage mixer, which had a copious amount of sausage emulsion adhering to the paddles and inner portion of the mixer. Such emulsions are excellent media for bacteria growth, and daily cleaning is a necessary operation. Some beef cuts hanging in the cooler showed evidence of soilage while in transit but none had been reconditioned by removing the soiled portions. Other insanitary conditions noted were ceilings with leaks dripping on exposed meat, causing serious contamination, and flaking paint in areas where exposed meat is normally handled. Some cockroaches were observed in the curing cellar where exposed meat is handled and stored."

MARYLAND—*No Mandatory Meat Inspection*

"There were a great number of live (and dead) flies in the department which were swarming on exposed meat and equipment. One end of a meat hopper on a grinder which appeared to have been recently used had a number of dead flies on it . . . the floor of the room was covered with filthy sawdust.

. . . . The wood portions of the tables of stainless steel tops were encrusted with dried blood and were not susceptible to proper cleaning."

NEW YORK—*Mandatory Inspection*[6]

"While the legislators were slashing the budget request, dead animals were being skinned out a block from the capital and sold for hamburger. Of 30 random samples of hamburger picked up in one week, 26 were found to be 'embalmed' with sulphite.

"Also detected were frankfurters containing about 20 percent skin, additive-loaded hams retaining five to ten times the amount of water permitted; sausage with up to 20 percent cereal and products containing hog blood, lungs, niacin, water, detergent, anti-biotics, etc.

"Chemical-wise, you name it and we have it in New York. About 90 percent of the uninspected processed meat sold in the State bears deceptive labeling."

NEW JERSEY—*Mandatory State Inspection*[7]

"Employees were doing the dressing operations. They skinned the carcasses hanging on a rail and although a sink was present, did not utilize it to wash their hands. They simply continued after skinning the carcasses by eviscerating the carcass with fecal-contaminated hands and knives. . . .

"Employes were using their hands and forearms to empty product from the silent cutter into a sausage truck and rinsing their hands in a metal drum containing tepid water. This is conducive to bacterial growth and the spread of contamination. After using his forearms to empty meat from the silent cutter, the employee would use his hands to scrape the meat still adhering to the cutter. The employee would use his hands to scrape the meat still adhering to his arms. This would remove the residues and at the same time probably loosen some hairs which would accompany the residue into a truck of sausage meat.

"Pork skins were put through an emusifier and used in bologna and frankfurter without declaration. Pork skins are not classed as meat and are not permitted in a product labeled 'all meat.' When used they should be declared as such on the ingredient statement to fully inform the consumer on the nature of the product he is buying.

"At the time of visit, when they were stuffing frankfurters and pumping tongues, management stated they knew of no limitations on the use of additives or adulterants.

"All chopped beef was weighed in a dirty wooden bucket before it was added to the silent cutter.

"Observed slaughter of calves in the morning. . . . Inspector was not in the plant during the preparation. Heads not identified with carcasses . . . Intestines removed and discarded. Hearts, lungs and livers removed and not identified with carcasses. Identification of carcasses and parts is essential for proper inspection."

New Jersey was always supposed to have one of the best state inspection setups. Yet, when inspection of meat was transferred from the State Department of Health to the State Department of Agriculture after the new meat law was passed, New Jersey Secretary of Agriculture Phillip Alampi said, "One of the major problems the state will face is locating the hundreds of meat plants officials are unaware of."

Alampi said that the meat plants had been hiring their own inspectors and "that a plant owner's relative could easily be the inspector."

He noted that 85 percent of the meat in New Jersey had been under federal inspection but that inspection of the remaining 15 percent is "quite difficult because they are mainly small plants—they're out in the hinterlands and not readily accessible."[8]

New Jersey is not one of the four states that have adequate poultry inspection.

Poultry may be marketed as dressed, eviscerated, or cut-up types of chickens, turkeys, or other fowl. These may be in the form of fresh, chilled, or frozen products. A large amount of cooked poultry meat is marketed as canned products or as ingredients in several types of frozen products.

Poultry, by its very nature, is contaminated with bacteria on the surface. The more is is handled, the more germs grow and the more likely it is to make you sick.[9] Clean birds or parts packed in ice or held at 32 to 34 degrees F. should have a shelf life of approximately four days without a marked rise in surface contamination. If the temperature is allowed to rise even a few degrees, serious contamination will occur. If birds are held at room temperature for only a few hours before being placed under chilled temperature, chances of causing illness are increased. If the surface of the skin or exposed flesh is slick, watch out! It is likely that the bacteria count on that piece of poultry is in the millions.

In January, 1968, federal inspectors discovered that one out of every five nonfederally inspected chickens was not fit to eat. They found that the "errors" in nonfederally inspected poultry included passing products with "gross lesions of disease as well as failure to remove infectious processes and contamination of the body cavity with stomach contents or fecal material."

Arthur N. Wilder, D.V.M., formerly Epidemic Intelligence Service Officer, Communicable Disease Center, and Robert A. Mac-Cready, M.D., Director, Diagnostic Laboratories, Massachusetts Department of Public Health, told of conditions in one poultry plant in Massachusetts:

"The processing equipment was crowded together and frequently inaccessible for proper sanitizing and cleaning during processing. The processing line was often understaffed and at times moved too rapidly. When this occurred, birds often fell off the line, or if improperly processed by an undermanned station, were removed from the line and stacked on the floor by an employee of the next station. The birds remained there, sometimes up to an hour, until someone was available to replace them on the line for reprocessing. The birds then continued with the others through the remaining processing stations. . . .

"The chilling vats, for whole birds and edible viscera, frequently contained water of a bloody consistence and were rarely replenished with fresh ice. The edible viscera and chicken necks frequently remained and soaked in the contaminated chilling vats before being conveyed to the wrapping table, which subsequently became a heavily contaminated area yielding 23 isolates of salmonella out of 57 samples."[10]

Senator Joseph Montoya, of New Mexico, in his statement before the Subcommittee of the Committee on Agriculture and Forestry of the United States Senate, in 1967, eloquently explained why more federal legislation of meat and meat products was necessary:

"Products ready for home use without further preparation have proliferated. They are more highly processed, with greater opportunity for adulteration and deception that a purchaser would not notice.

"All these advancements complicate inspection procedures. Inspection of meat for wholesomeness, without use of chemical analysis, is most effective when meat is fresh. Frozen meat must be defrosted prior to inspection. If there is suspicion of adulteration or unwholesomeness, it must be examined and tested closely, often requiring laboratory analysis.

"Adequate inspection of a fast processing line is far more difficult than is visual examination of carcasses and fresh meat. Also in modern processing, there is often less opportunity for inspectors to check each stage of operation.

"A significant disparity exists between Federal, State and local statutes regarding meat inspection. This disparity creates a form of economic separation that confers a very real competitive advantage upon the unregulated.

"Fifteen percent of commercially slaughtered animals—over 19 million head—are not slaughtered under federal inspection. Some of these are subject to state or local laws of varying stringency. Others are sold without any form of government inspection.

"About one quarter of the commercially processed meat products —an estimated 9 billion pounds—is processed without Federal inspection. This includes a wide assortment of products such as sausage, ham, bacon and canned and frozen meat specialty items. These products, usually made from two or more ingredients and often containing spices, flavoring, extenders or other additives are particularly vulnerable to adulteration.

"Many of these meats and meat products receive little or no inspection to assure their wholesomeness and freedom from adulteration."

Senator Mondale pointed out: "Modern science has developed and continues to develop new wonder chemicals—additives, preservatives and colorations—which can prevent the consumer from using the normal smell and sight tests to determine spoilage or deterioration, which will also provide a crude consumer test for toxic or diseased meat or meat products growing alongside the spoilage bacteria. Consumers have no chance at all to determine the safety of the meat they buy."

He and Senator Allen J. Ellender, Congressman Neal Smith, Congressman Thomas Foley, and many others all worked hard to get passage of the 1967 Meat Act after such measures were turned down in 1961, 1963, and 1965. Every consumer owes them a debt of gratitude.

The first Meat Inspection Act, March 18, 1907, was put into force after the author Upton Sinclair revealed conditions in meat plants in his book *The Jungle*.

The new meat bill passed on November 21, 1967, provides matching funds for states to improve their meat-inspection programs. It also:

• Extends the federal program to commerce wholly within the District of Columbia or within any territory not having a legislative body.

• Prohibits commerce in animal products not intended for human use unless denatured or in animal products properly identified as not intended for human use or naturally inedible.

• Provides for record keeping by certain slaughterers and handlers; registration and regulation of certain handlers of dead, dying, disabled, or diseased animals.

• Authorizes regulation of meat storage and handling to prevent adulteration or misbranding.

• Provides for withdrawal or refusal of inspection service, for detention, seizure and condemnation, injunction and investigation as new enforcement tools.

• Subjects meat imports to the same requirements as those for domestic meats.

• Otherwise revises and clarifies the Federal Meat Inspection Act.

In a letter to the author, Senator Mondale said: "I am totally satisfied with the new [meat] law, and I feel that it was the best possible bill that could have been passed."[11]

But, unfortunately, there is still plenty of opportunity—although certainly not so much as before—to slip adulterated meat onto the consumer's plate.

First of all, it will take several years to implement the meat bill. States had two years from the November, 1967, date of passage of the meat bill to better their inspection procedures. They had a third year to make improvements after being warned by the Secretary of Agriculture that their inspection was inadequate.

Even though the federal government will provide matching funds to states for inspections, some states are going to balk at federal interference. And even states that want to implement better inspection from the bottom of their legislative toes are still going to find it difficult to obtain trained meat inspectors.

Chet Huntley of Huntley-Brinkley fame created a tempest in an abattoir when he said that many New York truck drivers were quitting their jobs to become meat inspectors.

The fact remains that federal inspection is no guarantee of clean meat today. The majority of meat has been inspected federally for more than sixty years, but hog cholera and brucellosis are so prevalent in America that other countries, including England and Sweden, have banned the import of pork products from the United States. There is more trichinosis in the United States than in any part of the world. About one in six inhabitants of this country harbor the trichinae, with clinical symptoms displayed by 4.5 percent.[12]

United States Department of Agriculture inspectors grade fresh cuts of meat in descending order of quality: Prime, Choice, Good, Standard, Commercial, or Utility. Retail stores most often carry meat of "Choice" quality. The three upper grades indicate meat of excellent quality, flavor, and tenderness. The three lower grades are better for braising, pot roasts, stews, and so on.

Once a plant is in operation, every live animal is supposedly examined in its holding pen by a veterinarian or by an inspector supervised by a veterinarian. After slaughter, federal meat inspectors are supposed to examine each carcass, including internal organs and glands, to be sure that no unwholesome condition exists. A carcass that passes this inspection is stamped with a purple USDA shield mark.

During the production of processed meat, inspectors are supposed to examine both meat and nonmeat ingredients, and check a dozen or more steps to ensure that meat is wholesome and prepared according to approved formulas. They inspect curing solutions, check processing times and temperatures, and control the use of restricted ingredients. They must see that all containers are properly filled and labeled.

Sounds good on paper, doesn't it?

In New York City, a city health inspector walked into a *federally* inspected *kosher* sausage and frankfurter manufacturing firm on the lower east side in February, 1968. "Federally inspected" means that a USDA inspector had to certify the meat. "Kosher" means "clean" and prepared under the supervision of a rabbi trained in such work. The New York City inspector found approximately seventy-five violations, and noted, among them:

"The worm gears in the meat grinder were rusty and caked with bits of old fat and meat. Paint was scaling off the equipment and falling into the hot-dog mixtures. Fresh meat was being stored in rusty tubs.

"A sterilizer required in Federal plants to contain 180-degree water for sterilization of knives that are dropped on the floor was full of cold, greasy water. A dead roach floated in the scum of the water's surface.

"Evidence of rats was everywhere, even where meat was being handled . . . and there was a Federal inspector on the premises."[13]

Then there was the "Case of the Counterfeit USDA Meat Stamp." One must marvel at the officers of a wholesale meat company in New York for their brazenness. During 1963, the Feldman Veal Corporation of 410 West Thirteenth Street and two of its officers were charged with selling inferior, ungraded meat bearing counterfeit Department of Agriculture seals to the United States Military Academy at West Point. The company shipped 24,330 pounds of veal legs to the Academy for about $16,000. It was supposedly "Choice" cut.

One of the company's competing firms became suspicious of the low bids. A losing company has the right to inspect the product of the winner. This was done; and, according to Jack Kaplan, Assistant United States Attorney, it was discovered that the shipped meat was one and two grades inferior to Choice meat and that the USDA seals were counterfeit.[14]

The Feldman company received a $1 fine in Federal Court after conviction. Abraham E. Abrahamson, head of the New York City Department of Food and Drugs, declared: "It is always our hope that when we win a case in the public interest, there will be a suitable penalty."[15]

A poultry bill similar to the meat bill was drawn up. However, Drew Pearson, that fighting newspaperman from Washington, reported in 1968 that lobbyists quietly slipped a provision into the Federal Poultry Inspection bill that seriously weakened it. It is a provision that to be liable for prosecution, poultry distributors must have a willful knowledge of adulteration. Representative Thomas Foley, according to Pearson, "vigorously opposed the clause. He pointed out that it was highly difficult to prove willful knowledge against a defendant in court." Furthermore, the poultry bill exempts from inspection farmers and processors doing less than $15,000 a year in wholesale business.

But even the best law is no protection against unscrupulous operators and dealers in dirty and diseased meat.

Dr. M. R. Clarkson, then Associate Administrator of the Agriculture Research Service, United States Department of Agriculture, said before the Food and Drug and Cosmetic Law Section of the New York Bar Association, in New York City: "One of the toughest jobs in meat inspection—the task of certifying the wholesomeness of processed meats—grows increasingly difficult as new techniques are used . . . and as housewives depend more and more on the processor to prepare foods once cooked at home.

"We can't depend on laboratory analysis of samples to protect consumers against unfit or adulterated meat and poultry products. It is impossible to detect them—even microscopically—when mixtures have been chopped or blended or cooked."[16]

His comment becomes even more appalling when you read the National Livestock and Meat Board's booklet "Facts About Sausage." It states: "With over 200 varieties of sausage and ready-to-serve meats to choose from, menus built around them are literally endless.

"When selecting sausage or ready-to-serve meats, choosing some of the less familiar ones can add excitement to the menu. . . ."[17] Like Russian roulette?

Neil Peck, former Assistant United States Attorney, Southern District of New York, also pointed out the difficulty in identifying bad meat, even under the federal inspection system. In an article written in cooperation with James C. G. Conniff for *Pageant* magazine, in May, 1968, Peck said that he began an investigation into violations of the Federal Meat Inspection Laws in New York City in 1964. It required more than fourteen months to complete:

"This unhealthy meat, which came from various parts of the country, had been derived from so-called 4-D sources. It had been frozen into 50-pound blocks and then shipped east to the New York metropolitan area. In its frozen state—dark as a mahogany table top, so that you couldn't tell by looking at it what was in it . . . the shipment of frozen meat blocks was put directly into the machines that manufacture these processed meats.

Some meat, Peck said, came from animals that had rabies. On many occasions, the fifty-pound blocks of meat contained hide, teeth, pieces of hooves, whiskers, and other indigestible parts of the animal. "In one instance we found that every single block of meat in the entire truckload was contaminated with one or more of these filthy or inedible materials."

Peck said inspectors can spot-check only one or two cartons in an order containing 30,000 to 40,000 pounds of meat. If such a shipment goes to a plant with two federal inspectors, it would take them weeks to inspect the meat properly in that one shipment. They would have to melt down all the blocks to make sure it was all good meat.[18]

Improper use of legitimate chemicals is another hard-to-detect area of meat inspection.

Dr. K. E. Taylor of the United States Department of Agriculture Meat Inspection Service, writing in the *Journal of the American Veterinary Medical Association,* in 1962, said there are approximately twenty insecticides, eleven feed additives, and seven therapeutic agents that have been approved by the Meat Inspection Division. "However, if they are not used properly, even they leave a residue in the meat derived from cattle, sheep, calves, swine and goat."[19]

But how can you tell? Even the Meat Inspection Division's own regulations and instructions pertaining to biological residues in meats say: "In acute poisoning resulting from cholinesterase inhibiting pesticides, the lesions are never pathognomonic or particularly outstanding."[20]

As far as antibiotic residues are concerned, if the injection is not given in the usual place, the haunch, inspectors may miss the fact that the animal has been loaded with antibiotics just before slaughter. At best, even federal inspectors can just spot-check for signs that the animals have been injected recently.[21]

Although laboratory tests may not reveal some forms of contamination, they certainly are necessary. The visual inspection of meat alone, without chemical and biological testing, is as old-fashioned as crossing the ocean in a sailing ship.

David C. Tudor, V.M.D., Research Professor of Poultry Pathology at Rutgers, said in an article in *Veterinary Medicine,* in February, 1967:

"A reliable poultry disease diagnosis is based upon clinical and laboratory findings from several living and dead birds that typify the flock condition. It is essential that all parts of the bird be examined for gross abnormalities or evidence of disease."

Here are some of the laboratory procedures Dr. Tudor believes necessary for adequate poultry inspection:

• To establish the kind and extent of intestinal parasitism, fecal scrapings from four regions of the intestinal tract are examined under low-power microscopy.

• To establish rapidly the presence of bacterial infections such as tuberculosis and erysipelas, impression smears of the spleen and liver tissues are sometimes helpful. An acid stain must be prepared to identify tuberculosis organisms.

• Evidence of anemia, leukemia, or parasitism may be gained from blood smears prepared from the heart, blood, or blood taken from the brachial wing vein and stained with Wright's stain.

• Fowl cholera may be diagnosed when paradimethylamino benzaldehyde solutions added to the broth culture of fowl cholera yields a pink color. In the absence of this diagnostic tint, a diagnosis of the disease cannot be made.

• To identify salmonella infection, initial bacterial agar colonies may be transferred to nutrient peptone or tryptose broth and then to S.S. agar or MacConkey's agar.

In addition to the laboratory tests, there are about two hundred clinical observations that Dr. Tudor says can lead to a diagnosis of disease in fowl. Such diagnosis, of course, is difficult to make when birds go past an inspector—even a federal inspector—at the rate of approximately six a minute on an assembly line.[22]

As for the laboratory inspection of meat, the necessity was made clear in *Recommended Methods for the Microbiological Examination of Foods,* edited by J. M. Sharf and published by the American Public Health Association in 1966:

"Meat appears on the market in many forms and microbiological methods are needed to assay for quality, detect spoilage and determine the source of any quality defects. As a result of various methods of producing, processing and handling meat products, some meat foods act as selective or enrichment media for specific types of microorganisms."[23]

Some states have little or no facility for testing food for adulteration and contamination. A large percentage of food inspectors have no degrees beyond high school, and some are close to illiterate.

A few are dishonest. As one health officer of a large eastern city put it to me: "When you have underpaid inspectors in one spot for a long time, you are bound to get some hanky panky."

Under the present system, even a federal meat inspector may be assigned to the same plant for years. During this time, he is bound to become very friendly with the personnel. In other investigative branches of government, inspectors are periodically moved about to prevent such temptation.

But perhaps the biggest flaw in the protection of meat, even with the new act, is the lack of properly trained scientists and inspectors. Money cannot buy skilled employees who do not exist.

I wish I could say that shopping by name brand or in a well-known market is a good protection. It is not!

At the hearings on meat, it was brought out that companies such as Swift, the largest meat processor in the United States, maintained intrastate plants that avoided federal inspection. The reports of the 1962 and 1967 United States Department of Agriculture survey of such intrastate plants were not favorable to Swift. Here is W. F. Bonilla's report, dated July 31, 1967, concerning a Swift plant. Bonilla is a Department of Agriculture investigator:

"This plant is a wholesale meat jobber and conducts smoking

of hams. It is under the State of Arizona meat inspection system. The
building is new, but the facilities inadequate. Working areas are
crowded.

"General sanitation is poor throughout. Smokehouse area is
cluttered with storage of boxes, papers, bags, etc. Overall sanitation
could be greatly improved. No sterilizers in the working area. Wooden
tables are in use. Equipment is inadequately sanitized."

A September, 1962, USDA report of a Swift plant in Richmond,
Virginia, has been quoted; after it appeared in the *Congressional
Record,* the plant's activities were curtailed; it now distributes only
meat. In another 1962 report, a USDA inspector noted that in the
Swift plant in New Orleans, "There is no control over trichina and
no control in the use of 'restricted items' such as nitrite and
aureomycin."

Swift was not the only national company to get around the
federal law, but with the new Meat Act, and under the light of publicity, there should be considerable improvement.

As far as buying in a chain supermarket, Senator Mondale said
at the congressional meat hearings:

"This is based on some reports which I obtained from the Department of Agriculture—based on a laboratory analysis of nonfederally inspected meat products, 1967, and there were purchases
made at national chain grocery stores of national branded meats of
162 samples, purchased by the Department's laboratory, and of
those only 39 met all Federal standards, and a partial examination
of this study revealed that nonfederally inspected meat products
which do not meet Federal standards have been sold by such stores
as Safeway, Piggly Wiggly and A&P, Kroger and First National
Stores. And products not meeting the standards have been manufactured by the Nation's two largest firms, Swift & Co., and Armour
& Company, according to these same reports. There are many examples of this.

"A purchase made at the Safeway store in Phoenix, Arizona,
where the investigator bought skinless frankfurters, proved in laboratory analysis to contain 13 percent water and 7.6 percent fillers, that
is, nonfat dried milk, soy flour, cereal and the like, quite in excess
of Federal standards. In a Piggly Wiggly store in Mississippi, the
investigator bought some bologna which proved to contain four times
as much cereal fillers as would have been permitted under Federal

regulations. . . . And then there is another element that came out in these studies which, I think, is interesting and reveals the fact of the helplessness of the consumer in trying to deal for herself and her family in meat purchases. This was shown in terms of ascorbate. This is prohibited in processed meat or nonprocessed meat by Federal plants that are federally inspected. If I understand it, this is a kind of healthy formaldehyde. It makes meat that is starting to become stale look red and healthy. . . .

"There was a purchase made at Baltimore, Md., a purchase of pork sausage, which showed 445 parts per million of ascorbate, which would never be permitted in a federally inspected plant. Another purchase [was] made in Baltimore at a Safeway store of pork which contained 389 parts per million of ascorbate."

WHAT CAN YOU DO TO PROTECT YOURSELF FROM ADULTERATED FISH, MEAT, AND POULTRY?

In answer to the above question, most health officers to whom I spoke said, "Nothing." They explained that there is no way, in today's marketplace, for a consumer to be sure that the fish, meat, or chicken she is buying is wholesome. Sight and smell are no longer to be trusted because the chemicals that are in use today can doctor decaying, diseased, or just plain stale food. All a consumer can do, they say, is to rely on the federal, state, or local inspector, and put his faith in the brand name of the product and the store selling it.

However, it is apparent to me, after engaging in research for this book, that there are things that consumers can and should do to protect their food. Here they are:

1. Report any sanitary violation found in a store and any contamination of packaged food discovered at home.

2. Report any outbreak of suspected foodborne illness in the family. (While most boards of health and other protective agencies may be too understaffed to search out abuses effectively, they usually are only too happy to follow through on a suspected offense.)

3. Urge any group you belong to, or do-it-yourself, to find out how your state is implementing fish, poultry, and meat inspection. Some states are sure to claim insufficient funds or insufficient personnel, and to lag behind on food-inspection improvements.

4. Don't purchase any meat in a supermarket if its container has been damaged in any way.

5. Don't buy an unrefrigerated canned ham. Canned hams must be refrigerated at all times, and many supermarkets ignore this cardinal rule.

6. Don't contaminate the meat at home yourself. Fresh meat should be unwrapped as soon as it comes from the market. Store fresh meat uncovered or loosely covered in the coldest part of the refrigerator. Cured meat should also be stored in the refrigerator. Canned hams should be kept under refrigeration. Frozen meat should be stored at a temperature of 0 degrees F. or lower. It may be placed in the refrigerator under ordinary refrigeration if it is to be used immediately after defrosting. Never refreeze meat.

7. Do not leave frozen fowl unrefrigerated to defrost. Keep them in the refrigerator even if it takes several days for them to thaw.

8. Don't place other food in a container that previously held raw meat, and do not place other foods on a counter on which raw meat, fish, or poultry has been without first disinfecting the counter with soap and water.

9. Wash your hands after touching raw meat.

10. Practice good hygiene. Wash your hands after going to the bathroom, and don't handle meat when you are ill with a contagious ailment, especially an infected finger.

11. Never, never eat raw or undercooked meat.

12. Don't look for bargains. If meat, fish, or poultry in any form is being sold far below the normal price, there's a reason, and it is usually not for the benefit of the consumer.

4   NOTES

1. Edward Press, M.D., and Leona Yeager, M.D., "Food Poisoning Due to Sodium Nicotinate," *American Journal of Public Health,* October, 1962.
2. Rodney Leonard, Deputy Assistant Secretary of the Consumer Marketing Service, United States Department of Agriculture, testimony before congressional hearings on meat, November, 1967.
3. Stephen Kota, testimony at congressional meat hearings, November, 1967.
4. Leslie Orear, Division of Publications, United Packinghouse Food and Allied Workers, AFL-CIO, statement read at congressional meat hearings, November, 1967.
5. *Congressional Record,* Senate, August 3, 1967, S 10747.

6. Remarks of Dr. William E. Jennings, Director of the Division of Meat Inspection, New York State, quoted in *The National Provisioner,* April 20, 1963.

7. *Congressional Record,* Senate, August 3, 1967, S 10747.

8. Phillip Alampi, New Jersey Secretary of Agriculture, statements on WOR-TV, New Jersey Reports, as quoted in the *Newark News,* April 14, 1968.

9. *Recommended Methods for the Microbiological Examination of Foods,* edited by J. M. Sarf (American Public Health Association, 1966), p. 119.

10. Arthur N. Wilder, D.V.M., and Robert A. MacCready, M.D., "Isolation of Salmonella from Poultry," *New England Journal of Medicine,* June 30, 1966, Vol. 274, No. 26.

11. Personal correspondence, February 14, 1968.

12. World Health Organization Report, 1957.

13. *New York Times,* March 4, 1968.

14. New York Criminal Court, Judge Milton Shalleck, June 18, 1968.

15. "City Health Official Is Critical of $1 Fine in Sale of Dirty Veal," *New York Times,* July 3, 1968.

16. M. R. Clarkson, Associate Administrator, Agriculture Research Service, USDA, before the Food and Drug and Cosmetic Law Section of the New York Bar Association, New York City, January 24, 1962.

17. "Facts About Sausage," National Livestock Meat Board, 36 S. Wabash Ave., Chicago, Ill.

18. Neil Peck, former Assistant U.S. Attorney, Southern District, New York, as told to James C. G. Conniff, *Pageant,* May, 1968, Vol. 23, No. 11.

19. K. E. Taylor, D.V.M., USDA Meat Inspection Service, *American Veterinary Medical Journal,* November 15, 1962.

20. "Biological Residues in Meat and Meat Food Products," Instructions and Standards of Compliance, 11:27, November 7, 1964.

21. Ruth Winter, Newark *Star-Ledger,* March 5, 1965.

22. David Tudor, D.V.M., Research Professor of Poultry Pathology, Rutgers, in *Veterinary Medicine,* February, 1967.

23. *Recommended Methods for the Microbiological Examination of Foods,* edited by J. M. Sharf, (American Public Health Association, 1966), p. 111.

5

A Fish Story

BECAUSE A THREE-YEAR-OLD boy of Haddon Heights, New Jersey, was hungry a little earlier than usual, his mother cooked some fillet of flounder for him; the rest of the family was to eat their portion of the fish later. The little boy gobbled it down, ate his dessert, drank some milk, and then announced that he was going to his grandmother's, nearby.

The rest of the family sat down to eat their dinner after the boy had left.

The child had just reached his grandmother's when he complained of feeling ill. He turned blue and began gasping for air. An ambulance was summoned, but before it could speed its tiny burden to the hospital, the little boy died.

His parents and the rest of the family, all of whom were in the midst of their meal when they heard about the boy, stopped eating. But they began to suffer from dizziness, nausea, and cyanosis (lack of oxygen).

Later that same evening, the Poison Control Center in Philadelphia reported to the Chief of the Philadelphia Milk and Food Sanitation Section that three women who had eaten at a Philadelphia restaurant were hospitalized when they became ill within an hour after their meal. All three women had eaten flounder. All three had become faint, suffered headaches, dizziness, and vomiting, and were cyanotic.

Robert C. Stanfill, District Director of the Food and Drug Administration, and a neighbor of the boy's family was shaving when he heard a report of the youngster's death on the radio. He left immediately for his office.

He and physicians and other inspectors who became involved in the case concluded that a chemical which looks like ordinary table salt but which is illegally used to freshen rotting fish, sodium nitrite, was probably the cause of the poisoning. A chemist was assigned to run tests for nitrites on portions of the foods eaten by the victims.

Stanfill recalled: "Meantime, Philadelphia Department of Public Health Inspectors, New Jersey Department of Health personnel, the Camden County New Jersey Detective Bureau personnel, Haddon Regional Health Commission and many other local officials were investigating reports of illnesses and were sampling fish, searching for records of sales of sodium nitrite and otherwise participating in individual and group efforts to obtain all the facts.

"The facts pouring in definitely showed the presence of large quantities of sodium nitrite in the fillets delivered to the Yeadon chain-store warehouse and the one restaurant sale, but fillets sold to other stores by the same and other fish dealers did not show such evidence," he continued. "These findings narrowed the probable distribution of toxic fillets. Evidence of nitrites was present under the brine hoops on the concrete floor, and on the cutting table of Universal Seafood Company, Inc. The president and employees denied any use of nitrites. The proof was not yet definite as to how the incident occurred."

The health departments and the federal inspectors involved in the case issued public warnings concerning the possibility that people might have in their possession contaminated fillets of flounder.

"About the same time that Daniel DiOrio [president of Universal Seafood] was on a Philadelphia television program denying—as a spokesman for the fish industry—that anyone in the fish industry had or would use sodium nitrite, Dr. John Hanlon, the Philadelphia Director of Public Services, and I appeared on Station WRCV-TV after 11 P.M. to assure the public that the distribution of the poisoned fish didn't go beyond the nearby 3-state area around Philadelphia," Stanfill said.

"It was on Good Friday that the persistence of Food and Drug Inspector Frederick A. Cassidy resulted in the manager of a chemical and salt supply house joining Cassidy in a search of the firm's sales records covering a period of more than a year. The records showed a hurry-up early-morning delivery of 400 pounds of sodium nitrite had been rushed to Universal Seafood Co., Inc., on the Monday before the little boy died on Tuesday night. A smaller shipment had been delivered during Lent the year before. Investigation disclosed that DiOrio had personally authorized the order and personally accompanied the 400-pound drum from the truck to the filleting room. The drum bore bold red letters."

Stanfill told his colleagues at a Food and Drug meeting that the defendants, DiOrio and Universal Seafood Company, pleaded "no defense" to a charge alleging addition to fillets of a "poisonous and deleterious preservative for the purpose of misleading and defrauding."

He said the persistent investigational work by Food and Drug inspectors, police officers, health officers, public health inspectors and agents received recognition. But he pointed out that the quiet, efficient work done in the laboratory also deserves commendation. Stanfill described how the laboratory rapidly developed the proof that the fillets had been adulterated with nitrite to give them the smell and appearance of freshness when the fish were far from it.

"The facts were presented to a Federal Grand Jury," Stanfill recounted. "The Grand Jury indicted the fish processor, Universal Seafood Company, Inc., of Philadelphia, Daniel DiOrio, its president and treasurer; and Noel LoCastro, its foreman. . . . The corporation, which went out of business soon after the poisoning was publicized, was fined $100. DiOrio was fined $2,500 and sentenced to a year in jail, with 11 months suspended during a 3-year probation period. DiOrio's attorney petitioned the court to release DiOrio from jail and presented medical testimony that DiOrio had a heart disease and imprisonment was not good for his health. DiOrio was released after 16 days."

Stanfill said: "I am usually objective about matters pertaining to sentencing and serving sentences. Many citizens were indignant that DiOrio had only a month to serve and were more so when he was released after 16 days. . . .

"When DiOrio was in court for sentence after pleading 'Nolo Contendere,' a parade of fish dealers and other business associates and competitors appeared as character witnesses. A spectator remarked: 'But for the grace of God, it may have been any one of them.'

"I could not fully agree, but it seemed to be a sad commentary that a man who deliberately poisoned rotten fish, and whose deliberate action caused a child to die, was wholeheartedly supported by his fellow merchants. After dissolving Universal Seafood Co., Inc., Di-Orio has continued his lucrative fish business in his own name."[1]

Fortunately, such situations where death results from fish products are rare. Unfortunately, illnesses as the result of fish products are not rare, and are increasing all the time.

One of the problems is that, twenty-five years ago, there were relatively few types of fish products offered for sale compared with what is available today. In those days, the problems of ensuring freshness and preventing decomposition of fish products were paramount, according to J. Kenneth Kirk, Associate Commissioner for Compliance of the Food and Drug Administration.

Kirk said: "Recent years have seen a marked increase in the production of 'convenience' foods where the consumer has to do no more than heat the product to serving temperature. In the seafood area, this includes breaded shrimp, tuna potpies, breaded fish sticks and portions, crabmeat, deviled crab, etc. The elaborate and frequently untried production methods involved in processing of such foods have introduced new problems. These items require a great deal of handling in the producing plant and consequently plant sanitation is of prime importance to insure a safe and wholesome finished product."[2]

Such new developments, however, are not the only problem. They compound old problems—lack of inspection and outdated American methods of fishing and fish-product production. These problems are growing worse, not better, because of competition from foreign imports.

According to Harold E. Crowther, Director of the Bureau of Commercial Fisheries, United States Department of the Interior, there are forty American plants under voluntary inspection. The Bureau of Fisheries has sixty inspectors who inspect 265 million pounds of fishery products a year.

"When you compare the number of plants—there are approximately 2,200 processing plants shipping in interstate commerce—40 plants is not a large percentage of these," he said. "Two hundred sixty-five million compared to 1.4 billion pounds of products on the edible weight basis again is not a large percentage."[3]

Agents from another branch of government, Food and Drug inspectors, have discovered many serious deficiencies in fish handling and sanitary practices in a number of plants and vessels inspected, according to Philip R. Lee, M.D., Assistant Secretary for Health and Scientific Affairs, Department of Health, Education, and Welfare.

Testifying before a congressional committee trying to develop a fishery-products protection Act, on April 23, 1968, Dr. Lee said inspectors found conditions which include:

• "Vessels improperly equipped and maintained to handle and preserve the fish catch in a sanitary manner. For example, inadequate facilities to keep the fish iced and use of polluted water to wash both boats and fish.

• "Improper practices in unloading the fish. For example, allowing fish to sit on docks in open boxes in the sunlight for long periods of time, thus accelerating decomposition and allowing contamination by birds and other animals. Also the use of pitchforks in unloading the fish. [This creates an opening whereby bacteria on the skin or in the intestines are permitted to permeate the flesh and as a result deterioration is much enhanced.][4]

• "Grossly insanitary conditions and improper controls in processing plants. For example, failure to keep the establishments clean and clear of debris or refuse, as well as external influences such as fly and roach infestations which attack the fish during its processing. Also, failure to control properly sterilization and can-closing operations."

• "Improper sanitation measures by employees in fish-processing plants. For example, employees' failure to wash their hands after handling dirty objects such as garbage cans, and employees returning fish that have dropped on the floor to the processing line."

"In addition," Dr. Lee said, "to the problem of decomposed and filth-contaminated fish, we have the problem of insanitary processing and handling procedures which may result in diseases in man. Among the most frequently mentioned are botulism, Salmonellosis and other food poisonings of varying degrees of seriousness.

"In 1963, inadequate safeguards in processing smoked lake fish resulted in a major outbreak of botulism; nine persons died. During one weekend in 1966, about 400 cases of salmonella poisoning were reported. The illness was directly attributable to smoked fish.

"In 1966, more than 250 cases of food poisoning were reported in one city; imported shrimp was identified as the cause.

"Infectious hepatitis has been linked to shellfish in four different incidents since 1964. A total of 309 confirmed cases of hepatitis have been traced to shellfish from four eastern coastal areas. These are some of the reported cases. No one knows how many cases of illness attributable to fish go unreported every year. Clearly, unless consumer protection methods are strengthened, further cases of disease or death may be anticipated."[5]

By piecing reports together, a picture can be obtained of the factors that caused the contamination and how they led to the illness of the unsuspecting fish eaters.

On May 30, 1966, a bar mitzvah was held in Edison, New Jersey. A bar mitzvah is an occasion marking the time when a Jewish boy of thirteen years has attained the age of religious duty and responsibility. There were 121 guests in all, arriving in two shifts—one beginning at 2:00 P.M. and the second at about 8:00 P.M.

According to Dr. Eugene J. Gangarosa and his colleagues who documented the case in the January, 1968, *American Journal of Public Health*,[6] the next day, May 31, fever and upset stomach were reported by many who attended the party. Their symptoms developed from one to seventy-two hours after the affair. They had diarrhea, abdominal cramps, nausea, vomiting, fever as high as 104 F., shaking, chills, dehydration, headache, and general prostration. The uncomfortable illness lasted from two to ten days.

The bar mitzvah party was catered by a Newark, New Jersey, firm, and smoked whitefish was among the thirty items served. The same menu, except for the smoked whitefish, had been served by this catering firm at four other gatherings, with no reported illnesses following. By questioning those who became ill, it was discovered that the one thing they had eaten in common was the smoked whitefish.

Samples taken from the ill guests showed the presence of *Salmonella* identified as *S. java*.

The smoked whitefish was purchased from a delicatessen at 11:00 A.M. on May 30 and was taken directly to the bar mitzvah party arriving at noon. *The delivery truck was unrefrigerated.*

"The delicatessen had received its usual large shipment of smoked whitefish from its customary source, a fish-processing company in Brooklyn, New York, on Friday morning, May 27, 1966. The fish was stored in a large freezer which was in good operating condition. The delicatessen was open for business over the Memorial Day weekend, during which most of the whitefish was sold. None of the employees of the delicatessen had been ill prior to the Memorial Day weekend, but two of them who ate smoked whitefish developed the fever and upset stomach during this period.

Dr. Gangarosa said: "More than 12 separate outbreaks similar to the one bar mitzvah 'blitz' occurred during the Memorial Day weekend; more than 300 cases of fever and upset stomach were reported by local health departments throughout the greater metropolitan area of New York, New Jersey and Pennsylvania. Several patients required hospitalization, but there were no known deaths.

"The vehicle of infection was traced to one of the major whitefish smoking plants in the area. On April 1, the smoking plant had been seriously damaged by an extensive fire. Major plumbing and structural repairs were being made from the time of the fire until just before the outbreak. *During this time, there was some decrease in refrigerator and freezer space.* Careful investigation of the plumbing after the outbreak revealed no cross connections and no obvious source of sewage contamination.

"There was no known illness among the employees preceding the outbreak, although two individuals involved in the processing of salmon had fevers and upset stomachs simultaneously with the identical illness experienced in the outbreaks described above. Their stool cultures and the cultures of nine other employees were found positive for *S. java.*

"Although many denied it, it was generally accepted that almost all employees from the janitor to the manager ate processed products while on the job. Whitefish was especially favored; management accepted this as an inevitable part of the operation.

"Contaminated fish were voluntarily withdrawn from the market. The plant voluntarily ceased operation, and an extensive environmental survey was conducted a few days after the outbreak. Every phase of the operation was reviewed and numerous cultures were obtained. No evidence could be found of environmental contamination.

"Fish involved in the epidemic were caught in Canada. They were dressed frozen and then shipped by truck to Winnipeg, where they were repackaged, glazed and stored until February, 1966. Thirty-one cartons of fish were shipped by rail to another company in

Brooklyn which delivered four cartons to the smoking plant. On May 24, fish in three of these four cartons were responsible for the epidemic. *S. Java* was isolated from one fish in the remaining carton obtained from the freezer of the smoking plant.

"Subsequently, two other shipments from the Great Slave Lake, one of which did not go through Winnipeg, were found positive for *S. java*. These fish had been caught and processed in June, 1965.

"Shipments of contaminated fish were traced to two companies at Hay River on Great Slave Lake. Thus the source of contamination was clearly at Great Slave Lake.

"The most likely cause of the contamination," Dr. Gangarosa concluded, "was probably the practice of using raw river water to wash fish after dressing and to make ice to pack the fish in. A combination of circumstances that favored the growth and proliferation of salmonellae at the processing plant probably caused the epidemic."

What happened when federal Food and Drug inspectors examined fifteen plants in one section of the United States engaged in the processing of smoked fish?

W. B. Rankin, Deputy Commissioner of the Food and Drug Administration, described what the inspectors found during his testimony before a congressional hearing in July, 1967:

"Gentlemen, I would like to read you selected sections of a factual report we received on the operations of one of these producers:

" 'The fish were hung on wooden sticks for the processing operation. The sticks and nails were encrusted with rotten fish scales and particles from previous batches. The top of the table on which the raw fish were scraped and gutted was pitted. Debris from previous batches of fish were trapped in the nicked tabletop since no attempt was made to clean and sanitize the table between operations. These residues served to contaminate all batches of fish that passed over the table.

" 'No attempt was made to clean the rusty wire dip nets that were used to remove the fish from the thawing and brining casks. The nets had buildups of bits of rotten fish flesh and entrails.

" 'Rubber hoses in the wet work area were allowed to drop on the floor and [were] later inserted into casks of fish. No attempt was made to adequately clean and sanitize the wooden and metal tanks and casks. Old pieces of fruit and fish crates were used as floating identification markers in the casks of fish. Spoons and knives used in the fish-cleaning operation were encrusted with residues from previous batches of fish.

" 'A rust-perforated metal scoop was generally used to mix the brine solutions. In one instance, an employee picked a stick off the floor and used it to mix the brine.

" 'Employees handled dirty burlap bags, then handled the fish during the cooking and smoking process without making any effort to wash or sanitize their hands. In one case, the manager of the night shift wiped his hands on a rag in his pocket, then returned to his chore of the moment, packing the fish for shipment.

" 'After smoking, the fish were allowed to stand at room temperature for approximately four and a half hours before they were placed in a refrigerator."

Rankin said: "Practices in this plant did not represent the worst we found. I am glad to say that several plants were better.

"But in one of the other plants, there was a stainless-steel table for the cleaning and preparation of fish. An employee scrubbed the table before cleaning the next batch of fish. After scrubbing it, he sloshed it down with a sanitizing solution. Then he took a filthy rag from his pocket and carefully shined the table. It was then ready to inoculate the next batch of fish with a heavy load of bacteria from the rag."

Rankin said that three of the fifteen plants inspected voluntarily closed for a cleanup. One plant was closed under an injunction issued by the federal district court.

"We are currently considering further measures that may be required to effect complete clean up and satisfactory operation," Rankin said.[7]

Unfortunately, this attention is not directed to all smoking plants in this country or toward those that import fish into the United States. In the New York metropolitan area alone, hundreds of illnesses from smoked whitefish have been reported, with three deaths.[8]

Fish and fish products are highly perishable, even more perishable than meat and poultry, which have received more attention from government agencies.

In 1967 and 1968, hearings were held by the Consumer Subcommittee of the Committee on Commerce of the United States Senate under the chairmanship of Senator Warren G. Magnuson. The purpose was to draw up a bill "to protect the nation's consumers and to assist the commercial fishing industry through the inspection of establishments processing fish and fishery products in commerce."

Testifying before that committee in July, 1967, Harold E. Crowther, Director of the Bureau of Commercial Fisheries, said:

"Fish and fishery products are highly perishable and must be given proper care during handling and processing. Over the years, the United States fishing industry has improved the quality of its products. State inspection, the Department's Voluntary Inspection Program, the Public Health Service's Shellfish Inspection and actions of the Food and Drug Administration have contributed to this improvement.

"Much more needs to be done, however, if fish and fishery products are to enjoy a position of trust and confidence comparable to competitive meat and poultry products. It is a well-known fact that per capita consumption of fishery products has remained fairly constant over the past twenty years, while that of poultry and meat has increased substantially. It is our belief that uncertainty of quality is a major consideration in limiting consumer acceptance of fishery products. . . .

"We believe that the problem exists because of the lower-grade products being intermingled with these good products. This makes it difficult for the consumer to really determine what she is getting."

He was asked by Senator Philip Hart, of Michigan, who was also on the Senate Committee: "What special problems exist in fishery products as a food that are not present in other foods?"

Crowther said: "I believe one of the points I mentioned in my statement is that fish is even more perishable than meat and poultry and requires special handling from the time it is caught until the time it reaches the consumer.

"I think one of the problems we have with fishery products is that many of them are caught at sea. The fish die as they are brought aboard. And from that moment on they must be handled carefully and preserved in ice or by freezing and brought ashore.

"With meat and poultry products, an animal comes right to the plant itself. But from the time the fish does die, from that point on, it is highly susceptible to deterioration in quality. Therefore, I think it is a product that needs special attention."

He went on to say that because "we do catch fish in the oceans and the gulf and even in our inland waters, by necessity, many of

our plants are scattered along the entire coastline of the United
States. And in many respects they must be fairly small.

"Being small also presents problems, because you do not have
a large organization behind you. Adequate financing is needed to
make sure that the products can be held in proper storage until the
market can absorb them.

"Because the plants are small and in many cases inadequately
financed, I think many of them find it difficult to take all the precautions that must be taken to protect the fishery products adequately."

Senator Hart then said: "And the fellow who has the finest
plant in the world is handicapped by the existence of the problem
which your last answer implicitly suggests exists—namely, that once
the fish is on the shelf the consumer doesn't know whether it is from
the finest of all plants or the worst of all."

Crowther answered: "That is entirely true. For example, if
we had 100,000 pounds of top-quality fish in one lot and 10,000
pounds of lower quality in another lot which were offered for sale
at the same time, the poor quality fish would depress the price of
both lots of fish. Also, the consumers who bought the poor quality
product would be discouraged from buying any fish for some time.

"Unfortunately, in most segments of our industry, there is no
premium placed on top-quality fish as landed by the vessel. This is
not the fault of the processors, because in many cases, if they at-
tempted to restrict buying from a particular fisherman because his
quality was not up to par, in times when fish were needed this boat
would not go to him. It would seek another processor."

"Results of the survey showed the quality of the frozen fish
portions to be very low. On a sample basis, 6.7 percent Grade A;
27.8 percent Grade B and 55.5 percent substandard or Grade Not
Certified. The institutional samples were somewhat better than retail
but left much to be desired.

"Causes of low quality were processing defects, off-flavor and
odor and low fish flesh content. Of the 312 samples, one-fifth were
rated Grade Not Certified due mainly to rancidity, which indicates
that this damage occurred after processing and during distribution
and frozen storage."

Bureau of Commercial Fisheries 1964 Grading Survey B of
Retail Samples of Frozen Haddock Fillets and Frozen Raw Breaded
Shrimp (summary):

"This survey showed that the quality of haddock fillets available at the retail level was low, and that while the quality of frozen raw shrimp available at the retail level was considerably better, there was ample room for improvement. The samples were obtained in ten key cities from coast to coast. . . .

"On a sample basis, 25.2 percent of the haddock samples were Grade A; 32.0 percent were Grade B and 42.7 percent were Substandard or Grade Not Certified. On the same basis, 46.6 percent of the shrimp samples were Grade A., 15.9 percent were Grade B and 37.7 percent were substandard or Grade Not Certified. Principal causes for low quality of the haddock samples were poor flavor and odor, dehydration and processing defects. Dehydration and discoloration were probably due to poor and/or long storage conditions and poor packaging. On the other hand, processing defects were due to poor workmanship. Poor flavor and odor, however, may have been due to low quality starting material or to improper packaging and storage. Dehydration and discoloration can be controlled by better packaging and removal of all products from the market that have exceeded their normal shelf-life.

Mr. Crowther submitted surveys taken by the Bureau of Commercial Fisheries. Here are some of them:

Grading Survey of Retail and Institutional Samples of Frozen Fish Portions and Retail Samples of Frozen Halibut Steaks (summary):

"During the 1965 grading survey of frozen fishery products by the Bureau of Commercial Fisheries, U.S. Department of the Interior, 312 frozen breaded portions and 206 frozen halibut steaks were selected at random from commercial outlets located in ten key cities from coast to coast in the United States. The grading was done in accordance with provisions set forth in official U.S. Grade Standards for these products."[9]

The proposed Wholesome Fish and Fishery Products Act of 1968 was aimed at:

• Developing a comprehensive federal program for consumer protection against the health hazards and mislabeling of fish, shellfish, and seafood products.

• Setting standards and developing continuous inspection and enforcement.

• Supporting research, training, and inspection programs.

• Helping the states develop their own inspection programs.
• Assuring that imported fish and fishery products are wholesome.

According to Stanley A. Cain, Assistant Secretary for Fish and Wildlife and Parks, United States Department of the Interior, the bill would:

"1. Require a nationwide survey of the operations and sanitary conditions of commercial fish-processing establishments and commercial fishing vessels for the purpose of developing effective standards of sanitation and quality control under which such establishments and vessels must be operated and maintained. These standards would be published by regulation. The survey must be completed and regulations issued within one year after funds are appropriated for this purpose. The regulations would be effective no later than one year after publication, but if the Secretary deems it necessary the effective date can be extended for an additional year.

"2. Once the regulations are effective, the owner of every fish-processing plant and commercial fishing vessel which does not provide fish or fishery products for use as human food solely for distribution within one State must certify that they are complying with the regulations and must obtain a 'certificate of registration.' If he fails to do so, he cannot operate.

"3. Establishments of vessels that obtain the certificate and later fail to comply will have their certificate suspended until they take the necessary steps to comply.

"4. The bill would require continuous inspection of each such establishment. This means that a full-time inspector will be assigned to each plant except in cases where geographic distribution and plant size make it possible for one man to inspect more than one establishment on a substantially continuous basis in a manner that would carry out the objective of this proposal. The processing of fishery products is, in many cases, seasonal, and plants are located in close-enough proximity to permit an adequate inspection on such a basis. Because of the large number of fishing vessels, it would not be practicable, nor is it necessary, to provide a continuous inspection of them. Continuous inspection does not mean that every fish, as in the case of meat, would be inspected. This is not practical, but the fish would be spot inspected while in the plant.

"5. The bill would provide that fishery products processed for interstate or foreign commerce in an establishment with a certificate and packed in containers or wrappers shall be labeled.

"6. The bill would make it unlawful to transport or sell fish or fishery products in commerce that are both capable of use as human food and are adulterated or misbranded when sold or transported.

"7. The bill would authorize the issuance of regulations covering the conditions under which fish and fishery products capable of use as human food shall be stored or handled. These would apply to anyone buying, selling, freezing, storing or transporting or importing fish and fishery products in or for interstate or foreign commerce, to prevent adulteration or misbranding when delivered to the consumer.

"8. Once the regulations of the Secretary are effective, fish or fishery products cannot be imported into the United States if they are adulterated or misbranded or otherwise fail to comply with the provisions of the act or the regulations applicable to domestic fish and fishery products in commerce. Individuals who obtain these [products] for their own use are not subject to this requirement with a 50-pound weight limit.

"The bill also provides that if the Secretary determines that the country of origin has a system of plant, vessel and product inspection at least equal to the United States system, and that reliance can be placed on certificates required by United States regulations, and that the article complies with the system of the country of origin, such certificates may be accepted by the Secretary as proof of compliance with the comparable requirements of this act."

(According to Cain, there are about 105 countries exporting fishery products to the United States. Some, like Canada, have good inspection programs. Others have none. Over 50 percent of the edible United States fish supply comes from foreign countries.)

Mr. Cain continues to enumerate the benefits of the bill:

"9. In order to reduce costs the proposal would enable the Secretary to limit, with the approval of the Secretary of the Treasury, the number of ports where the imports could come in.

"10. Like the Meat Act, the bill would provide a cooperative program under which the Federal Government could assist the States in developing and administering a State fish inspection program where the State has adopted a State mandatory inspection law which is at least equal to the Federal law. This would apply only to persons, firms, or corporations engaged in the State in processing fish and fishery products for use as human food solely for intrastate distribution.

"11. The bill would authorize technical and financial assistance. The financial assistance would be in the form of up to 50 percent grants.

"12. The Secretary may appoint advisory committees consisting of State, consumer, and industry representatives to advise him on Federal and State programs.

"13. If after two years after the effective date of regulation, the Secretary believes, as in the case of the Meat Act, that the State has failed to meet its commitments and develop or enforce requirements at least equal to those imposed under this proposal for the Federal program, he shall tell the Governor and designate the State as subject to the Federal requirements. If, however, he believes that the State will carry out their responsibility within one more year, he may delay his designation."[10]

Naturally, the proposed bill met stiff opposition, as had other proposed fish bills in the past.

A legitimate point the fish industry has was expressed for all by Edward E. McCollum, Jr., chairman of the Committee on Wholesome Fish and Fish Products, Domestic Seafood Producers Association of New England, when he testified before the congressional committee in 1968:

"The seafood producing industry of New England has long suffered in the face of inadequate restrictive policy and competitive imports from heavily subsidized foreign fisheries. . . . In 1957, U.S. imports of fishery products were valued at $325 million. In 1966, this value had gradually increased to $720 million. It does not seem reasonable that any U.S. industry should be confronted with 82 percent importations into its markets."[11]

James Ackert, president of the Atlantic Fishermen's Union, made the point that if foreign fishermen are not required to meet the rigid standards of United States fisherman, and if United States fishermen have to sustain the additional costs of inspections, then they will be in an even more disadvantageous position then they are today. Furthermore, the American consumer cannot tell whether he is buying foreign or domestic fish when he purchases certain fish products.

Mr. Ackert said the Atlantic Fishermen's Union had a laboratory test made on foreign fresh fillets on May 19, 1967: "There was evidence of an additive being used to extend the shelf life of the fillet, namely chlortetracycline [an antibiotic]." He pointed out that the fisherman is uniquely dependent upon a rapid sale of his fish and unloading of his vessel. In contrast to the operations of the beef industry, he cannot place his fish in stockyards for leisurely inspection.[12]

American fishing boats are antiquated. Unlike many European ships, they still use wooden pens for their catch of fish instead of a hard-surfaced material, such as aluminum, which is easier to clean.

According to Leroy Houser, of the Standards Development Section, Shellfish Sanitation Branch, Division of Environmental Engineering, Department of Health, Education, and Welfare:

"It is said to be important that the fish be stored in the ice [aboard ship] so that any water from the melting ice drains away and does not form a pool of blood and slime along the dorsal part of the cavity. Otherwise, the gut cavity soon develops sour off odors indicating spoilage to those trained in public health, so some means of flushing the gut cavity with chlorinated sea water or potable water should be necessary as a public health measure.

"Most fish in the North American fisheries are landed in an uneviscerated form. However, extreme care is necessary in storing the fish in holds as the weight of the ice and fish may squeeze out intestinal material of fish stored in the lower levels. This material has been shown to contain up to 10 million bacteria per gram of gut content."[13]

When fish is stored from eight to sixteen days aboard an American fishing vessel, there are many opportunities for spoilage. A solution has been found by other countries in the form of floating fish factories. They compete with American fishermen.

Among the factory ships harvesting and processing fish is West Germany's *Tiki*. Her machinery can clean, fillet, and freeze 200,000 pound of fish a day.

The British trawler *Victory* has even done something to improve the fisherman's traditionally austere life, according to the National

Geographic Society. She has a recreation room, movie theater, library, and, most important, extra-high bulwarks to help prevent men from being washed overboard in high seas.

The Soviet Union is building a huge, multipurpose factory ship. The 43,000-ton *Vostok* will serve as flagship to fourteen fishing vessels, operate a cannery capable of filling 150,000 cans a day, store 13,000 tons of bulk cargo, and provide quarters for 600 crewmen. These supertrawlers, the society says, are equipped with electronic gear to find cod, machinery to process catches, and giant freezers to preserve the fish. When the ships reach port, the fish are ready for the grocers.[14]

It seems that the only innovation American fishermen have been able to make is to cut down on the number of seamen aboard ship to try to reduce the cost of bringing in fish.

Another who spoke out against passage of the Fishery Products bill was Dr. George A. Michael, Director of the Division of Food and Drugs, Commonwealth of Massachusetts, before the Committee on Commerce, on April 24, 1968:

"Gentlemen, it is my considered opinion after twenty-seven years in the Division of Food and Drugs, eighteen years of which were served as director of that division, that the concept of continuous inspection in regards to any area of the food business is archaic, obsolete and it does not take into consideration the great advances made by the scientists in our federal and state laboratories.

"We can determine many more of the items that are a hazard to the consuming public in our laboratories than an inspector looking at a product can determine by visual examination.

"It is a waste of money to insist on mandatory, continuous inspection in any food field except in the slaughtering operations."[15]

Though the bill was shelved in committee, Senator Warren G. Magnuson, chairman of the Committee on Commerce Hearings, said of the proposed Wholesome Fish and Fishery Products Act of 1968:

"Due to the difficult problems raised by several provisions of this bill and the late date at which it was introduced, it now appears that the Commerce Committee will not report out a fish inspection bill this year. We anticipate, however, that a similar bill will be introduced early in the next session of Congress, and I suspect that some legislation will be enacted at that time."[16]

With increasingly polluted water and wider distribution of fish, it is imperative that the American consumer be protected against disease-bearing or low-quality fish.

Many communities discharge human excrement into convenient rivers, lakes, or estuaries. It was always assumed that the contaminating material was naturally purified by dilution, aeriation, exposure to sunlight, and microbial action. However, a researcher from the Biological Sciences Laboratory at Fort Detrick, Frederick, Maryland, Werner A. Janssen, and a researcher from Chesapeake Biological Laboratory of the Natural Resources Institute, University of Maryland, Caldwell D. Meyers, found this was not true. They found that live fish may become infected with dangerous germs from man, and thus constitute a public health problem. They tested white perch from the rivers that flow into Chesapeake Bay through heavily populated areas.[17]

Researchers from the Department of Microbiology, University of New Hampshire, tested samples of seawater and oysters collected during periods from April to November, 1964, 1965, and 1966. They isolated a number of different *Salmonella* serotypes from such samples of seawater and oysters in shellfish-growing areas that met the current recommended standards for approved shellfish-growing waters. They commented: "It is apparent from these results that the current bacteriological criteria for approved shellfish-growing waters do not insure that the water or oysters harvested from such waters are free from pathogenic microorganisms."[18]

An editorial in the *Archives of Environmental Health* for May, 1966, entitled "The Shellfish Problem," said: "The ability of shellfish to act as vectors of human disease has been well documented. Early in this century the consumption of shellfish harvested from polluted water was shown to be the cause of typhoid fever outbreaks, and in the past ten years outbreaks of infectious hepatitis in this country and aboard have been associated with the consumption of raw oysters and clams.

"This epidemiological evidence has been supported by a number of laboratory studies which have shown that oysters and clams will not only take up a significant amount of virus or bacteria from contaminated water, but will also concentrate these organisms to a level up to 60 times that of the surrounding water. Naturally occurring contamination with certain types of echovirus and coxsackie virus has been demonstrated in oysters taken from water frankly polluted with human wastes.

"Paradoxically, shellfish grow best in areas most likely to be contaminated with human waste. . . ."[19]

California mussels become poisonous because they consume the tiny organisms that cause red tide. Poisoning in human beings from eating toxic shellfish has occurred in many places throughout the world.[20]

Current inspection procedures for fish and for water do not adequately protect us. Take the case of the 248,000 tins of salmon that had to be recalled from an Alaskan firm. The fish was distributed nationwide under thirty-nine brand names.[21]

A defect in the seam of a can was brought to the notice of the Food and Drug Administration, not by an inspector, but by a consumer. The FDA discovered signs of viable bacteria in the parent lot in Seattle, and termed the defect a potential health hazard. Though the company voluntarily recalled grocers' supplies, it had no way of reaching customers who had already made purchases.

The effect of lack of sufficient safeguards in America today was eloquently summed up by a member of the fish industry, Lowell Wakefield, president of Wakefield Fisheries, Port Wakefield, Alaska, while testifying before the Senate Committee:

"Frankly, the segments of the industry that I have been familiar with in this brief period I am afraid need cleaning up very, very badly. I am not all sure that as good a can of salmon is packed in Alaska today, Senator, as was packed when I entered the business forty-six years ago.

"The fish stench that is characteristic of seafoods in the minds of so many customers just should not exist at all. There is no more excuse for an off-flavor or an off-odor in fish than there is in meat or poultry. The existence of such things results simply from low-quality standards and improper practices that are characteristic of much of the fishing industry, in my opinion, both domestic and foreign. This situation costs our industry millions of dollars in lost sales.

"And I am not referring just to the spectacular and fortunately very rare instances when consumer deaths such as occurred in your State from botulism create havoc with large segments of the industry.

What I am referring to primarily is the everyday mishmash of excellent, acceptable, mediocre, minimum, and subminimum seafood products presented in the supermarkets to the housewife each day in such a fashion as to make shopping for seafood akin to playing a slot machine."[22]

HOW CAN YOU TELL WHETHER A FISH IS WHOLESOME?

In its frozen state, you can't!

When it is fresh, you should observe the following:

1. Is it of good color?

2. Does it smell? A fishy odor does not belong to fresh fish.

3. Are the eyes clear or clouded?

4. If you press down, does it leave an indentation in the fish? Fresh fish flesh springs up.

5. Is the skin smooth to the touch, and firm?

6. Are the gill sections clear and intact?

5 NOTES

1. Robert C. Stanfill, District Director, Food and Drug Administration, "A Case Study of a Chemical Food Poisoning Involving Fish," presented at the 44th annual meeting of the Central Atlantic States Association of FDA officials, Atlantic City, May 26, 1960.

2. Kenneth J. Kirk, Assistant Commissioner of Compliance, FDA, before the Consumer Subcommittee, Committee on Commerce, United States Senate, July 20–21, 1967.

3. Harold E. Crowther, Director of the Bureau of Commercial Fisheries, U.S. Department of the Interior, before the Consumer Subcommittee, Committee on Commerce, U.S. Senate, July 20–21, 1967.

4. Leroy Houser, Standards Development Section, Shellfish Sanitation Branch, Division of Environmental Engineering, *Journal of Environmental Health,* September–October, 1966.

5. Philip R. Lee, M.D., Assistant Secretary for Health and Scientific Affairs, Department of Health, Education, and Welfare, before the Consumer Subcommittee, Committee on Commerce, U.S. Senate, April 23, 1968.

6. Eugene J. Gangarosa, M.D., *et al.,* "Epidemic of Febrile Gastroenteritis Due to Salmonella Java Traced to Smoked White Fish," *American Journal of Public Health,* January, 1968, Vol. 58, No. 1.

7. W. B. Rankin, Deputy Commissioner of the Food and Drug Administration, U.S. Senate hearings, July 20–21, 1967.

8. Eugene J. Gangarosa, *ibid.*

9. Harold E. Crowther, *ibid.*
10. Stanley A. Cain, Assistant Secretary for Fish and Wildlife and Parks, U.S. Department of the Interior, Senate hearings, 1968.
11. Edward E. McCollum, Jr., chairman of the Committee on Wholesome Fish and Fish Products, Domestic Seafood Producers Association of New England, Senate hearings, April 22, 1968.
12. James Ackert, President of the Atlantic Fishermen's Union, testimony before the Senate Committee, April, 1968.
13. Leroy Houser, *loc. cit.*
14. National Geographic Society news bulletin, March 13, 1968.
15. George A. Michael, Director of the Division of Food and Drugs, Commonwealth of Massachusetts, Senate hearings, April 24, 1968.
16. Warren G. Magnuson, Senator, Washington, Chairman of the Committee on Commerce Hearings.
17. Werner A. Janssen and Caldwell D. Meyers, *Science,* February 2, 1968, Vol. 159.
18. L. W. Slanetz, Ph.D.; Clara Bartley, Ph.D.; and K. W. Stanley, B.S., "Coliforms, Fecal Streptococci and Salmonella in Seawater and Shellfish," presented before the Laboratory Section of the American Public Health Association at its 95th annual meeting, in Miami Beach, Florida, October 26, 1967.
19. May, 1966, Vol. 12.
20. Edward J. Schantz, U.S. Army Biological Laboratory, Fort Detrick, Md., *Biochemistry* 5:1191, 1966.
21. *Consumer Reports,* April, 1967.
22. Lowell Wakefield, president of Wakefield Fisheries, Port Wakefield, Alaska, Senate hearings, 1968.

6

Salmonella Sam and the Ptomaine Picnic

SALMONELLA ORGANISMS—NAMED FOR THE American veterinarian Dr. D. E. Salmon—occur in the intestinal tract and tissues of infected humans and animals. Many of the more than 1,200 different types can cause food poisoning.[1] They enter the food supply through meats or animal products from infected animals or from contamination by an infected animal or person. The common symptoms are diarrhea, abdominal cramps, fever, and sometimes vomiting. Infections range from moderate, with recovery in three to four days, to fatal.

In 1967, salmonella accounted for 12,836 reported cases in thirty-five outbreaks of food poisoning. But health officials say the true incidence is probably closer to two million cases a year, with a large percentage of those cases diagnosed as "flu." It is estimated that 1 percent of the population of the United States becomes infected each year.

In the fall of 1962, twenty-seven persons were hospitalized with acute digestive upsets in Spokane, Washington. The diagnosis was "salmonella."

Doctors studying the cases knew that the persons involved probably contracted the illness within three weeks of one another—but where did they get infected, and how? There seemed to be no logical pattern. The age distribution of the patients ranged from babies to persons in their seventies. They lived in widely scattered areas within a radius of fifteen miles. There was no recognizable genetic or social relationship among the patients. The only apparent similarity was that the two youngest victims were siblings. Many of the persons in-

volved were not much help because—as is often the case with food
poisoning—so much time had elapsed between ingestion of the contaminated food and the diagnosis of the symptoms.

Persistent questioning and complete medical histories did pay
off. Twelve patients had something in common after all. Six had
eaten chocolate meringue pie, and six had eaten banana meringue
pie from twelve to forty-four hours before becoming ill. The pie
had been consumed in eleven establishments; only two of the twelve
persons had eaten in a common restaurant.

One of the patients, a college student, remembered that there
had been an outbreak of illness among residents of dormitories at his
college at the same time that he had been hospitalized. Consultation
with the college physician and nurse revealed that forty-two persons
had been admitted to the college infirmary with upset stomachs on
October 1, the same day that the hospitalized student had become ill.

Further detective work on the part of the health officials investigating the case showed that the college cafeteria had received eighty
chocolate meringue pies at noon on September 29. The pies had
been baked early that morning and then served between 5:00 P.M.
and 6:00 P.M., without prior refrigeration.

Two of the hospitalized patients who first drew attention to the
outbreak reported eating banana meringue pie at the same hotel
dining room during a church luncheon on September 24. Sixty-five
of the 180 women attending the luncheon were reached by telephone
in several cities. Thirty reported having experienced the salmonella
symptoms. All of them had eaten the banana pie.

When the facts were in, the trail led to one bakery. Swabs were
taken from thirty-six surfaces around the bakery, and sixty-three
samples of nineteen ingredients in the pies were cultured in the laboratory. All the cultures proved to be negative for salmonellas. There
had been no recent illness of any kind, and no diarrheal illness
within the past year in any of the fourteen employees, according
to interviews.

Only two ingredients were suspect as far as salmonellas were
concerned. One of these—spray-dried egg albumen—used in the pie
filling and produced in Kansas City, Missouri, was cultured. The
cultures of fifteen samples were found negative. The other suspected
ingredients, frozen egg white, produced in a Spokane plant and

supplied regularly to the bakery for meringue production, proved a stumbling block.

There was no egg white left that had been used in the suspected pies. The eggs were obtained by the creamery for breaking from a large egg-production area spanning twenty states. The plant manager was unwilling to provide samples for laboratory testing or detailed information regarding the purchase of eggs, production of frozen and dried eggs, or the sale of these products.

The next fall, at the same college previously involved in the salmonella outbreak, sixty-four hapless students again came down with gastrointestinal symptoms of infection. Public health officials asked two nearby hospital laboratories to culture samples from patients hospitalized with gastrointestinal illness. Again, salmonella was reported in a number of cases, and once more the patients had eaten meringue pie at one of several local restaurants from ten to thirty-two hours before onset of their symptoms. The pies were from the Spokane bakery.

This time, a decision was made to investigate the egg-breaking plant. On October 4, 1963, the plant's records were seized by court order, and the entire stock of frozen and dried egg whites, yolks, and whole eggs were placed under seizure after being identified in several cities.

Suppliers of the eggs to the breaking plant were still numerous and widely scattered. Yet, representatives of the Food and Drug Administration and the Washington State Department of Agriculture found that the eggs used for breaking were, in general, those that could not be graded. They consisted largely of checked, cracked, and dirty eggs. Samples examined in the laboratory showed that approximately 20 percent of the eggs were unfit for human consumption according to FDA and the Washington State Health Department standards.

Furthermore, it was found that the production of bulk frozen egg whites, yolks, and whole eggs in this plant involved hand-breaking into cups and separation of whites and yolks by employee's fingers! The eggs were then sold to bakers, candymakers, and other users of raw, frozen liquid eggs.

Of the 1,131 specimens tested, salmonella was isolated from 20.8 percent of the cans of frozen eggs and 30 percent of 81 lots.

The Spokane case was reported by Ernest A. Ager and others in a paper entitled "Two Outbreaks of Egg-Borne Salmonellosis and Implications for Their Prevention" in the February 6, 1967, issue of the *Journal of the American Medical Association*.[2]

Eggs are frequently the cause of salmonella infection, and have been for a long time. In fact, we Americans almost finished off our British allies during World War II with spray-dried eggs. We gave them twenty-two types of salmonella they had never had before, and when Churchill referred to "blood, sweat and tears," he may have meant more than we thought he did.[3]

Egg powder as a constituent of cake mixes has been frequently implicated in salmonella outbreaks. When the Canadians tested samples of cake mixes, 54 percent of them yielded salmonellas. (I stopped letting the children lick the cake-mix bowl after I discovered that!)

Dr. Agar and his associates feel that one of the most threatening outbreaks of salmonellosis ever studied in this country occurred in the spring and summer of 1963 in at least fifty-three hospitals in thirteen states. More than one thousand individuals—including both patients and employees—became infected with *S. derby,* a type of salmonella, either directly from the ingestion of raw or undercooked eggs or as the result of contact with individuals previously infected. It was estimated that eggs from as many as twelve thousand farms, after being handled by processors, wholesalers and distributors, could theoretically have reached any fifteen of the hospitals in three states. With persistent detective work, it was determined that only a limited number of farms in two localities were involved.

Another spectacular outbreak occurred among 1,850 mental patients. One hundred and four became ill after drinking raw eggnog.

But no matter how prevalent, egg-borne salmonellosis is just one fraction of the problem.

In a case reported in the *New England Journal of Medicine,* Dr. David J. Lang and his group described how they were confronted with twenty-one cases of infection of salmonellosis in a short period of time. In each instance, the offending organism was detected as *Salmonella cubana.* Fearing "an explosive common-source outbreak," admissions to the pediatric service were halted.

All food in the kitchen and all personnel were tested for salmonella. None proved to be the carrier. Half of those affected were children, including tiny infants. The remainder were elderly. After weeks of searching, no common denominator was found. Then someone suddenly realized that all the patients affected had had tests for gastroinestinal function.

Among the diagnostic solutions used to test the digestive organs was carmine. With this lead it didn't take long to trace the mysterious outbreak to this red dye made from dried ground, female scale insects and larvae found in Central America and Mexico. These insects sometimes harbor salmonellas.

One of the patients—a nine-month-old child with congenital kidney disease—died after acquiring an overwhelming salmonella meningitis and blood poisoning.[4]

Sixty-nine deaths were associated with salmonella infection in 1966, but the "true reflection of the mortality rate due to salmonellosis in this country is not known," according to the National Communicable Disease Center.

A report made in April, 1968, in Boston to the annual American College of Physicians meeting, by doctors from Memorial Hospital in New York, noted that 12.5 percent of the cancer patients in that hospital who caught salmonella infections died. "Salmonellosis in such a population is a most serious complication," they noted.[5]

The possibility that salmonella may cause the death of unborn babies has also been raised. Dr. Daniel Widelock, Deputy Director of the Bureau of Laboratories, New York City Department of Health, reported that after injections with killed *S. typhimurium salmonellae*, pregnant mice experienced hypoglycemia and an increased sensitivity to histamine. When both factors were present, he said, fetal wastage occurred. Increased malformations were also noted.[6]

Former Food and Drug Administration Commissioner Dr. James Goddard said: "Salmonella has become a major public health problem which is continually increasing in complexity. Despite new sanitary procedures for manufacturing, handling, storing, preparing and serving food, the incidence of the disease is rising throughout the world.

"In addition, formerly predictable epidemiological patterns appear to be changing. For the past thirty years, *S. typhimurium* has been the most common isolate. It was often the unwelcome guest at 'church socials.'

"Now, *S. heidelberg,* considered rare prior to 1950, is the runner up to *typhimurium.*

"Evidence is accumulating that warns us that salmonella sero-types are mutating and finding a wider range of hospitable hosts among the various animal species," he said in a 1967 article in *Nutrition Today*.

"Milk and milk products spread salmonella too. Disease transmission through pasteurized milk and milk products is rare. But the experience with the instant non-fat dry milk in 1966 shows the potential.

"Swine and cattle are also prime sources of salmonella infection," Dr. Goddard said. "Meat chosen at random in retail markets has shown a high incidence of contamination. This is especially true for pork products. A study in Florida revealed that salmonella contamination of fresh sausage and pork ranged from 8 percent in samples from national distributors to 58 percent from local abattoirs."[7]

In a Massachusetts study, 40.4 percent of chickens inspected in a plant were contaminated with salmonella.[8]

Dr. Goddard said animal feed is another source of contamination; and although the Food and Drug Administration has laid down the law about using feed containing salmonella, they have no real way of policing it. The former FDA commissioner said that household pets are also a source of salmonella infection:

"This is especially true when children feed their pets such products as dog candy. It isn't uncommon for children, particularly crawling infants, to eat the candy too. In addition, the infection of a household pet, even if low grade and not acute, may be a source of infection to human members of the household. One study in Florida showed that 15 percent of 1,626 normal household dogs and 12 percent of 73 normal cats were harboring salmonella."[9]

Some other things around the house can also carry salmonella. Cockroaches, which all too frequently contaminate our food in processing plants, warehouses, restaurants, and supermarkets, as well as in the home, have been incriminated in the transmission of the "bug." Studies indicate that if roaches deposit their fecal pellets on food or food utensils, the salmonella organisms will remain alive for many weeks. Like the housefly, the odious cockroach, by its indiscriminate movements from excrement and other filth to our food, mechanically transmits diseased organisms to humans.[10]

Rats and mice are other carriers of salmonella. The *American Journal of Public Health* reported that salmonella would remain viable in rat feces for 148 days. The presence of whole or ground rat or mouse excreta in feeds of laboratory rodents and other animals has caused outbreaks of salmonellosis and other diseases. The salmonella serotype responsible for mouse typhoid is also responsible for food poisoning among humans.

If you don't believe that it is possible for you to get insect- or rodent-contaminated food, all you have to do is read one page of the monthly *FDA Papers*. Take page 30, in the February, 1967 issue:

- Chocolate-drink mix, Memphis, Tennessee: contains poisonous salmonella microorganisms[11]
- Bread crumbs, Boston, Massachusetts: insect-contaminated[12]
- Cookies, Oklahoma City, Oklahoma: prepared and packed under insanitary conditions; insect- and rodent-contaminated[13]
- Egg noodles, Norfolk, Virginia: insect-contaminated[14]
- Flour, Omaha, Nebraska: rodent-contaminated[15]
- Crackers, Los Angeles, California: insect-contaminated[16]

These are just a few of the many items on one page in one magazine. Because inspectors do no more than spot-check, you can be sure that such contaminated food does get to your dinner table.

An epidemiological investigation of a gastroenteritis outbreak aboard a Navy ship shows how easy it is to spread salmonella and how vulnerable a health inspector may be. The outbreak occurred in two phases. The first had a symptom attack rate of 2.6; the second had a rate of 4.4 percent among those eating the suspect meal. All the men suffering from nausea and diarrhea had eaten the suspect food. Culture studies disclosed that at least 10 percent of the personnel carried the salmonella infection without symptoms.

In the first outbreak, roast loin of pork was the suspected food; in the second, turkey sandwiches prepared and served several days later seemed to be the culprit. Prior to Thanksgiving aboard the ship, frozen turkeys were removed from the freezer and placed on a thawing table. During this process, the roast pork was carved on a cutting board placed on the thawing table. The juices from the thawing turkeys apparently contaminated the cutting board. In the second outbreak, the same cutting board, which evidently had been improperly cleaned, was used to slice the leftover turkey for sandwiches.

Investigators took surface samples following both outbreaks. In the first outbreak, the sample taken from the thawing table yielded a culture of *S. chester salmonella*. In the second incident, one of the investigators, while inspecting the galley, touched only one item: the cutting board. He then smoked a cigarette without first washing his hands. Two days later, he was the only sick member of the investigating team. He yielded a culture of *S. chester*.

Adequate surface disinfection and sanitation could easily have prevented the entire episode.[17]

The ability to stop salmonella and the misery it causes seems almost impossible today. Dr. Goddard believes that one of the most dangerous sources of the disease is "Salmonella Sam." He compares him or her to "Typhoid Mary," who was an innocent carrier of that disease. Though such people are free of symptoms, they contaminate all they touch.

"Unfortunately, there appear to be a great many carriers among those who handle our food," Dr. Goddard said. "It isn't that the food industry has a peculiar attraction for Salmonella Sams. Rather, food handlers have a greater exposure to infection because of the presence of salmonella in the food-processing environment. In fact, in some institutions, salmonellosis is regarded as an occupational hazard, and workers suffering infection are compensated for time lost from the job."

Dr. Goddard said that with all the meals now being eaten away from home, and with the increasing use of convenience foods, infected food handlers have increased opportunities to contaminate your food. He summed it up when he said: "The centralization of American cooking is in the hands of relatively few people. One cannot help worry that in one kitchen feeding so many, one contaminated food handler could produce a real crisis if the elusive salmonella slips by the Department of Agriculture and the U.S. Public Health and the state and municipal authorities and our Food and Drug inspectors."

Though this sounds like a formidable barrier, in reality inspection is spotty and infrequent. Furthermore, you can't smell, see, or taste salmonella. It must be diagnosed from symptoms of illness or in a laboratory. Dr. Goddard admitted that "it is quite plain that we are today a long way from guaranteeing salmonella-free products in the marketplace. What levels of contamination in processed food are a health hazard to the consumer? Unfortunately, we are still far from providing a precise answer to that thorny question."

BOTULISM

"Why don't you come over for lunch?" Helen Brown asked her friend and neighbor Barbara Mason. "I'll make some tuna-fish sandwiches and we can chat."

While the two women talked, Mrs. Brown took some salad dressing she had made and mixed it with the tuna fish.

"That fish smells kind of funny," Barbara said, picking up the can and sniffing it. "Do you smell anything?"

"No, it smells all right to me. Let me taste some," Helen replied. "It tastes all right!"

She finished making the sandwiches, and then decided to open a can of soup because it was such a chilly day. They were almost through with lunch when Mrs. Brown's mother, Mrs. Konners, dropped in.

"Hi, Mother," Helen said. "Why don't you have some lunch with us?"

"I'm not very hungry," Mrs. Konners replied, "but I'll take a taste of that tuna fish. I want to see if you made it as good as I make it."

The three chatted for a while until it was time for the children to return from school.

That night at dinner—about 6:00 P.M.—Helen Brown complained to her husband that her vision was blurred. She kept taking off her glasses and putting them on again. Without finishing the dishes after supper, she went to bed.

"It's hard to breathe," she told her husband, "and my throat feels tight."

She and her husband thought she was coming down with the flu. They believed she would be all right in the morning.

But at 6:30 A.M., Mr. Brown was awakened by the sounds his wife was making. She was breathing convulsively and could speak only in a whisper. He called the emergency squad, and his wife was taken to the hospital. But before the ambulance arrived, at 7:30 A.M., Helen Brown was dead.

Her luncheon companion, Barbara Mason, had also begun to feel the same symptoms about dinnertime on the day of the lunch. She complained of feeling dizzy and of blurred vision, and had difficulty in breathing. Later, her movements became somewhat uncoordinated, and she vomited frequently during the night. She and her husband both thought it was the flu until they heard about Helen Brown.

Barbara Mason was hospitalized half an hour after her friend's death. She was given Polyvalent Type A and B Botulinus antitoxin.

Her symptoms continued to progress. On the fourth day after the luncheon, she was given Type E antitoxin. She did not improve. At 5:00 P.M., five days after the fateful lunch, Barbara Mason joined her friend in death.

Helen Brown's mother, Mrs. Konners, did not suffer the symptoms until about twenty-four hours after eating a small portion of tuna salad. She began vomiting, and also complained of a sore throat and some difficulty with her vision. She was hospitalized and given 10,000 units of A and B Polyvalent Botulinus antitoxin. Her recovery was relatively rapid and she was released from the hospital three days later.

Laboratory tests confirmed that the illness that struck the three women was botulism.

Samples from Mrs. Brown's garbage can, including some of the salad dressing, the soup can, and the tuna can, were given to the public health laboratory. Even the can opener was brought in. A pure culture of botulinus was isolated from the tuna can.

The health departments of Michigan and California, of Wayne County, Michigan, and the Detroit district of the Federal Food and Drug Administration immediately began tracking down cans from the same lot of tuna fish. The California State Department of Health closed down the cannery that packed the Dagim Tashorim Brand Tuna. The tuna fish had been imported frozen from Japan, and canned in the California plant.

On the same day the plant was closed down, the New York City Health Department picked up a large number of cans in that city. In all, the health officials retrieved 1,200 cans. Tests showed that at least twenty-one contained the deadly botulinus.

Ralph W. Johnston, John Feldman, and Rosemary Sullivan, bacteriologists with the FDA in Detroit, reported the case in Public Health Reports in July, 1963. They said the cans showed defective seams, revealing that the contamination had taken place after sterilization.[18]

The toxin responsible for botulism is the most powerful and deadly poison known to man. Cobra venom, curare, and arsenic are mild by comparison. Controlled experiments at the University of Michigan have shown that 1/100,000,000,000 part of a gram of pure botulism toxin is enough to kill. It is so potent, it has long been recognized as a prospective weapon for bacteriological warfare.[19]

Botulism was first recorded as a disease in 1735, in Germany. The poisoning at that time appeared to be associated with sausage, and the disease was named "botulinus" from the Latin word for sausage, *botulus*. Not until 1895 was the organism discovered and described as occurring in ham and pork. It was called Type A. Thirty years later, a second type, named B, was found in California soil. Since then, it has been found in soils all over the world. Types A and B are both often associated with vegetables and fruit.

In subsequent years, two more types were discovered, C and D. Type C was found occurring in birds, and has, periodically, created havoc in the population of wild ducks. According to Professor Elizabeth McCoy, of the University of Wisconsin, no human case of type C has yet been authentically reported.

Type D was found associated with disease of grazing animals—horses, cattle, sheep. It has been called "forage poisoning" because animals pick it up by feeding on decomposed vegetation that often contains the growing bacteria. This type, like C, also appears incapable of affecting human beings.

The last type found to date, Type E, was discovered in saltwater fish. Poisoning from it occurs most frequently in countries where much preserved fish is consumed. It wasn't until 1951 that scientists discovered that Type E could also come from freshwater fish.[20]

The victims of botulism usually get it by eating improperly canned foods—meat, fish, or nonacid vegetables. Once in the body, the toxin is absorbed sluggishly by the intestines. But when it gets into the bloodstream, the consequences are swift. The poison sets up "roadblocks" between nerves and muscles, causing paralysis. Breathing muscles are usually the first to suffer, then the heart muscle.

The largest outbreak of botulism ever recorded occurred in Russia in 1933. Some 230 cases, with 94 deaths, resulted from Type-A toxin contained in stuffed eggplant.

The botulism caused by tuna fish at the beginning of this chapter was the first incident in the United States arising from commercially canned foods in nearly forty years. One exception may be a reported incident, caused by commercially canned mushroom sauce, which occurred in 1941. The United States canning industry has maintained a very good record for safety.

In 1963, the same year as the deaths from poisonous tuna fish, nineteen more cases of botulism were reported as being caused by commercially smoked fish. Seven persons died. In the same year, home-processed foods were responsible for twenty-two cases of botulism, including five deaths.[21]

But no one knows how many cases of botulism there really are each year.

An editorial in the *Journal of the American Medical Association,* November 1, 1965, pointed out that because of the relative rarity of botulism, "the diagnosis could not be in the front of the physician's mind and botulism could be overlooked."

"During publicized epidemics, every news reader will know as much about botulism as the physician," the editorial said. "How many physicians know that they can obtain types A and B antitoxin from ready commercial sources and Type E from the Public Health Service Communicable Disease Center in Atlanta, which began to stockpile significant quantities more than a year ago?"[22]

How well are we being protected from botulism?

Wesley E. Gilbertson, of the Division of Environmental Engineering and Food Protection, United States Department of Health, Education, and Welfare, testifying before a congressional committee, said of the plant where smoked fish had caused death from botulism:

"We were astounded to see . . . that the finished products very often were not separated in the processing rooms from the raw materials coming in. So instead of having the usual type of food operation, one was looking at something that really in a sense lacked the technology we think the food industry should have." He indicated also that the machines used to smoke the fish lacked instruments for measuring heat intensity.

In his testimony, Gilbertson summed up the danger from botulism in America today by saying, "We are on the borderline of a hazard."[23]

Lloyd Kempe, professor at the University of Michigan College of Engineering, has been working on the problem of botulism for more than ten years. He and research bacteriologist John T. Graiskoski helped identify the strain that killed the women in the case at the beginning of the chapter.

Their studies have shown that the bacteria can produce toxin at normal refrigerator temperatures. The poison, however, can be rendered harmless by cooking it at about 150 degrees F. for 15 minutes, although it takes one hour's cooking at 195 degrees to kill the poison-producing botulism bacteria.

Kempe and Graiskoski showed that Type E botulinuses can grow and form toxin at temperatures below 40 degrees. In fact, they said, they can incubate botulinuses for research in laboratory refrigerators.[24]

STAPH—PTOMAINE POISONING

Company picnics can be dangerous—not just because someone might say the wrong thing to the boss or because the shy secretary in the office becomes a femme fatale on the field, but because picnic food is highly susceptible to spoilage.

At a company picnic in northern Florida, some 150 employees ate ham, potato salad, and cake. Just as everyone was about to start a baseball game—about ninety minutes after lunch, five persons became extremely nauseated and had severe stomach pains. Within half an hour, fifteen more joined their miserable ranks. Before 10:00 P.M. that night, twenty-three persons required temporary hospital treatment and sixty-three were admitted overnight.

At a church dinner, over half of those who had eaten chicken—about one hundred persons—had become ill within six hours.

Investigation into the company picnic case showed not only that the ham and potato salad had been prepared under insanitary conditions by a caterer but also that a company truck had conveyed the food about one hundred miles the day before without any type of refrigeration. It was placed under refrigeration at the picnic grounds, but by then it was too late.

At the church dinner, the chickens had been cooked the day before and immediately refrigerated. The next morning, the chickens were reheated and cut into quarters with a butcher's meat saw. The chickens were without refrigeration from 10:00 A.M. until 5:00 P.M., when they were again reheated. The hands of the cook who prepared the chicken had numerous small cuts and abrasions.[25]

What had ruined the company picnic and poisoned the church parishioners? The staphylococcus germ. It rivals salmonella as the culprit in food poisoning, and there is much controversy over which causes more cases.

Staph is present on human skin, in the human throat, and in the human nasal areas, as well as in festering human wounds. At mealtimes, skin eruptions and cut fingers are common sources of staph germs. Many foods, once infected, will allow the organisms to grow and produce toxins unless the food is refrigerated. Even if the organism itself has been killed by heat, if sufficient toxin has been produced, the food is still capable of causing the symptoms of staph poisoning. The toxin produced by staph is heat-resistant.

Foodborne illness from staphylococcus is often referred to by laymen as "ptomaine" poisoning. This term has been consistently used since its introduction in 1870. Actually, there is no specific entity or group of substances that properly might be called "ptomaine." The word is derived from the Greek word *ptoma,* which means "carcass" or "dead flesh."[26]

The foods most often connected with staph poisoning are custards, cream-filled pastry, milk, and processed meat and fish. Food handlers with staphylococcal skin infections are the primary source of the illness.[27]

The incubation period is usually two to four hours after ingestion of food containing enterotoxin, or "poison." Then the onset is abrupt, with nausea and vomiting. The attack lasts from three to six hours, which is too long if you've ever had it. Fatalities are rare, and complete recovery is the routine. Diagnosis is usually based on the sudden onset of illness after eating infected food, brevity of symptoms, and rapidity of recovery. Furthermore, the patient is usually one of a number of similarly affected victims.

Considerable progress has been made in the past few years in the procedures for detecting staph poisons in food in the laboratory.[28] In fact, new laboratory techniques saved a cheese manufacturer from financial ruin. Staph toxin was discovered in samples of four million pounds of cheese that had been distributed around the country. Even though the live staph germ itself was not present, the cheese was ordered removed from the market. Faced with bankruptcy, the manufacturer had the cheese tested for the presence of enterotoxin, using the new laboratory techniques. As a result, he was able to release all but approximately 62,000 pounds of the cheese. No report of food poisoning followed the consumption of the released cheese.

Unfortunately, the ability to detect enterotoxins and enterotoxigenicity by seriological methods in the laboratory is limited to only a few laboratories because necessary supplies are not generally available. Furthermore, not all staph poisons have been identified.[29]

SHIGELLA

On the evening of April 20, 1965, a group of Army personnel and civilians and their dependents held a banquet in a private hall in San Antonio, Texas, to celebrate the end of the bowling-league season. Some 320 persons heard short speeches and long jokes and everyone had a good time.

Within a week, almost everyone who had attended the banquet was miserably ill. The sickness came on suddenly. They had fever, felt drowsy, lost their appetites, began to vomit, had severe diarrhea, and abdominal pains with distention. Three days after their symptoms began, blood, pus, and mucus began to appear in their stools. Actually, the epidemic was under way for a week before its existence was recognized. The first victims were treated at scattered civilian and military medical facilities. Their cases had been erroneously diagnosed as flu.

Then Lieutenant Colonel Jerome H. Greenberg, M.D., and other health investigators stepped in. They looked over the menu of the food eaten at the banquet. They immediately suspected the potato salad because it is a food often implicated in such illnesses.

The investigators went to the potato-processing plant. They found numerous flies. The bathroom lacked soap and towels. After potatoes were peeled and cooked, they were cooled, unprotected from flies, in front of a fan for several hours. The potatoes were then diced and placed in plastic bags and baskets. During the process, some of the potatoes spilled onto the floor, while others were partly in contact with the floor through the latticework of the baskets. Upon completion of dicing, some four hours after the potatoes were cooked, the bags and baskets were placed in a walk-in refrigerator.

On the day of the banquet, the temperature of the refrigerator had been 52 degrees F., and the internal temperature of the bag of potatoes that had been in the refrigerator approximately three hours was 64 degrees F. No further processing was done until the potatoes were delivered, in an unrefrigerated truck, to the restaurant where the salad was made. Additional periods of time during which the potatoes remained unrefrigerated occurred at the restaurant while the salad was being prepared and later, during delivery to the banquet hall. The durations of the periods could not be determined accurately.

In any event, the unhygienically prepared potato salad was capable of giving three hundred people shigellosis, or bacillary dysentery, which is an acute infection of the bowel caused by organisms of the shigella group and characterized by bloody diarrhea.

The incubation period is one to four days. This is one reason that diagnosis is often erroneous. Suspect food after that length of time is often not available for examination. Another reason is that laboratories often fail to use techniques that will detect a small number of shigellae in the presence of larger numbers of other bacteria.

Shigella infections are usually spread by contaminated water, defective plumbing, or food contaminated by unwashed hands or by flies. Good sanitation, with exclusion of flies and protection of food from contamination, is of prime importance in preventing the infection.

Dr. Greenberg pointed out in an article in *Public Health Reports,* November, 1966, that the disease is endemic throughout a large part of the United States. In epidemic form it has been less common than salmonellosis, but when it occurs, it usually strikes down a majority of those exposed.[30]

From 1951 to 1960, 108 outbreaks of shigellosis were reported. The number of cases ranged from six to 1,400 per outbreak. Food, other than milk, and person-to-person contact accounted for twenty-nine outbreaks each, and water accounted for ten. Only three were from milk. Unfortunately, for thirty-seven outbreaks no source could be determined.

There were 13,000 cases reported in 1963, but with shigellosis, as with other foodborne diseases, the true incidence is greatly underreported.[31]

CLOSTRIDIUM PERFRINGENS

One day, an exclusive girls' school had almost 100 percent illness. From the headmistress to the youngest student, everyone was crowding the bathrooms with diarrhea and colic-like cramps. The suspect meal was roast beef and gravy. The beef and gravy had been prepared the day before and allowed to cool in open trays, without refrigeration, for twenty-two hours.

The cause of the illness? *Clostridium perfringens.*

Clostridium perfringens is widely distributed in feces, sewage, and soil. It is so prevalent it is a probable contaminant of nearly all foods. The spores of *C. perfringens* are present in a large percentage of meat products, both raw and cooked.[32] The cooked foods most frequently associated with outbreaks in America are meats, fowl, and gravies that have been cooked, and allowed to cool slowly.

Herbert E. Hall, Ph. D., and Keith H. Lewis, Ph.D., writing in *Health Laboratory Science,* October, 1967, said: "We do not know how many outbreaks involving *C. perfringens* occur each year in the United States. The syndrome is a mild one, and unless an isolated group is involved, medical and epidemiological attention is rarely directed toward its occurrence."[33]

In the American Medical Association publication *Let's Talk About Food,* edited by Philip White, Sc.D., it was pointed out that symptoms from *C. perfringens* last one to one and a half days. "Since the patients recover quickly, and since people learn to tolerate minor episodes of discomfort, thorough surveillance by public health authorities is difficult."[34]

Dr. Hall and Dr. Lewis pointed out that public health laboratories that routinely examine food for isolations of *C. perfringens* usually find outbreaks caused by this organism.

"Further, we know that over 75 percent of food handlers carry one or more strains of these organisms in their feces, and that recovery of these organisms from the food preparation environment is not difficult and that 37 to 82 percent of raw meats and 4.7 to 37 percent of processed meats contain these organisms. It is, therefore, reasonable to expect that the etiology of many more outbreaks would be determined if all laboratories examined suspect food anaerobically."[35]

ESCHERICHIA COLI

As Christmas lights were being hung along the streets and while carols poured from loudspeakers in December, 1965, babies began to sicken and die in Newark, New Jersey. The infants had severe diarrhea, a condition that does kill millions of infants in underdeveloped countries around the world every year. But what had caused it in New Jersey's largest city? What did the babies have in common?

They came from families of all economic levels and from all ethnic groups.

By the time officials realized it was an epidemic, sickness had struck scores of babies. Public health officials who began investigating the case found that there was one thing 30 percent of the babies did have in common. They had been hospitalized in the recent past, but for a variety of conditions. Without knowing what was causing the sickness, doctors tried desperately to save the infants. They used a wide spectrum of antibiotics, but none seemed of much use.

By the time the epidemic had ended, four hundred infants had been seriously affected and twenty-eight had died. Of those that succumbed, almost all had been in the 30 percent previously hospitalized for other conditions.

Laboratories finally succeeded in isolating the organism that had caused the diarrhea. It was *Escherichia coli*.[36]

Little is really known about the "bug." It is known that *E. coli* is normally present in the intestines. Abroad, it has been reported as a cause of both food and waterborne illness in adults, and it is associated particularly with infant diarrhea in this country. The symptoms range from those of a mild disease to a severe illness with high fever, acute diarrhea, and prostration. In addition to the overt illness caused by ingesting EEC, both the acutely ill and those displaying no symptoms become carriers for variable periods of time, and are potentially dangerous to small infants.[37]

Although they are not sure, public health officials believe that the Newark infants picked up the disease in hospitals, either from food or personnel, during their stay for treatment of other conditions; then they spread the disease to other infants in the community.

There is no doubt that *E. coli* is contaminating some of our food. In 1967, FDA inspectors discovered it in:

- Potatoes, crushed and dehydrated, in Trenton, Missouri.[38]
- Pecan pieces at Fort Worth, Texas.[39]
- Prepared cake mixes, Chicago, Illinois.[40]

Approximately 20,000 pounds of the prepared cake mixes, valued at $3,000, were destroyed voluntarily because the products were contaminated with *E. coli*.

But how much of our food is contaminated with the organism?

How many of our illnesses are caused by *E. coli?* Although proper laboratory tests could tell us, no one knows.

FOODBORNE ILLNESSES FROM VIRUSES

A kitchen worker in a hospital in St. Louis, Missouri, went about her duties, although she was worried about her husband. He didn't complain much, but he acted as if he didn't feel too well. The date was July 2. As she mixed the frozen orange-juice concentrate with water for the next morning's breakfast, she thought to herself that she was glad she was well and able to hold down a job to supplement the family's income. She placed the orange juice in the refrigerator, and went home.

The next morning, interns, resident physicians, nurses, and cafeteria employees filed in for breakfast. Most of them, as is the custom in America, took orange juice.

Between July 21 and August 12, fourteen of the orange-juice drinkers came down with hepatitis. This was in spite of the fact that the orange juice had a pH (acidity-alkalinity content) in the range of 3.5 to 4.0 and had been left in the refrigerator at least overnight. At the time the hospital personnel came down with hepatitis, so did the kitchen worker's husband. The public health officials believe that he had the virus and that his wife carried it without symptoms.[41] For some reason, young people seem to be affected most frequently by hepatitis. The peak season apparently is in the fall. The incubation period for hepatitis is estimated at two to six weeks.[42] The onset of the symptoms is abrupt, with loss of appetite, nausea, fever, and malaise. Tenderness and enlargement of the liver and pain in the right upper quadrant are usually early symptoms. About five days after the onset, jaundice appears, and fever tends to subside. The gastro-intestinal symptoms persist for about ten days, and subside with regression of the jaundice. Swollen glands, severe generalized itching, hives, and intermittent diarrhea may occur. Usually, the patient recovers uneventfully after six to eight weeks. Relapses occur in 5 to 15 percent of the cases, and are usually attributed to premature resumption of activity, poor diet, or alcoholism. Ninety percent of the patients recover.

Dean O. Cliver, writing in the October, 1967, issue of *Health Laboratory Science,* said foodborne viruses are usually too small to be seen with a regular microscope.

"Since the laboratory diagnosis of virus disease is relatively new, the greatest emphasis in the epidemiological record has necessarily been placed upon diseases whose clinical pictures were so distinctive as to permit them to be diagnosed on that basis by the attending physician. The first of the clinically distinctive human agents reported to be transmitted by foods was poliomyelitis. Ten outbreaks took place between 1914 and 1949 . . . milk, particularly raw milk, was the predominant vehicle."

He went on to say, "Although there is no reproducible method of cultivating the virus of hepatitis in the laboratory, the clinical picture is frequently highly distinctive, and epidemiologists are coming increasingly to consider food as a possible vehicle for the virus." He added that since the incubation period for hepatitis is approximately four weeks, it is extremely difficult to compile definitive information once an outbreak has been recognized.[43]

In another article, in *Public Health Reports,* February, 1966, Dr. Cliver said that the majority of foods implicated in the outbreaks of hepatitis had been cooked very little: "It is to be noted that contamination which takes place almost immediately before consumption is the least likely to be counteracted by inactivation of the virus as a result of cooking or other treatment of the food. As a result, the infected human who works either as a food handler or a kitchen worker in final preparation constitutes a potentially quite significant source of virus in foods."

As with the spread of bacteria-borne food poisoning, good sanitation is one step in prevention. As far as the hepatitis virus is concerned, public health officials agree that the virus is shed by infected individuals in the feces, so that considerable mishandling of food must occur before a foodborne outbreak.

FOODBORNE PARASITIC DISEASES

Corner grocery stores are fast being replaced by the impersonal supermarket. But some small stores still exist in ethnic neighborhoods. Practically everyone went to one such market to get "homemade" pork sausages. "They taste just like the ones in the old country," people would say. Even young children who had never been out of the boundaries of the neighborhood liked them.

One spring, eleven people in the neighborhood, ranging from a four-year-old to an eighty-year-old, came down with high fever, muscle pain, stomach cramps, chills, and general weakness. They were members of seven families, but the cause of their symptoms wasn't hard to track down. All had eaten raw smoked sausage prepared from the same hog at the corner grocer's. The hog was infected with *Trichinella spiralis,* a small parasite.[44]

Trichinella spiralis requires two hosts, animal and man. Trichinosis results when humans eat insufficiently cooked flesh of infected animals. Pork is the most common source of the trichina-infected meat.[45] The larvae originally held in the animal are released from their "space capsule" in the small intestines of the person who consumes the meat. Their parasites mature within a few hours and mate within two or three days. The male worm of *T. spiralis* is eventually passed out of the human body. The females, on the other hand, burrow deep into the intestinal wall, and there they discharge many larvae over a six-week period. These offspring enter the bloodstream, and are carried to the heart, where they are then pumped to all parts of the body. Only those that lodge in muscle tissue are capable of further development. Within a month, they are encapsulated by fibrous tissue, and the cycle is complete. They may live indefinitely in these cysts without causing any significant symptoms.[46]

However, persons who have eaten a large number of the worms in their food usually develop such symptoms as swelling of the upper eyelids, muscular tenderness, headaches, diarrhea, and fever. They may have an eye hemorrhage, eye pain, and shy away from light. If the worms affect the heart, respiratory system, or the nerves, severe symptoms and even death may result. But permanent disability rarely ensues, although symptoms may persist for several months.

Though it is hard to believe, it is conservatively estimated that 25 to 50 million Americans carry trichina larvae in their muscles and internal organs. Every American is estimated to consume at least three servings of infested pork annually. Up to 10 percent of the pork sausage in large city markets has been found to be infected, according to Howard Earl in the October, 1965, issue of the American Medical Association's publication *Today's Health.*[47]

Between two and three hundred human cases of trichinosis are reported each year in the United States in spite of the fact most states do not make such reporting compulsory. The fatality rate from trichinosis is listed at about 5 percent, but in epidemics it has been known to reach more than 30 percent.[48]

The prevention of trichinosis should be simple. Thorough cooking of all fresh pork and the feeding of only cooked garbage to hogs would go far toward reducing it. About one-fourth of 1 percent of the grain fed to swine, and considerably more of the raw garbage, are estimated to be infected. Although the law states that garbage should be cooked, it is difficult to enforce, and infected animals are still on the market.[49]

TOXOPLASMOSIS

In 1965, the National Academy of Sciences urged further research in the field of parasitology. Tapeworms, protozoa, and other parasites can cause all sorts of symptoms, from ulcers to weight loss to dysentery.[50]

Disease from the protozoa *Giardia* is present in 7.4 percent of the people in the United States and only 6.9 percent of the people in other parts of the world.[51] Amebic dysentery is endemic throughout the world, affecting 17.6 percent of the population. In the United States, it affects 13.6 percent.[52] All can be spread through unsanitary food. No one, as we have said before, really knows the extent of the parasites and the diseases they cause.

An example of how important research can be may be found in the example of toxoplasmosis. Since the 1930's, it has been known that *Toxoplasma* can cause significant disease in man. It was then shown by physicians at Columbia University that this parasite could be transmitted from mother to unborn child. But in the intervening years, it was never revealed:

• How the mother becomes infected.
• What the true incidence of congenital toxoplasmosis is.
• How an early diagnosis can be made.
• How preventive measures can be taken.
• How widespread mental retardation, compromised vision, epilepsy, hydrocephalus, and so forth, are because of toxoplasmosis.[53]

There is no doubt that toxoplasmosis cripples unborn children. One study showed that of 150 infants with proved congenital toxoplasmosis, approximately one-third showed signs and symptoms of an acute infectious process with splenomegaly, jaundice, enlarged liver, anemia, retinal damage, and abnormal cerebrospinal fluid.

How many babies have been born with damaged brains and blind eyes because of toxoplasma gondii?

Dr. Jack S. Remington, Chief of the Division of Allergy, Immunology, and Infectious Diseases, Palo Alto Medical Research Foundation, reported in 1967 that detailed recent studies supported the view that ingestion of infected meat or water may be the mode of transmission. He noted that studies of animals chronically infected with toxoplasma had shown that the cysts obtained from muscle were resistant to gastric acidity and digestive juices. The findings thus suggested that undercooked meat played a role in spreading the disease.[54] In studies by his own group of fifty samples each of beef loin, lamb and pork loin, obtained from local stores, Dr. Remington said toxoplasma was found in 4 percent of the lamb samples, 32 percent of the pork samples, and none of the beef samples.

Further support to the meatborne theory was the case study of a French hospital for tubercular children. At the time of admission, 641 children showed no toxoplasma antibodies; but after admission, 204 did. The risk of infection per month of hospital stay was approximately five times as high as for the general population. When the usual ration of undercooked meat was increased, the number of infections showed a significant increase, and the risk almost doubled.

Dr. Remington said of the French hospital study: "The custom in this hospital of eating raw or very undercooked meat was probably the cause of the abnormally high number of toxoplasma infections. The authors stated that the prevalence of toxoplasma infections in France is higher than in other countries with similar climate and culture. The difference is particularly pronounced among children."[55]

Dr. G. Richard O'Connor, Associate Director of the Francis I. Proctor Foundation for Research in Ophthalmology, is studying the effect of toxoplasmosis on the eyes of newborn infants. "We think there is a possibility that mothers may transmit the disease to their infants. When the disease occurs, we find the one thing many of these mothers have in common is that they have eaten raw meat sometime early in their pregnancy." Mothers, he emphasizes, should not eat raw meat during pregnancy and should also avoid raw eggs.[56]

OTHER FOODBORNE DISEASES

There are many other foodborne diseases. In fact, more than 40 percent of all human diseases are contracted through food.

Typhoid fever, although it crops up once in a while, is not too much of a problem in America today. It can still be a danger in water, milk, and shellfish that is contaminated at the source. Food contaminated by unwashed hands or by flies may still give a person typhoid fever.

Streptococcus, which causes septic sore throat and scarlet fever, may still be obtained from raw milk contaminated at the source. Diphtheria is a remote danger from dishes or silverware contaminated by a carrier.

Brucellosis, or undulant fever, is an infectious disease with an acute high fever but few other signs. Vague body aches, weakness, and sweating may also be associated with it. Brucellosis is too common in the United States today. The three causative microorganisms belong to the genus *Brucella,* of which three species primarily affect animals: *Br. abortus,* cattle and hogs; *Br. suis,* hogs; and *Br. melitensis,* goats. Any of these may be transmitted to man by direct contact with secretions and excretions and by the ingestion of milk or milk products containing viable brucellae. Though brucellosis is a worldwide disease, it is most prevalent in rural areas, and is an occupational disease among meat-packers, veterinarians, farmers, and livestock producers.[57]

The symptoms may simulate a number of human diseases, making diagnosis very difficult. In the heart of Newark, at the United Hospitals, a number of women who had miscarriages were tested. The lesions in their placentas were similar to those seen in the placentas of cattle who had lost their calves. The brucellosis organism was recovered from the women.[58]

NATURAL FOOD POISONS

Dr. Walter MacLinn, Director of the Agricultural Experiment Station at Rutgers University, says: "You must remember that animals and plants were not put on earth for the benefit of man. Everything has just as much right to exist as man. Man is a predator. Some of the things he eats are going to make him sick."[59]

Potatoes, Brazil nuts, and tangerines are among the items that are inedible for some people. Dr. Thomas Golbert, a fellow in medicine at Northwestern University, described thirteen cases of anaphylactic shock due to common foods. Besides potatoes, nuts, and tangerines, there were pinto beans, halibut, rice, shrimp, milk, a cereal mix, and garbanzo (chick-peas).[60] All the reactions were acute and potentially fatal, with skin, respiratory, and blood-pressure involvement. Swelling, hives, or both, occurred in every case. Thirteen of the patients lost consciousness.

In several instances, Dr. Golbert said that he and his colleagues examined the patients in the emergency room. In others, a complete medical and allergic history was done. In eight cases, the cause was incontrovertibly proved: the patients developed anaphylactic shock a second time after ingesting the same food.

In eleven cases, once the cause was proved or was presumptively identified, there were no recurrences. In two cases the cause of the reactions remains uncertain. One patient has had several recurrences after eating foods with a large mold content: cheeses, old breads, certain kinds of sausage—and he has reacted strongly to a test with mold antigen. The last patient is still a mystery, although an investigation of hidden additives may explain why he shows no reaction to extracts of the pure foods during tests.

A. D. Campbell, Chief of the Food Contaminants Branch, Division of the Food Chemistry, Food and Drug Administration, discussed "natural food poisons" in the September, 1967, *FDA Papers:*

"Generally, through a trial-and-error process, man has been able to place plants and animals into safe and unsafe food categories. This trial-and-error process has been useful in eliminating those which produce acute toxicity; the results are usually sudden illness or death. However, the manifestations of chronic toxicity of some of these substances are not readily associated with the source; symptoms may occur after a considerable lapse of time. More sophisticated research studies are usually necessary to find the cause-and-effect relationships for chronic toxicity."

He went on to say that plants may contain toxic substances, such as protein digestion inhibitors, toxic proteins such as those found in castor beans, estrogenic substances, substances containing cyanides, solanine substances such as toxins from potato sprouts, and other toxic materials.

"In some instances, the toxicant is at such a low level that it does not present a health problem when eaten; the estrogenic substances of soybeans are examples. In other instances, the toxicant can be inactivated by heating the foodstuff before it is eaten. For example, the protein digestion inhibitor of soybeans and the cyanide substances in lima beans are inactivated, as toxicants, by heating.

"The toxic portions of some plants are usually removed and discarded. Those found in the skin and sprouts of potatoes which have been exposed to sunlight are thus avoided. Stalks of rhubarb are eaten, and the toxic leaves are discarded.

"Harvesting at the proper stage of maturity is a means of avoiding other plant toxicants. For example, unripened grapefruit contain a toxic substance which is not present in mature fruit. The use of selective breeding by the plant geneticist is another means of eliminating toxic substances from some plants."

Dr. Campbell pointed out that some animals or animal products that are normally suitable as food can contain toxic substances under unusual circumstances:

"Oysters, clams, and other shellfish have been shown to contain a toxic substance known as 'the paralytic shellfish poison' when they grow under adverse conditions. The puffer fish, considered a delicacy by some, contains a highly toxic substance in its skin and sex organs. Toxic animal metabolites (substances produced by the life processes) are known to contaminate some animal products when some toxic substances from molds are eaten by the animals. Detection by analytical means and discarding the contaminated lots may be the only means of avoiding them."

The FDA scientist then launched into an extensive discussion of the mycotoxins that have been with "man since the beginning." He referred to the incident in 1961 when hundreds of English turkeys died from a toxic substance produced by the mold *Aspergillus flavus.* The substance was called "aflatoxin."

"It is known that the aflatoxins are produced by a number of molds in addition to *Aspergillus flavus,"* Dr. Campbell said. "These are very potent toxins for some animals, and the sensitivity varies over a considerable range for different species. Rainbow trout are the most sensitive animals that have been found so far."

Dr. Campbell said it is not uncommon for the mycologist to isolate molds from cereal grains and other foodstuffs. He said that American scientists began to work on the mold toxin problems after 1961. As a result of FDA's early efforts, and through the cooperation of industry and the United States Department of Agriculture, contaminated peanuts have been diverted from food channels.

Each lot of peanuts, he said, is examined as it comes from the farm, and the lots likely to be contaminated with aflatoxins are analyzed. If the contamination is found too high, the lot is used only for the production of peanut oil, because the refining process eliminates aflatoxins.

The aflatoxin problem has not been confined to peanuts. Dr. Campbell concluded:

"Much has been learned by the scientific community from the great amount of research which has gone on in many laboratories since the aflatoxins were discovered in 1961. This information has been quickly put to use to protect the health of the people throughout the world. These studies indicate that much is still to be learned about naturally occurring food poisons. Only through concerted research efforts of many laboratories will the basic scientific information be obtained for a sound evaluation of this newly recognized problem."[61]

If aflatoxin is a newly recognized problem, death from mushrooms is a very old one.

In New Jersey, an English professor and his wife picked mushrooms in a field near their home. They cleaned them, peeled and boiled them, and ate them. Being a member of the intellectual élite, the professor was confident he knew the difference between poisonous mushrooms and edible mushrooms. Fifteen minutes after eating the mushrooms, he and his wife became dizzy and numb. They began vomiting. An ambulance was called, and they were taken to the local hospital. The professor's condition rapidly deteriorated. The police were called, and he was rushed by ambulance to a hospital twenty miles away that had a hyperbaric unit. The doctors felt that oxygen under pressure might save the professor's life. He died the next day. His wife, who was put in the hyperbaric chamber six hours later, also succumbed.

But mushrooms are far from the only plants carrying deadly poison. Although they kill rapidly, some may kill slowly.

A detailed report on foods that contain substances known to have toxic effects on man under some conditions was issued by the Food Protection Committee of the National Research Council in 1967. The Academy of Sciences release said of the report: *"Toxicants Occurring Naturally in Foods* suggests the need for continuing research in a field that has received comparatively little study and which contains many unknowns."[62]

The report concludes that the primary medical challenge lies in "the question of the long-term chronic toxicity, or lifetime effects, of many of the known as well as the yet unrecognized natural chemical components of our foods. Long-delayed harmful effects that might result from normal patterns of consumption are of the greatest potential importance since they would be expected to affect a large number of individuals."

Among the many natural food chemicals with possible long-term harmful effects are those that can produce goiters, tumors, and cancers. The foods that carry the greatest amount of goitrogenic chemicals include rutabagas, turnips, kale, and cauliflower. These chemicals are also present in wild turnips and in such weeds of the mustard family as lesser swine's-cress, pepper cress, and shepherd's purse. The report said that the chemicals "appear to be transferable to the milk of cows consuming these plants and to be capable of interfering with the thyroid function of humans who drink such milk."

In discussing the chemicals that have produced cancer in laboratory animals and that are found in some humans' foods, the report cautioned: "The role played by these carcinogens in the occurrence of certain cancers in man in regions where these agents are found is still unknown. An informed approach to the hazards for these agents and the synthetic chemicals in our environment is necessary. . . ."

Some of the carcinogens considered in the report are ergot, a fungus substance sometimes found on rye; a mold that causes rice to turn yellow and bitter; an aflatoxin.

Stimulants and depressants are found in many plants. Jimsonweed, used frequently in home medicines as a tea, produces hallucinations. It is estimated that four to five grams of the crude leaf or seeds is fatal. Nutmeg, used by some individuals for its narcotic effects, also produces burning abdominal pain, delirium, stupor, low blood pressure, liver damage, shock, or death. The amount of nutmeg found to cause poisoning is inconsistent, but the report cites one study that sets the amount at five grams or more.

The report confirms that caffeine, in the amounts present in coffee, tea, and many cola drinks (a six-ounce bottle of cola contains about one-third the caffeine of a cup of coffee) tends to facilitate mental and muscular effort, and diminishes drowsiness and psychic and motor fatigue. Heavy coffee drinking, along with several other factors, have been associated in a Chicago study with the development of coronary heart disease. The coffee association does not become apparent, physicians pointed out, unless six or more cups a day are consumed.[63] Coffee has also been designated as a food allergen. It has been known to cause migraines, stuffy nose, and upset stomach.[64]

Tea contains, in addition to caffeine, a second, less powerful stimulant—theophylline. Both it and caffeine can be fatal in doses far greater than can be ingested ordinarily in coffee or tea.

Honey made from nectar of the Carolina jessamine, also known as yellow jessamine and trumpet flower, has caused death in man.

Many common foods—such as bananas, pineapples, tomatoes, some cheeses, lemon, and wine—contain large amounts of toxic amino compounds, enough to have disastrous consequences if they were injected into the veins. Among the factors that are believed to be responsible for rendering these amino compounds harmless in foodstuffs is detoxification after consumption through the action of another chemical, monoamine oxidase (MAO). However, severe complications have been reported among patients on tranquilizers following the consumption of pickled herring.

Another type of complication from combinations of foods is mentioned briefly in the report on toxicants: acute illness caused by drinking an alcoholic beverage following the consumption of the edible "inky cap" mushroom. A chemical in the mushroom interferes with normal metabolism of the alcohol.

The list of naturally occurring food poisons and possibilities is endless.

Spinach has been implicated several times. One West German baby died and thirteeen others between the ages of two months and ten months developed an anemic blood condition after eating spinach or drinking the water in which it was cooked. Nitrites in the spinach were blamed.[65] A Milwaukee cardiologist warned that heart patients taking anticoagulant drugs should not eat spinach or other leafy vegetables containing vitamin K. Vitamin K aids blood clotting.[66]

An Ohio doctor believes that large amounts of mustard, pepper, and ginger in the diet can produce high blood pressure.[67]

The Food Protection Committee of the National Research Council report on *Toxicants Occurring Naturally in Foods* sums up the situation very well: "The possible presence of significant amounts of these [aflatoxins] and other carcinogenic agents in human food deserves the attention of the epidemiologists in considerations on the etiology of cancer in man. A corollary requirement is the need for much more information on the composition and toxicological properties of previously ignored or unknown non-nutritive constituents of human foods."

6 NOTES

1. "FDA and Salmonella," *Sanitation Review*, February, 1967.
2. Ernest A. Ager, M.D.; Kenrad E. Nelson, M.D.; Mildred M. Galton, Sc.M.; John R. Boring, III, Ph.D.; Janice R. Jernigan, "Two Outbreaks of Egg-Borne Salmonellosis and Implications for Their Prevention," *Journal of the American Medical Association (JAMA)*, February 6, 1967, Vol. 199, No. 6, pp. 372–378.
3. *Ibid.*
4. David Lang, M.D., *New England Journal of Medicine*, 276:829–832, 1967.
5. Donald Armstrong, M.D.; Martin Wolfe, M.D.; Donald Louria, F.A.C.P.; Anne Blevin, R.N., Department of Medicine, Memorial Hospital, N.Y., 49th Annual Session, American College of Physicians, April 15, 1968, Boston.
6. Daniel Widelock, Ph.D., Deputy Director, Bureau of Laboratories, New York City Department of Health, "Salmonella Link in Fetal Death?", *JAMA*, December 19, 1967, Vol. 202, No. 12, p. 32.
7. James Goddard, M.D., Commissioner of U.S. Food and Drug Administration, "Incident at Selby Junior High," *Nutrition Today*, September, 1967.
8. Arthur Wilder, D.V.M.; Robert MacCready, M.D., "Isolation of Salmonella from Poultry," *New England Journal of Medicine*, June 30, 1966, Vol. 274, No. 26.
9. Goddard, *op. cit.*
10. "FDA and Salmonella," *Sanitation Review*, February, 1967.
11. *FDA Papers*, June, 1967.
12. *Ibid.*, February, 1967, p. 30.
13. *Ibid.*
14. *Ibid.*
15. *Ibid.*
16. *Ibid.*
17. Lt. Warren Sanborn, M.S.C., USN, "The Relation of Surface Contamination to the Transmission of Disease," *American Journal of Public Health*, August, 1963, Vol. 52, No. 8.
18. Ralph W. Johnston, M.S.; John Feldman, A.B.; Rosemary Sullivan, B.S., *Public Health Reports*, July, 1963. The names of the victims are fictitious.
19. University of Michigan News Service, October 9, 1968.
20. Dennis Blakeslee, feature story, University of Wisconsin News Service, December 10, 1963.

21. *Ibid.*
22. Editorial, *Journal of the American Medical Association,* November 1, 1965, Vol. 194, No. 5.
23. Wesley E. Gilbertson, Division of Environmental Health Engineering, U.S. Department of Health, Education, and Welfare, testimony before House, HEW Appropriations Subcommittee, 1965.
24. University of Michigan News Service, October 9, 1963.
25. Public Health Service Publication 1105, November, 1963.
26. Howard Earl, "Food Poisoning," *Today's Health,* October, 1965.
27. *The Merck Manual,* 11th edition, 1966.
28. E. P. Casman, Ph.D., "Staphylococcal Food Poisoning," *Health Laboratory Science,* October, 1967.
29. *Ibid.*
30. Jerome H. Greenberg, M.D., "Common Source Epidemic Shillegosis," *Public Health Reports,* November, 1966.
31. Herbert Hall, Ph.D.; Keith Lewis, Ph.D., *"Clostridium Perfringens* and Other Bacterial Species as Possible Causes of Foodborne Disease Outbreaks of Undetermined Etiology," *Health Laboratory Science,* October, 1967.
32. *Food Facts from Rutgers,* October–November, 1967.
33. Hall and Lewis, *op. cit.*
34. *Let's Talk About Food,* ed. Philip White, Sc.D., American Medical Association, 1967.
35. Hall and Lewis, *ibid.*
36. News coverage and *Medical World News* report, "PHS Traces Epidemic of Fatal Diarrhea," June 4, 1965.
37. Hall and Lewis, *ibid.*
38. *FDA Papers,* May, 1968.
39. *Ibid.,* May, 1968.
40. *FDA Papers,* April, 1968.
41. Dean O. Cliver, Ph.D., "Implications of Foodborne Infectious Hepatitis," *Public Health Reports,* February, 1966, Vol. 81.
42. *The Merck Manual.*
43. Dean O. Cliver, Ph.D., "Food-Associated Viruses," *Health Laboratory Science,* October, 1967, Vol. 4, No. 4.
44. U.S. Public Health Service Publication 1105, November, 1963.
45. *Let's Talk About Food, loc. cit.*
46. *The Merck Manual.*
47. Howard Earl, "Food Poisoning: The Sneaky Attacker," *Today's Health,* October, 1965.
48. *Ibid.*
49. *The Merck Manual.*
50. C. Cheng, "Parasitological Problems," *Journal of Environmental Health,* December, 1965.
51. *Ibid.*
52. *Ibid.*

53. Richard O'Connor, M.D., Associate Director of the Francis I. Proctor Foundation for Research in Ophthalmology, lecture before the Society for the Prevention of Blindness, Science Writers' Seminar, October, 1967.
54. *Medical Tribune,* January 22, 1968.
55. *Ibid.*
56. O'Connor, *op. cit.*
57. *The Merck Manual.*
58. Samuel A. Goldberg, D.V.M., Ph.D., M.D., "Bacterial and Parasitic Diseases Common in Animals and Man," *New Jersey Public Health News,* January, 1961.
59. Walter A. MacLinn, Director of the Agricultural Experiment Station, Rutgers University, in a taped interview with author, January, 1968.
60. Thomas Golbert, M.D., American Academy of Allergy meeting, Boston, 1968.
61. A. D. Campbell, Ph.D., "Natural Food Poisons," *FDA Papers,* September, 1967.
62. News from the National Academy of Sciences and the National Research Council, April 19, 1967.
63. Paul Oglesby, M.D., Professor of Medicine, Northwestern University, and Mark Lepper, M.D., Professor of Preventive Medicine, University of Illinois, "Circulation," *Journal of the American Heart Association,* July, 1963.
64. Martin Green, M.D., "Coffee as a Food Allergen," *Journal of the New Jersey Medical Society,* June, 1960, Vol. 57, No. 6.
65. *British Medical Journal,* January 29, 1966, report of Drs. A. Sinios and W. Wodak.
66. Armand J. Quick, M.D., *Science News Letter,* January 25, 1964.
67. Jackson Blair, M.D., *Medical Times,* November 5, 1966.

7

Water: Unfit for Drinking

A FUNERAL PARLOR IN ATLANTA, Georgia, had its hydroaspirator—a device used to withdraw body fluids during embalming—improperly connected to the local drinking-water supply. Several doors down the street, some people were getting something unexpected from their faucets. One man who was questioned by local authorities said, "I thought the water looked rusty, but it wasn't rust."[1]

In October, 1961, in a midwestern city, ethylene glycol antifreeze was being pumped from a large storage tank to an antifreeze distribution system. This system was cross-connected to city water supply lines, and it was estimated that over one hundred gallons of 60 percent ethylene glycol were pumped into the water mains. Samples from the waterpipes showed the presence of from 1.5 to 2.0 percent, or up to 20,000 parts per million, of this toxic chemical agent. This time, a homeowner reported the water's bitter taste and reddish color to the water department. Radio announcements, a shutdown of the water supply to the area, and repeated flushings of the pipes were required to keep the townspeople from being unknowingly "fortified" against the winter's cold.[2]

After an outbreak of gastroenteritis in an Oklahoma school, public health inspectors found that none of the flushometer valve toilets with submerged inlets were provided with the vacuum breakers that prevent atmospheric pressure from forcing waste water into the supply lines. Each night, to conserve water and eliminate the possibility that classrooms might be flooded if a leak developed, the custodian turned off the valve from the main supply line. As the pressure in the supply lines was cut off, atmospheric pressure in the toilet bowls moved the waste water up to the drinking-supply reservoir. Most of the people affected were those who drank from the faucets on the first floor of the school; there were progressively fewer cases on the second and third floors as the atmospheric pressure moved less of the waste water to those heights.[3]

Though these are rather startling cases, they are not so unusual as you might think. The fact is that 95 million Americans drink water that is below federal standards or of unknown quality.[4]

No book on food safety would be complete without a chapter on water. In the average community, over 140 gallons of water per person per day are used. Of this amount, about 60 gallons per person are used by each household, another 45 gallons by industry, 7 gallons by public services such as fire fighting, and 25 gallons by commercial firms. About 3 gallons are lost through leaks in underground water pipes.[5]

It takes 325 gallons of water to make one gallon of alcohol, 375 gallons to grow a one-pound sack of flour. The combined consumption of a cow, hog, sheep, and chicken will average about 40 gallons of water a day. And more than 77 billion gallons of water a day are pumped from rivers, reservoirs, and ponds in the widespread irrigation network that feeds western agriculture.[6] If contaminated water is used for any of these drinking and food-processing purposes, and proper treatment safeguards are not applied, the result may be human illness.

How do you know whether the next glass of water you drink will be safe and pure?

The State Board of Health of Wisconsin, in a brochure directed at farmers, said: "People are likely to feel that odor-free, crystal clear, cold water, free from unpleasant tastes, is also safe water.

"True, these are all desirable qualities, but a water supply can meet these standards and still be as deadly as poison. Many a death has been caused by waterborne diseases. Many less serious diseases and intestinal disturbances are caused by impure water."[7]

In 1965, for instance, an outbreak of waterborne intestinal illness made 16,000 people sick in Riverside, California. Within a few days, several died, including an infant.[8] In the same year, an additional 24,000 cases of waterborne illnesses were reported in the nation.

This, of course, is not a true representation of the total number of such illnesses, since, as in foodborne disease, there is faulty reporting.

Dr. Luther L. Terry, as Surgeon General of the Public Health Service in 1961, said: "When I entered the Public Health Service some twenty years ago, I was taught by the senior physicians of our Corps that whatever else in our environment was dangerous to health, our water supplies were safe. But three dangers—one potential and two actual—are causing us to re-examine our water's spotless reputation."[9] Dr. Terry listed virus diseases, new chemicals, and radiation.

"The United States Public Health Service Drinking Water Standards," 1962 revision, states:

"Drinking water shall not contain impurities in concentrations which may be hazardous to the health of consumers. It should not be excessively corrosive to the water supply system. Substances used in its treatment shall not remain in the water in concentrations greater than required by good practice. Substances which may have a deleterious physiological effect, or for which physiological effects are not known, shall not be introduced into the system in a manner which would permit them to reach the consumer."

Virus diseases are borne in human feces. Water inspectors determine the level of contamination of our drinking water by measuring *Escherichia coli,* which is present in fecal matter from humans and other mammals. Its presence is an indication of contamination.

Two families of viruses are excreted from the feces: the enteroviruses—which include polio, Coxsackie, and Echo viruses—and the adenoviruses. The enteroviruses multiply in the human intestines, and are discharged in the feces. Adenoviruses apparently multiply in the human intestines, too, and are also found in the feces, but less is known about them. Adenoviruses are associated with upper respiratory diseases causing inflammation of the mucous membrane of the respiratory system and the eyes.

The classic case of waterborne disease occurred in Chicago in 1933. As it was later proved, old, defective, and improperly designed plumbing fixtures and plumbing permitted the contamination of drinking water. As a result, 1,409 people came down with amebic dysentery. There were 98 deaths.[10]

This incident led to a tightening of water standards and expanded inspection, but public health officials today are still very much concerned about faulty plumbing. Cross-connections make possible the contamination of potable water, and are "ever-present dangers," the Public Health Service maintains.[11]

In its publication "Water Supply and Plumbing Cross-Connections Hazards in Household and Community Systems," Public Health Service officials say: "The probability of contamination of drinking water through a cross-connection occurring within a single plumbing system may seem remote, but considering the multitude of similar systems, the probability is great. The only proper precaution is to eliminate all possible links or channels whereby such pollution may occur."

Why do such cross-connections exist?

One reason is, the Public Health Service says, that a connection is made by a plumber unaware of the danger. He does not realize that water flow may occur in a reverse direction or even uphill. Other reasons why such connections are made is the simple one of convenience, combined with a false reliance on a valve or other mechanical device or water pressure as adequate protection. Valves may fail or be carelessly left open.

Such cases are legion. One of the most famous occurred in 1932, when, during a five-week period, more than 10 percent of the 347 children in Huskerville, Nebraska, contracted polio. A study of the water supply revealed that the afflicted children lived in areas where flush-valve water closets lacked vacuum breakers.

In 1952, faulty plumbing almost "sank" a large oceangoing vessel. The luxury liner put to sea in apparently shipshape condition. A day or so later—three hundred miles out—more than a thousand persons on board developed dysentery. History did not record who manned the ship during the siege, but it did speculate that while the ship was tied up at its moorings, somehow its freshwater tanks were contaminated with sewage.

But sewage in our drinking water is not the only danger. In the past twenty-five years, at least a half-million new chemical compounds have come into existence. Many of them are discharged into our rivers and streams or dumped on the ground to seep into our underground water supplies.

According to Dr. Luther Terry, the durability of some of today's new substances was demonstrated by the national water-quality headquarters in the Robert A. Taft Sanitary Engineering Center in Cincinnati, Ohio. One day a water sample from St. Louis produced a peculiar new mark on a routine infrared test procedure. A week later, the same mark appeared in a test made from water sent in from New Orleans. The chemical had traveled hundreds of miles in the Mississippi River without undergoing any change, and showed up in one liter of water taken from the billions of gallons of water that pass New Orleans every day.

Fish are good indicators of the dangers of polluted water. In 1963, for instance, more than 50,000,000 fish were killed in United States coastal waters and rivers. Radioactive wastes were blamed for kills in the Colorado. Many streams in Pennsylvania and West Virginia were fouled by acid draining into them from mines. Elsewhere, the wastes of septic tanks seeping into underground waters, as well as chemical pesticides and oil spills, were involved in fish kills.

Amazingly small amounts of pesticides can kill shrimp, crab, and other aquatic life. One part DDT in a billion parts of water was found to kill blue crabs in eight days. The relationship is the same as one ounce of chocolate syrup to 10 million gallons of milk.[12]

Water begins to foam if there is as much as one part of alkyl benzenesulfonate, a component of hard detergents, in a million parts of water. Hard ABS detergents, were being dumped into the water supply by housewives and industry, and staying there. The Public Health Service allowed one half of one part of ABS in a million parts of water. When the foam choked rivers and streams, and people complained about turning on the faucet and having the water "foam" out, the federal government insisted that detergent manufacturers change to "soft" detergents, which do not foam.

However, according to the experts who prepared *A Strategy for a Livable Environment* for the Secretary of Health, Education, and Welfare in 1967, the new detergent compounds are suspected of killing large numbers of fish by affecting their eggs.

It has not been proved that detergents in water affect human health directly. However, in 1962, 1,727 incidents involving ingestion of detergents, as well as soaps and cleaners, in children under five years of age were reported to the National Clearinghouse for Poison Control Centers.

Dr. Jay M. Arena, of the Poison Control Center, Duke University Medical Center, said in the *Journal of the American Medical Association,* on October 5, 1964, in an article entitled "Poisonings and Other Health Hazards Associated with Use of Detergents":

"Because they are such necessary and familiar household items, cleaners are not usually regarded as hazardous substances. . . .

"Unfortunately, the terms 'soap' and 'detergent' are synonymous to many laymen, and I know of an incident, for example, in which significant injury occurred from the misuse of detergent instead of a soapsuds enema."

In explaining the toxicity of various detergents, Dr. Arena said:

"The cationic detergents or quaternary ammonium compounds are available commercially as ointments, powders, tinctures and aqueous solutions and are used to destroy bacteria on skin, surgical instruments, cooking utensils, sickroom supplies and diapers.

"The toxicity of quaternary ammonium germicides has not been definitely established, but the human fatal dose by ingestion has been estimated to be between 1 and 3 gm. . . . The principal manifestations of poisoning from ingestion of these agents are vomiting, collapse and coma. Specifically there is local and gastrointestinal irritation, restlessness, apprehension, confusion, dyspnea, cyanosis, convulsions, muscle weakness, and death due to paralysis of respiratory muscles.

"There are numerous anionic surface-active agents. All are only moderately toxic. . . .

"Packaged detergent granules: . . . manufacturers classify these products as (a) light-duty for dishes and baby clothes, (b) all-purpose, sudsing products for laundry and general use, and (c) washday, low-sudsing detergents made especially for automatic washers. However, with respect to their toxicity and the treatment of patients who have ingested them, all of these products may be considered as a single group. . . .

"Although the systemic toxicity of carbonates and silicates is low, their solutions can be very alkaline and may produce corrosive burning of the mucous membranes. . . . The ingestion of sodium tripolyphosphate and hexametaphosphate has caused severe gastroenteritis, with vomiting and diarrhea, and at least one child has developed esophageal stricture.

"Liquid detergents: . . . The formulations of the liquid household detergent preparations are similar to those of the detergent granules; the main difference is that they are in aqueous or hydroalcoholic solutions; . . . Manifestations associated with the swallowing of appreciable quantities should be no different than those expected from the ingestions of detergent granules. . . .

"However, several highly advertised general-purpose liquid cleaning agents contain petroleum distillates or pine oil made soluble by the addition of synthetic surfactants. . . . Aspiration of petroleum distillates, which may occur at the time of ingestion or later in association with vomiting, may produce hydrocarbon pneumonitis: involvement of the lungs has not been reported in cases in which the ingested product did not contain substantial amounts of this substance. Pine oil causes irritation of the eyes, mucous membranes, and gastrointestinal and genitourinary tracts, and depression of the central nervous system with hypothermia and respiratory failure. . . ."[13]

After a two-year Food and Drug investigation into dishwater detergents, the Food and Drug Administration began seizures of products its scientists said contained "hazardous chemicals." The detergents contain sodium metasilicate, a substance that is toxic when swallowed. It can cause severe eye irritation and has caused blindness in rabbits.

Since detergents are found in our water, in our food, and on our dishes and silverware, the possibility that, even in small amounts, they may be toxic to our systems is not so remote as manufacturers would like us to believe.

Here is a simple test to determine the presence of detergents or other organic materials present in a river, well, or glass of water. It was devised by George J. Crits, Assistant Technical Manager of the Cochrane Division of the Crane Company, Philadelphia.

Take a tall, cylindrical bottle similar to an olive bottle. Fill it half full of water, stopper it, and shake it. Presence of high amounts of detergents or soap will cause a noticeable foam. Small amounts will cause a film that will travel upward on the side of the glass bottle. The film rises until it disappears at a height dependent on the contamination in the water. The greater the contamination, the greater the height of the film or ring.

Perhaps the Public Health Service will reconsider its permissible limits for detergents, as it did for other chemicals in our water supply in 1962. Take arsenic, for instance. In the revision, the Public Health Service said:

"The widespread use of inorganic arsenic in insecticides and its presence in animal foods, tobacco and other sources make it necessary to set a limit on the concentration of arsenic in drinking water.

"The toxicity of arsenic is well known and the ingestion of as little as 100 mg. usually results in severe poisoning. Chronic poisoning from arsenic may be insidious and pernicious. A considerable proportion is retained at low intake levels. A single dose may require ten days for complete disappearance.

"Recent evidence supports the view that arsenic may be carcinogenic. The incidence of skin cancer has also been reported to be unusually high in areas of England where arsenic was present in drinking water at a level of 12 mg. per million parts.

"Formerly, the U.S. Public Health Service drinking water standards from 1946 established an arsenic limit of 0.05 mgs./1. In light of our present knowledge concerning the potential health hazard from the ingestion of inorganic arsenic, the concentration of arsenic in drinking water should not exceed 0.01 mg./1."

And take nitrate, which is deliberately added to food, including infants' food. The Public Health Service says:

"Serious and occasionally fatal poisonings in infants have occurred following ingestion of all waters shown to contain nitrate. This has occurred with sufficient frequency and widespread geographic distribution to compel recognition of this hazard by assigning a limit to the concentration of nitrate in drinking water.

"From 1947 to 1950, there were 139 cases of methemoglobinemia, including fourteen deaths due to nitrate in farm well-water supplies in Minnesota. Wastes from chemical fertilizer plants and field fertilization may be sources of pollution.

"Breast-fed infants drinking from mothers who drank nitrate-contaminated water may be poisoned. Cows drinking water containing nitrate may produce milk sufficiently high in nitrate to result in infant poisoning. Both man and animals can be poisoned by nitrate if the concentration is sufficiently great."

Cadmium from zinc-galvanized iron and from electroplating plants also gets into our water. According to the Public Health Service, cadmium is a biologically nonessential, nonbeneficial element, and it is highly toxic:

"Recognition of the serious toxic potential of cadmium when taken by mouth is based on poisoning from cadmium-contaminated food and beverages, epidemiologic evidence that cadmium may be associated with renal arterial hypertension under certain conditions and long-term oral toxicity studies in animals," the Public Health Service said.

"Several instances have been reported of poisoning from eating substances contaminated with cadmium. A group of school children were made ill by eating popsicles containing 13 to 15 mg./1 part cadmium. All levels of dietary cadium so far tested have shown cadmium accumulation in the soft tissues down to and including 0.1 mg./1 in drinking water."

And, just as scientists have found that individually harmless chemicals when combined in food or drugs may become toxic, they have also found the same thing in water. Water chemists refer to such combinations as "gunk."

Dr. Terry reported an incident that happened in Alabama. A textile mill, operating there for years, dispensed waste into the river. Later, a plant manufacturing pesticides opened. It, too, used the river. Still later, a bleachery was established. This industry also discharged waste into the river.

As far as any scientists could tell, the waste-disposal practices of all three industries were entirely safe. But soon after the bleachery opened, people began to complain about taste and odor in their drinking water. Moreover, the physicians of the town noted an increase in patients suffering from nausea and digestive disorders. When water samples were studied more intensively, it was found that discharges from the three industries had combined to form a new and harmful chemical.

Phosphate residues found in detergents, municipal sewage, and industrial wastes and agricultural products overfertilize aquatic plant life and result in a process known as "eutrophication." When water supplies are taken from lakes or streams that are undergoing eutrophication, the algae affect treatment plant operations, cause clogging of filters, may cause undesirable tastes and odor, and impair water quality.[14]

The old dangers from our water have subsided. The death rate from typhoid fever declined from 31.2 deaths per 100,000 population in 1900 to 0.01 in 1960.[15] But there are new dangers. The Public Health Service in its revised water standards of 1962, said: "The development of the nuclear industry has been attended by a small, unavoidable increase of radioactivity in the environment.

"The advisory committee, in considering limits which should be established for drinking water, recommended limits for only two of the nuclides—Radium 226 and Strontium 90.

With Radium 226, above-average levels of intake generally occur only in unusual situations where the drinking water contains naturally occurring Radium 226 in greater-than-average amounts, as in the case of ground waters or from the pollution of the supply by industrial discharges of waste containing radium.

"The principal source of Strontium 90 in the environment to date has been due to fallout from weapons tests, and human intake of Strontium 90 to date has been primarily from food."

As the nuclear industry expands and the weapons race continues, the dangers from radioactive wastes in our water will increase. For instance, another radionuclide that was not included in the "United States Public Health Service Drinking Water Standards" of 1962, tritium, has been recognized as "of health significance." It is a radioactive isotope of hydrogen with an atomic weight of three, and a half-life of 1226 years. Tritium has the same chemical properties as hydrogen, and combines with oxygen to form water ($^3H_2 0$). It cannot, by any standard treatment procedures, be separated from ordinary water. Extreme care is taken in the application of nuclear energy so that maximum permissible concentration of tritium in water will not be exceeded. This concentration at present is 0.003 microcuries per ml. above natural background.[16]

Modern man has also deliberately added chemicals to his water. Chlorine and fluoride are well-known additives, but water-softening chemicals are sometimes overlooked.

Congestive heart failure is a common cardiovascular problem today. Fluid retention in liver and kidney disease and in pregnancy is also widespread.

Dr. Peter Braun and Dr. Alvin A. Florin, of the New Jersey State Department of Health, writing on "Drinking Water and Congestive Heart Failure" in the *Journal of the Medical Society of New Jersey,* in 1963, said: "The restriction of sodium in the diet has become a cornerstone of medical treatment in edematous [water-retention] states.

"Recent literature contains well-documented examples of sodium from drinking water as a cause of cardiac decompensation. In many areas, sodium in water supplies may be a significant factor in chronic congestive heart failure and other edematous states."

Drs. Braun and Florin said persons on a restricted salt diet should drink water containing no more than twenty milligrams per liter. But, they pointed out, commercial and domestic water-softening equipment can raise sodium concentrations to levels far beyond those desirable for such patients. In some New Jersey water supplies, the doctors found concentrations as high as 260 milligrams of sodium per liter.

In most American communities, public drinking water is one of the world's greatest bargains. The average cost of the sixty gallons or more of good water delivered into your home each day via the tap is a fraction of the cost of one bottle of soda.[17] But you may be getting more from your kitchen tap than you bargained for. Our rapidly changing technology has had an adverse impact on our water environment, and the manner in which your drinking water is treated, as well as delivery systems, is becoming obsolete.

G. M. Hansler, Regional Assistant Administrator of Consumer Protection and Environmental Health Service, Health, Education, and Welfare, New York, emphasized the seriousness of the drinking-water problem in America today. [18] He said that in suburban communities in New Jersey, for instance, there were outbreaks of hepatitis and gastro-enteritis after spring flooding in 1968. Drinking-water systems in these communities were suspect. Although unusually heavy rains can be construed as "acts of God," *proper* construction, maintenance, and routine surveillance of water systems can prevent such occurrences.

Mr. Hansler told of a new hospital in Mississippi that inadvertently had the water from its boiler control system connected with the drinking-water supply. People were drinking chromate ions in their water. He said this also happens as the result of air conditioners being cross-connected with water supplies. "Water goes into every household," Hansler said. "Some surveillance procedures and water systems are very, very good. Others are really unsafe."

At present, the level of chromate ions that can be tolerated by man for a lifetime without adverse effects on health is unknown. It is known that, when inhaled, chromium causes cancer.[19]

No section of the nation is without at least one major water problem, either in distribution, supply, quality, pollution, floods, or variability.[20] And the situation is going to get worse. By 1980, we are expected to use almost 600 billion gallons daily of fresh water, but only 515 will be available.

As the levels of water in our streams, rivers, and reservoirs goes down, pollution goes up. Less open land for natural purification and more chemicals from our farms and industries will compound the problem. More people will make more sewage. We shall have to begin using the same water over and over again. Yet, even now, viruses can escape our present water-purification and disinfection processes.[21]

But with all the talk about water pollution, relatively little research is going on concerning the health effects of the metals, chemicals, sewages, and viruses in our drinking water. Hopefully, the modern scientific and engineering technologies that created our water problems can be better applied to provide us with safe and healthful drinking water. If not, in the not too distant future, a phrase from Samuel Coleridge's *Rime of the Ancient Mariner* will apply to us all: "Water, water, everywhere, nor any drop to drink."

7 NOTES

1. G. M. Hansler, Acting Assistant Regional Director, Environmental Control Administration, U.S. Health, Education, and Welfare Department, New York region. Tape-recorded interview with author, July, 1968.
2. "Water Supply and Plumbing Cross-Connections Hazards in Household and Community Systems," U.S. Health, Education, and Welfare Publication No. 957, 1963.
3. *Ibid.*
4. *A Strategy for a Livable Environment,* a report to the Secretary of Health, Education, and Welfare by the Task Force on Environmental Health and Related Problems, June, 1967.
5. U.S. Department of Health, Education, and Welfare, "Water Supply Activities," Publication No. 1511, 1966.
6. Howard Earl, "Water Pollution, That Dirty Mess," *Today's Health,* March, 1966.
7. State Board of Health Publication, Wisconsin.
8. U.S. Department of Health, Education, and Welfare, "Water Supply Activities," No. 1511, 1966.
9. Luther, Terry, M.D., Surgeon General of the U.S. Public Health Service, "Let's Stop Poisoning Our Water," in *This Week,* December 3, 1961.
10. "Water Supply and Plumbing . . . ," HEW Publication No. 957, 1963.
11. *Ibid.*
12. Howard, Earl, *op. cit.*
13. Jay M. Arena, M.D., Poison Control Center, Duke University Medi-

cal Center, "Poisonings and Other Health Hazards Associated with Use of Detergents," *Journal of the American Medical Association,* October 5, 1964, Vol. 190, pp. 56–58.

14. Dr. Gerard Rohlich, Professor of Civil Engineering and Director of Water Resources Center, University of Wisconsin, on "Eutrophication," presented to 41st annual convention, Soap and Detergent Association, New York, January 25, 1968.

15. "Patterns of Disease," Parke-Davis, July, 1963.

16. Atomic Energy Commission, *Regulations,* 10 CFR, Part 20.

17. U.S. Department of Health, Education, and Welfare, "Water Supply Activities," No. 1511, 1966.

18. G. M. Hansler, interview cited above.

19. "Public Health Service Drinking Water Standards Revision," 1962.

20. *Patterns of Disease,* July, 1963.

21. Luther, Terry, *op. cit.*

8

Eating Out Tonight?

As I STOOD IN LINE at a barbecue in an exclusive tennis and swim club whose members are among the most intelligent and well-to-do in New Jersey, the French chef behind the table, cigarette dangling from his mouth, was dishing out spaghetti with his fingers. He was sweating profusely. An elderly gentleman in front of me complained loudly at such an obvious breach of sanitation, and stalked out of the club. I stayed, fascinated by a flagrant violation of the most elementary health practices involved in serving food to the public.

Farther down the line, I saw a young assistant spooning desserts on a plate, and stopping every once in a while to lick his fingers. The waitresses, hired for the summer, had long hairdos that hung loose over the food they served. Flies were plentiful. I looked at the silverware; and some of it was encrusted with food. A meat sandwich that was served had obviously been sliced from meat that had been cooked the day before, for it was dry and unappetizing.

I was reminded of what I had learned from food inspectors: much of what I saw actually goes on in many of the more than half a million eating places in the United States. The difficulty is that the patrons just don't see it, for most of it takes place behind the scenes, in the kitchens and larders.

We Americans buy 28 billion meals a year, and more than 540,000 eating and drinking places serve approximately 78 million customers daily. That number of patrons represents nearly half the population in the nation.[1]

The Bank of America did a two-year survey, and found that the business of serving food totals $27 billion at retail annually. Separate eating and drinking places now rank as the Number One type of retail outlet in the nation. "They outnumber grocery stores. They outnumber service stations," the survey said. "American families now spend $400 to $500 annually. In fact, we are now spending more to 'eat out' than we do to buy new and used automobiles."

Yet the survey quoted recent figures, compiled by Dun & Bradstreet, indicating that over half of the restaurants in the United States show no taxable profit. Each year, the survey said, eating and drinking places account for around 20 percent of all retail failure. Only half of all food-service operations maintain the same ownership for five years or more.[2]

But such financial perils may not be the only hazard. The Public Health Service, in a publication directed at food-service personnel said:

"Yours is a dangerous business, . . . dangerous because food and drink that are not carefully handled and prepared too often are a source of disease—and death.

"A single germ in 24 hours will under favorable conditions produce 281,000,000,000,000,000 other germs capable of doing the same.

"People have died because they ate and drank heartily, trusting in those who prepared and served the food. And people will continue to sicken and die because they eat out, unless you protect them. You cannot always tell by tasting whether food is safe or not."[3]

Since the early 1930's, professional sanitarians have been urging health departments to include eating and drinking places within the framework of food-sanitation programs. Most health departments do have some sort of restaurant program, but the number of eating places and catering establishments has multiplied to such an extent that the understaffed and underfinanced health departments have curtailed or stopped restaurant surveillance altogether. Some municipalities have no health departments at all.

James L. Shoemaker, M.P.H., Director of the Environmental Health Demonstration Project, Merced, California, pointed out in an article in the *Journal of Environmental Health* in 1965 that accomplishments of a program inspecting public eating and drinking establishments are difficult, if not impossible, to assess in terms of accurate, objective measurements.[4] He said that justification for such programs is currently based on morbidity and mortality data that are largely nonexistent nationally.

Mr. Shoemaker noted an evaluation that was made in California in 1962. He said there were 34 outbreaks of foodborne illness in public eating places, affecting 298 persons; there were 28 in private homes, affecting 191; 14 at clubs and social gatherings, affecting 1,035; 11 in hospitals, affecting 895; and 3 in labor camps, affecting 232.

The Public Health Service does have thick files on outbreaks of food poisoning, although personnel admit that their records are just the very tip of the iceberg. Such illnesses are not all from germs. Take the case of the barbecue-stand patron who loved chili. He ate some "mexihot." Six hours later, he was dead. On the same day, when several other patrons became ill, food sanitarians traced the case to a roadside stand. The chef refused to believe it, and ate some chili himself to prove his point. He died.[5]

Though there were no disease germs in the food, the laboratory discovered a quantity of sodium flouride, a poison used for killing roaches, in the chili. In another incident, 236 people on the West Coast got sick because roach powder had been mistaken for powdered milk and mixed with some scrambled eggs. Forty-seven died.

Though most of the restaurant slip-ups are not so deadly, they are far more prevalent. The East Orange, New Jersey, Health Department has a budget for four inspectors (which means all the positions are not always filled). The inspectors also investigate dog bites, ragweed pollution, swimming pools, sewage, garbage, pet shops, gasoline stations, citizens' complaints, rodents, smoke, and other nuisances. The population of the city is 77,259.

During one year, 622 inspections of 305 East Orange food establishments were made; an average of five violations of the Sanitary Code was found on each inspection.

• Forty-two samples of potentially hazardous foods were checked; only twelve were found to have bacterial counts in compliance with recommended standards.

• One hundred and eighty-three swabs were taken from utensils in eating establishments; less than 25 percent (or about 45, a not inconsiderable number) were found to be in excess of bacterial standards.

• Twenty-three embargos were placed on food where misbranding or adulteration were questioned.[6]

What exactly does an inspector look for when he goes into a restaurant?

According to William Clinger, Regional Sanitation Consultant, Environmental Health, United States Public Health Service:

"The most frequent violation concerns temperature. The cold foods are not kept under proper refrigeration and the hot foods are not kept hot enough. Refrigeration should be below 45 degrees. Steam tables should be 140 degrees.

"The second most common violation is improper storage. Flour and onions stored on the floor, for instance.

"Inspectors look to see whether foods which are displayed are protected by glass . . . whether cream pies and custards are refrigerated.

"Does food splash on single service items such as paper cups? This is a problem today.

"Are there open sugar bowls? Sugar should be served in individual packages or in a closed container.

"What are the toilet facilities like? Can help wash their hands in a convenient place?

"There should be no cross-connections with or back-siphonage into the water supply from sinks, dishwashing machines, lavatories, or toilets.

"A frequent violation is that the drain from the steam tables reflush over the tables.

"Grease traps should be cleaned to avoid clogging and should be in good repair.

"Vapona insect strips are used improperly in many places today. They are sometimes hung over tables used for preparation of food, and condensation from the heat causes them to drip into the food and milk.

"No food should be left out overnight.

"Garbage should be covered and disposed of promptly.

"Insect and rodent killers should be kept far away from the food.

"Dishes should be washed either by hot water in a dishwashing machine or disinfected with chemicals.

"The inspector must know the source of the restaurant's food supplies.

"There should be no smoking while food is being prepared.

"Employees should wear headbands, hairnets, or caps, and all uniforms should be clean."[7]

Federal Food and Drug inspectors did a survey in New Jersey of the restaurants in one small town and one large city. They found many breaches of sanitation. They even found that one food inspector who was supposed to fill out reports could barely write his name.

Restaurant inspection itself is a controversial thing. When Dr. George Kupchik, Director of Environmental Health of the American Public Health Association, was asked by the author whether he felt confident when he went into a restaurant that was not inspected by a health department, he said, "I don't feel confident when I go into a restaurant that I know is inspected! Restaurants inspected every three months for ten years are no better than restaurants that have never been inspected," he said. "There is no question in my mind that some of the fanciest-name restaurants lack adequate sanitation. On the other hand, some small, family-run eating places have excellent sanitation."[8]

The fallibility of inspection was demonstrated in an item from *FDA Papers* in February, 1967:

"Two Philadelphia FDA inspectors were too close to a recent food poisoning case for comfort. Wayne Stafford and Kenneth Martin developed severe symptoms of food poisoning after eating at a diner in Allentown, Pa., in October. Inspector Stafford required hospital treatment. Investigation showed that the diner used drinking water from a contaminated well and stored and handled food in an insanitary manner. Bacteriological findings in sausage and butter samples taken at the diner were reported to the State of Pennsylvania Department of Health."

The question of health examinations for food handlers is highly controversial.

Dr. Aaron Haskins, Health Officer for Newark, New Jersey, abolished physicals for food handlers after he was "embarrassed" in 1952:

"Just before Easter, a certain bakery in Newark prepared exceptionally large amounts of cream pies, much more than the capacity of its refrigeration system. The owner was compelled to keep half his cream pies outside the refrigerator, on a hot day. This period of nonrefrigeration was about eight to ten hours. About two weeks before the outbreak, he burned his forearm and treated himself. The burn became infected and in this condition, he prepared the cream fill for the pies. Almost two hundred persons came down with staph aureus poisoning.

"My face was red when it was brought out that the man had a health card from the City of Newark Health Department testifying that one month prior to the outbreak he was examined and found healthy.

"In 1921," Dr. Haskin explained, "the City of Newark passed an ordinance requiring the physical examination of food handlers, the theory being that a sick food handler would transmit disease through food.

"While the theory is commendable, the actual practice cannot be considered so. The physical examination consisted of an X ray of the chest, blood serology, and a mouth smear. The examination also included a very cursory screening for superficial skin infections. If we realize that the diseases most apt to spread through food are of the salmonella, typhoid and dysentery groups and the staphylococcus and streptococcus organisms, you can readily see that the type of examination as carried out is not directed at these organisms; the program has degenerated into a case-finding program for tuberculosis and venereal disease.

"The fallacy of the physical examination for the prevention of the spread of disease through food becomes more obvious when we realize that even if we were able to carry out the proper type of examination, it would only show that at the time of examination the food handler was well. But the next day he could easily become infected with any of these important diseases, and be a source of infection, and still have in his possession a health card from a health department testifying that he is well and that it is safe for him to handle food.

"In my opinion, this gives the public and the food handler a false sense of security, because unless that food handler is acquainted with the disease that he may have and unless he knows how to properly conduct himself so that he may not infect the food, the public is not safe. I believe that no physical examination of the food handler is the answer to this problem and certainly the public should not be lulled into this false sense of security.

"In 1951, I made an evaluation of the program of food handler examination and I found that we spent $40,000 to $50,000. As a result of the expenditure of this amount of money, we found two cases of tuberculosis not heretofore known and several cases of syphilis.

"In view of the fact that this had turned out to be a case-finding program in tuberculosis and syphilis, I was sure that the $40,000 to $50,000 spent in a different manner for case finding would discover a great many more cases."

Dr. Haskin said that when he abolished food-handler examinations in 1952, he was warned that dire consequences would fall upon the citizens of Newark. Instead of the examination, however, Dr. Haskin has required all food handlers to go through a week's course in sanitation. The course informs the food handler of the types of diseases he may have that will spread through food, chiefly the diarrheal diseases, staph and strep infections and Vincent's infection of the mouth. The food handler is taught how these diseases appear on the body, how he as a food handler may infect foods with these various organisms, and how he as a food handler could prevent the infection of food. The food handlers are taught good sanitation practices, including dishwashing and hand washing.

Dr. Haskin also pointed out that a survey conducted by the Sanitation Foundation found that the average intelligence of a food handler is that of an eighth grader. He said food handlers' training programs have to be adapted to their IQ level.

Dr. Haskin believes that the Newark program is working well and that no food handler should be permitted to operate unless he can show a certificate testifying that he has successfully passed this form of instruction. He said his inspectors ask to see the certificates when they go into a food establishment.[9]

East Orange Health Officer Robert Lackey said that food handlers in his jurisdiction are required to have X rays of the chest only. He expressed doubt that this was of much use. He did point out that many food handlers in American restaurants today are immigrants from other countries, from Puerto Rico, and from the American South. He said that many of them have parasites that can and are being transmitted to the food they handle. He said experience has shown that even if you do rid the food handlers of their worms and other parasites, they soon become reinfected by members of their own households.

Mr. Lackey thought that perhaps stool cultures might be of some help in detecting food handlers carrying parasites.

Dr. Haskin, on the other hand, said, "If we did stool cultures on all food handlers in Newark, our laboratory would be a cesspool, and the people still wouldn't have adequate protection."

Mr. Lackey believes that education of food handlers is very difficult to implement. He said that the turnover of restaurant help is almost 100 percent. "If a town has one thousand positions for food handlers, two thousand will have filled them in a year," he explained. He feels that vocational schools will have to play a larger part in the education of persons who intend to work in food-handling jobs.[10]

In the *Journal of the American Medical Association,* on November 6, 1967, in answer to a Florida physician's question about food-handling certificates providing a "false security and totally inadequate control of communicable disease," Dr. Robert W. Harkins of Chicago answered for the AMA:

"Public Health officals can do much to encourage food sanitation by providing educational services for both the manager and the employee. Periodic, realistic inspection of all food service operations can pinpoint weak gaps. A sense of urgency among public health officials must be conveyed to the owners, and it should be conveyed to the courts as they levy penalties on those establishments which fail to maintain adequate standards. Everyone wins when food service sanitation is high—the customers, the employees and the owner."[11]

An additional safeguard, and perhaps one of the most effective, in addition to education of food handlers and inspection by health departments, is an informed patron.

I asked food inspectors what they would not order when they go into an unfamiliar restaurant. Most agreed that they would not order raw shellfish unless they knew that the product came from uncontaminated water. They would not order egg salad anywhere, and would be hesitant about ordering any cooked salad such as potato or chicken salad. Many were even cautious about ordering ham sandwiches because they said cooked ham is a frequent source of foodborne infection.

A prominent cookbook author told me that she would never order chicken salad or lobster thermidor unless she knew the chef and he liked her. She said leftover chicken may be used for the salad, and the shells of lobsters may be taken from the plates of patrons who had whole lobsters, and kept around the kitchen for several days before being filled.

Based on the opinions of the experts, here are the things you should look for when patronizing a restaurant:

• Is the outside clean? Are the bathrooms clean? Although

different personnel may handle food, these factors are a good indication of whether the management insists on good sanitation.

• Are the dishes chipped? All equipment—including utensils and dishes—that touches food or drink should have a hard, smooth finish.

• Is garbage exposed? Are the counters and tables dirty?

• Are there flies or evidence of insect and rodent contamination?

• Are the food handlers smoking? Ashes from cigarettes or cigars and contamination from saliva are, of course, unsanitary.

• Is the restaurant in the basement? If it is, there is a greater possibility of contamination by flooding, sewage, and rats.

• Are the uniforms of the food handlers and servers clean? Do they wear caps to keep their hair from falling in the food?

• How do the waiters and waitresses set the silverware down? How do they serve the food? Are their fingers over and in everything?

• Are the glasses and silverware clean? Is there lipstick on the glasses or are there coffee grounds in the cup? (Water spots are not an indication of contamination.)

• Does the cream for the coffee feel warm? If it does, it is a good indication that it has been kept at room temperature and that temperature and time control are not observed by the management.

• Is the help coughing, spitting, or sneezing near the food?

• Are custards and cream-filled foods refrigerated?

• Are foods kept covered until they are served?

• Are the floors clean?

• In a restaurant other than a very small one, does a busboy remove your dirty dishes? Contamination from dirty plates may contaminate your food by way of the hands of the server if busboys or proper sanitation are absent.

• When your food is served, does the server use a utensil instead of his hands?

• Are the menus dirty?

• Do the waiters or waitresses have sores on their skins or do they have improperly bandaged fingers if they have been injured?

• Are the salads warm or wilted?

THE CATERED AFFAIR

One day in June, 1965, health officials in the Washington, D.C., area became aware of an outbreak of diarrheal disease. Some of

Washington's most important citizens were affected. Investigation showed that those afflicted had attended one of nine catered parties held on either June 5 or June 6. At each of the catered affairs, a variety of foods from the same caterer had been served. Of approximately 570 persons who had attended the parties, 431 were interviewed. One hundred and ninety-eight—45.9 percent—reported an illness that began at a mean interval of twenty hours after the festivities.

The most common symptoms included moderately severe diarrhea, abdominal cramps, and low-grade fever. Ages of the victims ranged from three to eighty years. One patient was hospitalized, and sixty-five required the services of a physician.

Isolated both from the foods served and from sick persons who had attended the party were *S. meleagridis, S. chester,* and *S. tennessee* forms of *Salmonella*.

In an effort to determine the extent of the secondary spread within the households of the affected, a telephone survey was made. Only one possible secondary case showed up. The husband had attended the party and had had severe diarrhea for several days. The wife had not attended the affair, but one week after her husband became ill, she too had the same symptoms.

An additional 142 illnesses not related to any of the parties were reported following newspaper publicity concerning the outbreak.

It was learned that prior to the June outbreak, several cases of salmonellosis related to the delicatessen in question were known by health authorities. In fact, stool specimens obtained from employees at the time were taken. Seven of the food handlers behind the serving counter were found to be excreting *S. meleagridis*. All denied any clinical illness. The employees were removed from their jobs and were treated with antibiotics. They were instructed not to return to work until three successive rectal cultures were negative. On June 2 and 3, just before the outbreak, four of these employees known to have been actively excreting the organism were working nevertheless. In all, a total of 356 known cass of salmonellosis occurred between May 10 and June 7, 1965.

The enterprise involved was a combination caterer-delicatessen-restaurant. It was physically divided into a delicatessen store, dining area, kitchen, bakery, second-floor banquet room, and basement storage area. It catered up to ten parties a month, and handled a large-volume restaurant delicatessen trade. It was estimated that more than four thousand people consumed food there between June 4 and June 7.

Following the closing of the firm by health authorities on June 7, of the 103 specimens cultured from employees, fifty-seven were found to be positive for *S. meleagridis*. Employees were treated with antibiotics. In the meantime, a complete environmental investigation of the premises was made. Here are some of the blatant violations found:

1. Lack of hand-washing facilities.
2. Inadequate employee rest rooms.
3. Presence of many cockroaches and flies.
4. A malfunctioning automatic dishwasher.
5. A nonrefrigerated delivery truck.
6. Inadequate refrigeration facilities.
7. Inadequate routine cleanup of food-processing areas.
8. Corned beef was cooled in a kitchen sink that had its drain plug situated several inches below a stationary grid.
9. Raw foods were not kept separate from cooked foods.
10. A can of frozen eggs was found in a temperature of 80 degrees.
11. Display cases in the delicatessen were used for cooling rather than holding, which placed a burden on the refrigeration units.
12. The slicers were contaminated, resulting in cross-contamination of sliced meat such as salami and bologna.

This case was reported in the *American Journal of Public Health,* in April, 1968, by Arnold Kaufmann, D.V.M.; Charles R. Hayman, M.D., M.P.H.; Frederick Heath, M.D., M.P.H.; and Murray Grant, M.D., D.P.H.[12]

The catering business, health officials admit, is one of the weakest links in food-protection efforts in the United States. The majority of local and interstate caterers are not inspected, and can operate without supervision.

Vernon E. Cordell, Director of Public Health and Safety for the National Restaurant Association, said that the proliferation of multiple-unit operations, franchised operations, and food services performed by management contractors had brought the food industry up against the problem of lack of uniform sanitation regulations.

Instances of poisonings from all sorts of catered affairs are numerous, and involve large numbers of people. For instance, the New York City Health Department reported that three thousand persons were made ill between April 5 and 11 in 1967. They attended catered affairs in the area. The desserts for these parties were made by Country Club Frozen Desserts, New York. The firm immediately shut down and ceased production and distribution until proper equipment and processing modifications could be made. The contamination was ultimately traced to nonpasteurized, sugared egg yolks used in the desserts, and manufactured by the Manhattan Egg Company, New York. The firm halted distribution of nonpasteurized egg products. The eggs were linked to other food-poisoning outbreaks in New Jersey, and were suspected of causing similar ailments in Massachussetts, Connecticut, and Michigan.[13]

Private clubs, fraternal orders, societies of various types, churches, and religious-affiliated organizations are not closely inspected. In fact, the church supper has become one of the most common events for such unwelcome guests as salmonella and staph poisons.

Current practices relating to this category of food service varies throughout the country. Some health agencies include such organizations in their inspections. Others exempt private clubs, church-affiliated, or certain educational organizations from permit or license requirements and regular sanitary inspections. "When this is the case," the Public Health Service says, "a rather substantial segment of the population receives no official health protection in this area of food control."[14]

East Orange Health Officer Robert Lackey also points out the difficulty of inspecting delicatessens and caterers of any sort. "The health agencies do not have the manpower or the money to bring these under surveillance," he said. He gave as an example cooked salads:

"Potato salad is brought in 50-pound containers from Brooklyn or Pennsylvania; and, historically, when we tested it we found contamination. Even though these products travel interestate, they are not necessarily inspected, and we do not have the inclination to go to another state and inspect the processing plant."[15]

In May, 1965, New Jersey started a sampling and inspection study of wholesale manufacturers and distributors of potentially hazardous foods, with particular attention paid to potato salad, macaroni salad, and coleslaw products. According to Robert E. Johnson, Principal Sanitarian, Bureau of Food and Drugs, New Jersey State Department of Health:

"Human contamination has been evident in the preparation and subsequent handling of these foods. We have related causes for high laboratory results of analyses to insanitary processing practices, use of contaminated ingredients, too slow cooling after preparation, improper storage facilities, improper repacking procedures and/or improper transportation facilities."

He said that in one study New Jersay did of ninety-four samples of potato salad, 35 percent had bacteria counts of 100,000.[16]

William Clinger, federal sanitation consultant said local, state, and federal health officials are well aware of the problem of catering, and they met in July, 1968, to try to draw up standards and cooperative procedures between them.

How do you know if a caterer handles food properly?

In East Orange, Mr. Lackey pointed out that health departments don't know when a caterer is going to cater a specific party. Furthermore, there are many widows and small food establishments who go into the catering business, and the local health department doesn't even know about it.

Some food inspectors suggest that a person who wants to give a private party, or who is in charge of arrangements for an organization, first get in touch with the local board of health to determine if the caterer has a license. Big caterers usually have good equipment, including temperature-control trucks, experienced help, and good sanitation know-how. But it pays to ask questions. In the meantime, after checking with the local health department, readers should see that potentially hazardous food is not exposed to improper temperatures during the party and that food is not contaminated by improper handling, either by the food handlers or by the guests.

VENDING MACHINES

One afternoon, a woman having her nails done and the manicurist doing her nails both did not feel well. Neither wanted to say anything, but as they sat opposite each other they both began to feel nauseated. Finally, the customer, with nails half polished and still wet, stood up from the table and rushed to the ladies' room. She was soon followed by the manicurist.

The fact that both had become ill almost simultaneously was not a coincidence. A chain of well-known restaurants had placed a shop containing automatic vending machines on the Short Hills, New Jersey, mall. The mall contains branches of many Fifth Avenue, New York, stores, and caters to a clientele drawn from many of the lush suburbs in the state. Both the customer and the manicurist had eaten sandwiches at noon from the vending machines. As with such illness, although typically foodborne, no report was made of the possible source of the illness to the local board of health. Perhaps there were too many such illnesses or the operation proved unprofitable, but the shop was closed and a conventional restaurant established in its place.

Though sales of products from vending machines are now in the billions, vending machines, like catering establishments, are a very weak link in the food-inspection protection program. Actually, vending machines are not new. Their existence has been recorded since a machine dispensed holy water in Alexandria, Egypt, in 200 B.C.[17] Vending machines first made their appearance in America in 1880. During the Second World War, as the shortage of all food-service personnel became acute, vending machines multiplied to fill the gap. There were no regulations concerning the vending of food, and it wasn't long before public health officers found that the machines were a source of trouble. Fruit juices, syrups, and other products would leave residues on the machines and in the machines and contaminate the fresh products. Delivery tubes were not sanitized, and microorganisms flourished in such an environment.

In the early fifties, a number of persons were made violently ill after drinking soda from vending machines. Defective valves had permitted carbon dioxide to back up into the copper water valve. Copper was leached, thus contaminating the soda, and the unwary drinkers suffered copper poisoning.

The British have been more aware of, and stricter with, potential hazards from vending machines.[18] In 1966, the *Public Health Inspector,* a British publication, revealed that there had been a great deal of trouble and many complaints concerning unsound meat pies and meat sandwiches purchased from vending machines. Upon investigation, they found that the delivery truck had no form of temperature or humidity control. Though pies and pastries were put into preheated, heat-controlled containers, no thermometers were used. The vending machines were cleaned in a perfunctory way—when time and staff were available. Internal lighting in the machines raised the temperature more than 40 degrees.[19]

In *The Medical Officer,* another British publication, in September, 1961, health officers recognized a potential hazard we have yet to see. They wrote:

"With the increasing habit of chewing gum, slot machines for dispensing gum have multiplied. Sometimes the operators would drive up in the night, remove the top, collect the money, and put new gum in it. During the later months of 1960 and 1961, a series of machines were brought before the justice of the peace.

"The slot machines dispensing unwrapped ball gum were examined bacteriologically. Three out of 60 were found to be contaminated by human bacteria. *Streptococcus pyrogens* lived for a week or 16 days. Staph and *E. coli* survived 33 and 40 days.

"Any machine with unwrapped sweets into which children can poke their fingers is fundamentally unsound."[20]

The English no longer permit the dispensing of unwrapped sweets in vending machines. The Americans do. How many American children have picked up "one of those viruses" from a vending machine?

An Evaluation of Public Health Hazards from Microbiological Contamination of Foods, a Report of the Food Protection Committee of the Food and Nutrition Board, National Academy of Sciences, said of vending machines:

"The industry has, by self-regulation and education and by use of public health consultants and outside evaluation agencies, established a good operating control of food-vending machines.

"Recent findings cause some doubt on the efficiency of the lower temperature in restraining the growth of potentially hazardous bacteria. The upper level is, of course, insufficient to prevent growth of some thermophilic bacteria which, while not dangerous per se to health, could render the food unattractive. However, the primary risk in the case of food-vending machines seems to be related to improper processing and mishandling of foods prior to introduction into the machine, or to malfunction of the machine itself so that temperatures rise above 10 C. or drop below 66 C., even though machines are provided with controls designed to render them inoperative automatically when this happens."[21]

Public Health Service standards state:

"Vending machines dispensing potentially hazardous food shall be provided with adequate refrigerating or heating units, or both, and thermostatic controls which insure the maintenance of appliable temperatures at all times. Such vending machines shall also have controls which prevent the machine from vending potentially hazardous food until serviced by the operator in the event of power failure or other conditions which result in noncompliance with temperature requirements in the food-storage compartments.

"The machine location shall be such as to minimize the potential for contamination of the food, shall be well lighted, easily cleanable and shall be kept clean. Conveniently located handwashing facilities shall be available for use by employees serving or loading bulk food machines."[22]

Have you seen machines that do not follow this description?

The problems of inspection and supervision seem almost insurmountable. I personally watched a man refill a popcorn machine. He opened the bottom part of the device, and popcorn was strewn about the floor like snow. Though he didn't take the popcorn from the floor and place it in the machine, he did handle it. Without washing his hands, he put new popcorn on top of the old buttered popcorn in the machine. Health officials say that there is some supervision of commissaries that prepare the food for vending machines but that there is almost no inspection of the machines themselves or of the men who service them.

Robert Lackey, the East Orange health official quoted earlier, said: "We discourage the type of vending machine that sells sandwiches. Some industries do have banks of vending machines instead of cafeterias. That is all right if they employ 3,000 people and there is a rapid turnover. But not in a marginal operation."

Many vending machines are operated on a concession basis, and sometimes the individual operator may be careless. Too often, vending machines are licensed, but that is all.

What can the customers do to protect themselves and their families against contaminated vending machine products?

"Nothing," said Dr. George Kupchik. "It is a closed mechanism. You simply have to rely on the operator."

But why not post a sign stating when the machine was last inspected, just as in elevators? Why not a list of standards for the product sold by the machine, and a visible temperature gage? If the machine is supposed to dispense hot food above a certain temperature, why not say so, and have a thermometer that can be read by the buyer?

IT CAN BE DONE

Harold Simpson, a former chef, is now Corporate Director of Purchasing Control for Restaurant Associates Industries, an organization that owns everything from vending machines and snack bars to some of the best gourmet restaurants in the world, such as The Four Seasons and Forum of the Twelve Ceasars in New York. He said:

"We have self-inspection and we hire two professional firms to check our sanitation, in addition to the checks by local and federal inspectors.

"We run our own classes for our food handlers, and the City of New York has a food-handling course in sanitation. There is no substitution for proper food-handling techniques.

"We also reject a lot of food if it does not meet our standards, which are very rigid," he continued. Mr. Simpson says that their standards are so rigid that they have not found a frozen-food manufacturer that measures up to their requirements.

"Some restaurants have gone into portion-cut, prepared convenience foods. This is a costly thing in itself, but they think it will reduce their own labor costs. We haven't been able to find the quality and the portion cuts we want. Furthermore, if all restaurants buy food from the same frozen-food manufacturer, then all restaurants would be alike."

Mr. Simpson, who was once a chef at the Greenbrier, Mount Washington, and Boca Raton hotels, said the reasons restaurants go under financially is poor location and lack of business knowledge:

"A man can be a hell of a cook, but without the other knowledge he won't succeed. People have to be trained in temperature control, how to care for perishable foods, how to rotate food items, how to prepare a menu.

"With the number of meals being served in this country, the number of bad results is very small," he said.[23]

There is no doubt that many readers of this book have experienced bad meals during a car trip. Even in the bush country of Africa I have never experienced meals as unappetizing and probably dangerous as some of those I had along American highways and at tourist spots.

However, as our federal food inspectors point out, you may be driving from New York to Florida, and become ill with food poisoning, but you won't know in which of the many restaurants you were served the "poison," for, as we mentioned earlier, symptoms may take as long as seventy-two hours to develop.

The Federal Food and Drug Administration has jurisdiction over airline, bus, train, and ship food services because they move interstate or are American-owned. Some foreign vessels request our federal food inspection, although they are not legally required to do so.

No one wants to poison a patron, but even the most efficient operation can be hazardous. An airline wanted to serve gourmet meals on its flights. Meals prepared by approved processors were frozen; there were temperature controls on each "stack" of meals, and the trucks that carried them were properly temperature-controlled, as were the kitchens aboard the planes. However, no one could predict which meals the passengers would order. Some meals were taken on and off airliners thirty-two times, often with a loss of temperature control. A potentially hazardous situation developed, and the airline lost more than a million dollars, finally changing back to the old system.[24]

Several federal food inspectors and I were discussing the hazards of eating in some restaurants while traveling by car. They pointed out that the FDA actually has legal jurisdiction over places along the highway because they can inspect food that is used in interstate commerce. They wondered whether it would not be possible for federal inspectors to give a "seal of approval" to tourist places that qualified, saying they were sanitary.

The value of such a seal is obvious, and if you think so too, and have had some bad experiences while traveling, you could encourage such a step by writing to your congressman.

8   NOTES

1. "From Hand to Mouth," U.S. Department of Health, Education, and Welfare, Public Health Service Publication No. 281.
2. Report of Bank of America Survey, *Newark News,* July 7, 1968.
3. "From Hand to Mouth," *loc. cit.*
4. James L. Shoemaker, M.P.H., "Public Eating and Drinking Estab-

lishment Sanitation," *Journal of Environmental Health,* January, 1965, Vol. 27, No. 3.

5. "From Hand to Mouth," *loc. cit.*

6. Board of Health, City of East Orange, New Jersey, Annual Report, 1966.

7. William Clinger, tape-recorded interview with author, July, 1968.

8. Dr. George Kupchik, Director of Environmental Health, American Public Health Association, tape-recorded interview with author, February 26, 1968.

9. Aaron H. Haskin, M.D., Health Officer, Newark, N.J., "Physical Examination of Food Handlers Is Not a Useful Requirement," *Public Health News,* New Jersey State Department of Health, June, 1967. Also, author's interview with Mr. Haskin in July, 1968.

10. Robert Lackey, East Orange Health Officer, tape-recorded interview with author, June, 1968.

11. Robert Harkins, Ph.D., Chicago, "Food Handling Certificates," *Journal of the American Medical Association,* November 6, 1967, Vol. 202, No. 6.

12. Arnold Kaufman, D.V.M.; Charles Hayman, M.D.; Frederick Heath, M.D.; Murray Grant, M.D., "Salmonellosis Epidemic Related to Caterer-Delicatessen Restaurant," *American Journal of Public Health,* April, 1968, Vol. 58, No. 4.

13. *FDA Papers,* July–August, 1967, p. 35.

14. *Food Service Sanitation Manual,* 1962, Public Health Service Publication 934.

15. Tape-recorded interview with author, June, 1968.

16. Robert E. Johnson, Principal Sanitarian, Bureau of Food and Drugs, New Jersey Department of Health, "New Jersey's Program to Control Quality in Potentially Hazardous Foods," *Public Health News,* June, 1968, Vol. 49, No. 6.

17. *Public Health Reports,* October, 1958.

18. *Ibid.,* April, 1957.

19. *Public Health Inspector,* November, 1966.

20. *The Medical Officer,* September, 1961.

21. *An Evaluation of Public Health Hazards from Microbiological Contamination of Foods,* a report of the Food Protection Committee, National Academy of Sciences and National Research Council, Publication 1195, 1964.

22. *The Vending of Food and Beverages,* 1965 recommendations of the Public Health Service.

23. Harold Simpson, Corporate Director, Restaurant Associates Industries, interview with author, July, 1968.

24. G. M. Hansler, Acting Assistant Regional Director of Environmental Control, Health, Education, and Welfare, tape-recorded interview with author, July, 1968.

9

Those Convenient
New Foods

S. NEWBRUNSWICK IS A SEROTYPE of *Salmonella* isolated from a
baby chick in New Brunswick, New Jersey, in 1937. It had not
received much attention because between 1947 and 1966, out of
50,782 salmonella isolations from human sources, only thirteen were
the same as that identified from that tiny ball of yellow fluff.

The State of Michigan had never had a known case of human
S. newbrunswick until January, 1966, when two male infants—both
less than six months of age—developed severe gastroenteritis. Even
though they lived in different parts of the state and their families had
never met, both had *S. newbrunswick* forms of salmonellosis.

The Michigan State Department of Health began an investigation. Both babies were fed the usual baby foods, and each had been
on a formula made with widely distributed brands of instant nonfat
dry milk. Inspectors from the Health Department purchased samples
of dry milk at local retail stores, and the laboratory examined the
products. No salmonellas were found.

Public health officials asked other state health departments
whether they had any reported cases of *S. newbrunswick* illness.
Seventeen did. In all, there were twenty-nine cases that had been
reported across the country between March, 1965, and February,
1966. The product that carried the rare organism had to be something
distributed nationally. But what?

One thing became quickly apparent when the cases were gathered
together: 48 percent of the victims were infants less than a year old.

But what did the limited diet of infants have in common with the diets of adults? Solving the puzzle was made easier by the fact that one adult victim was a strict vegetarian, and thus a large number of dietary sources of salmonellas, such as chicken and cake mixes, could be eliminated.

The one thing that all the victims had in common was dried milk. Though multiple brands of milk were named, this did not discourage the researchers, since they knew that there was a frequent interchange of base powder among various producers of the final instantized product and that the majority of producers drew on the same large milksheds in the Midwest.

The trail finally led to a processing plant that produced an estimated 11 million pounds of nonfat dry milk in 1965, approximately 4 percent of the total instant nonfat dry milk in the nation. Some eight hundred farms routinely supplied the milk for the plant. A number of materials produced by the plant in question were found to be contaminated with *S. newbrunswick;* two of the employees involved in sifting and bagging operations were found to be infected with *S. newsbrunswick;* the air filter of the spray driers was contaminated with *S. newbrunswick.*

The mode of the first contamination of the plant was never identified. Health officials suspect that one of the eight hundred farms supplying the plant provided raw milk contaminated with *S. newbrunswick* and that the heat treatment in the plant was insufficient to kill the organism.

The case history of the outbreak, which occurred over a period of a year in seventeen states, was reported by Richard N. Collins, Michael D. Treger, James B. Goldsby, John R. Boring, III, Donald B. Coohon, and Robert N. Barr, in the *Journal of the American Medical Association,* March 4, 1968.[1]

The case illustrates two points:

1. THAT WE DEMAND CONVENIENCE—Most mothers have given up breast-feeding, and an increasing number are giving up mixing their babies' formulas in their own kitchens. Although there is little enforcement of standards in premixed formulas, and the possibility of contamination of dried milk is high, we are willing to take the chance, through ignorance or laziness.

2. THAT PUBLIC HEALTH OFFICIALS FIND IT DIFFICULT TO RECOGNIZE AN EPIDEMIC IN CONVENIENCE FOODS. Outbreaks may occur

over a long period of time and in widely separated areas; and because of faulty reporting, the source may not be discovered. The vast increase in new convenience products can be appreciated when we learn that of all the food products available for the housewife today, 66 percent did not exist ten years ago.[2]

According to a report of the Food Protection Committee of the National Academy of Sciences and National Research Council:

"The most outstanding development in the food industry has been the transfer of food preparation from the home to the factory. At the local level, food service organizations provide prepared meals and other food items on a large scale for industrial employees, schoolchildren and special groups. A wide variety of perishable prepared ready-to-eat foods is being distributed for home consumption by "carry-out" food services. In general, food production of this type is under purely local public health supervision.

"On the national level, large quantities of products are manufactured in individual plants for distribution throughout the country and internationally. In earlier years, such foods were primarily "sterilized" or "stabilized" canned or dehydrated products. However, the improvement in food distribution methods in recent years, particularly in applications of refrigeration, has made it possible for perishable products to be shipped over long distances and retailed in good condition."[3]

In 1940, the average housewife spent about five hours each day preparing three meals for her family of four. Currently, it takes her less than one and a half hours.[4]

Half or more of the sales of most major companies are of products developed in the past ten years. Inquiries by *This Week* magazine showed that fifty new products are presented to food-chain buying offices during an average week, and the typical chain adds 1,300 new items and drops 1,050 items each year.

An article by Dr. Abel Wolman, "Man and His Changing Environment," in the *Journal of Public Health,* November, 1961, pointed out: "The increase in the number and variety of processed foods is considered by some to be synonymous with a better and easier life. It seems to be assumed that most individuals for one reason or another are unwilling to accept foods in their natural state. Hence, every conceivable effort has been made to modify color, taste, structural appearance, texture, stability, nutritive value and substitute commodities. Such successful efforts to supplement, modify and conceal nature introduces innumerable problems of identification, of evaluation, of control and of assessment of long-term biological effects.

"To the orthodox problems of biological hazards in food, industry has added the major issues of chemical, biochemical, physical and other adjustments. The natural and artificially induced shifts in food habits, new methods of food technology, and the intentional and inadvertent use of additives find the health officer confronted with a baffling set of conditions unheard of even a decade ago."[5]

No one in America wants to go backward. We want both convenience and an abundant choice of food. Yet we want it, and should have it, free of hazard, and it should be of good quality. Too often, we are not getting what we expect and pay for. As proof, here are some examples that are just a fraction of such infractions on the market:

KANSAS CITY DISTRICT—Dehydrated potatoes and frozen custard pies were seized in April, 1967, because of *E. coli,* excessive coliforms, and total bacteria.[6]

LOS ANGELES DISTRICT—Because of salmonella contamination, a pie company of Los Angeles, California, recalled more than 100,000 frozen-custard and pumpkin pies in April, 1967. Inspection of the firm that supplied liquid eggs to the bakery revealed inadequate pasteurization.[7]

ATLANTA DISTRICT—A Florida macaroni company and its president were fined a total of $12,000 on February 2, 1968, on charges of insect infestation.[8]

BALTIMORE DISTRICT—A railroad car of yellow shelled corn was seized at Greenville, North Dakota, on June 8, 1967, owing to an unsafe pesticide residue, Captan.[9]

COLORADO DISTRICT—Prompt identification of salmonella by the Colorado Department of Health in a food-poisoning case resulted in a nationwide recall of frozen Chinese dinners manufactured in Minneapolis, Minnesota.[10]

At an American Public Health Association meeting on November 12, 1968, researchers from General Foods reported finding *Cl. botulinum,* Types A or B, in six samples of frozen vacuum pouch-pack spinach in butter sauce. The samples were among one hundred randomly selected, commercially available cut green beans and frozen chopped spinach.

The authors of the report, N. F. Insalata, section head, General Foods Corporation, Post Division Research; J. S. Witzeman, J. H. Berman, and E. Borker, denied there was an "eminent hazard" because if housewives followed instructions and boiled the pouch for fifteen minutes, the botulinum would be destroyed.[11]

But what if they didn't follow instructions?

If six out of a hundred randomly selected packages showed botulinus, how many more on the supermarket shelves show the same thing? And what about the new do-it-yourself vacuum pouch-packs? Housewives are not as careful as large food manufacturers in observing sterile techniques. What else will mothers and wives be putting into the pouch with the leftovers?

FROZEN FOODS

Former FDA Commissioner James Goddard said in an interview with the author that the "major area of concern of the Federal Food and Drug Administration in the food-protection system is providing safe, good-quality frozen foods right from the time of manufacturing and processing into housewives' kitchens."[12]

A news release of the American Public Health Association put it in stronger terms in April, 1968: "Bargain day for TV dinners may be a bad bargain for your stomach.

"A study, 'Incidence of *Clostridium perfringens* in Fish and Fish Products,' by Dr. Mitsuru Nakamura and Katherine D. Kelly, reveals that the incidence of *Clostridium perfringens,* a bacterium which may cause acute gastroenteritis, is twice as high in TV dinners and potpies containing fish as in fresh or smoked fish."

Health Laboratory Science, a journal published quarterly by the Laboratory Section of the American Public Health Association, has featured a variety of studies of food contamination in the past. This study, based on selective sampling taken in Missoula, Montana, points out that frozen foods are often subjected to thawing and refreezing several times prior to sale. On sale days, when the packages are stacked high and displayed under inadequate refrigeration, the bacteria present in the fish may reproduce and initiate food poisoning when the food is consumed.

The APHA article concluded: "The moral of the story? Turn off your TV and go catch your own fish!"[13]

Actually, patents for freezing fish were issued to H. Benjamin in England in 1842. Before that, cooling with natural ice or in caves was practiced for centuries. Mechanical refrigeration, developed in the late 1800's, allowed foods to be stored at about 40 degrees F., but frozen foods didn't really get started until 1940. Clarence Birdseye and others helped to develop quick-freezing processes, thus promoting frozen foods as a consumer item.[14] Annual consumption of frozen foods has risen from six pounds per capita, around World War II, to thirty or more pounds.

Because of their high water content, most foods freeze easily at temperatures between 25 and 32 degrees F. Although each food has a specific freezing point, quick freezing takes place in thirty minutes or less. If freezing is rapid, damage to the food is reversible. Slow freezing permits large, uneven crystals to build up; these puncture the food cells, and make the food mushy when it is defrosted.

According to *An Evaluation of Public Health Hazards from Microbiological Contamination of Foods,* a report of the Food Protection Committee of the Food and Nutrition Board, National Academy of Sciences and National Research Council, the primary hazard in frozen products lies in contamination and perhaps microbial growth or toxin production during preparation and processing and in failure to observe proper temperature control during storage, distribution, retailing, and especially in the home.

Frozen foods are very sensitive to temperature increases. In "Quality and Safety in Frozen Foods," published in the *Journal of the American Medical Association,* it was pointed out by Dr. Horace K. Burr and Dr. R. Paul Elliott, that most chemical reactions are 20 to 30 percent more rapid when the temperature rises 5 degrees F.; but certain deteriorative reactions in frozen foods may double, triple, or even quadruple their rate with such a temperature rise. They said that deterioration begins even at 0 degrees F. but that, if packaged suitably, frozen foods retain high quality for many months.[15]

Under present regulatory conditions, the manufacturers themselves are trusted to make sure their products are not contaminated with food-poisoning bacteria. No federal law sets limits on the amount of food-poisoning bacteria that can be present in frozen foods, although the United States Army sets such standards for the food it buys. Generally, federal and state authorities don't step in until the contaminated food has reached the market.[16]

Though 50 percent of the live organisms are killed in frozen food in six months and 75 percent in one year, the low count does not mean that the food is safe. It may have been handled in a very unsanitary manner and may have food toxins and other contamination.[17]

At the Frozen Food Packers National Association meeting in Chicago, in 1964, former FDA Commissioner George P. Larrick said:

"Routine bacteriological controls are not sufficient to detect potentially pathogenic microorganisms which may be present in raw ingredients.

"Pesticide residues in frozen foods are a problem requiring unique controls where raw agricultural commodities of a perishable nature are purchased.

"An ever-present problem, both for the frozen-food packer and the FDA, is the care employed in adding just the right amount of direct food additives for which there are tolerance limitations. There is a basic assumption in the use of these that the food manufacturer will take the necessary precautions to avoid misuse.

"When our inspectors visit your plant—*about once every two years on the average*—they need to know how good your controls are so we can evaluate how you are carrying out your responsibility day in and day out."

Mr. Larrick concluded: "The extent to which some in industry adopt control methods is influenced by the attention given the problem by federal, state and local officials."[18]

When the FDA conducted a survey of frozen-food plants which covered sixty-three factories in eighteen states, some three thousand samples were collected and examined. The results led to the conclusion that "sanitary and operating practices in plants were considerably below the level desired" for this kind of food product.

Even if the commercially frozen food is not of the quality we would like it to be, for the most part it is safe. The really dangerous frozen food is that prepared by the independent small-time merchant who wants to freeze something he makes himself. Delicatessens and specialty stores do it, most of the time without proper equipment and without any inspection at all. In such cases, one man's frozen dish may truly be another man's poison.

CANNED FOODS

When Napoleon had his hand in his shirt, he may have been hiding the first can of food.

All eighteenth-century soldiers traveled in peril of their diets of putrid meat and other inferior food. In order to improve the condition of his fighting men, Napoleon offered a prize of 12,000 francs for the invention of a method of food preservation for his army. A confectioner, Nicolas Appert, observed that food cooked in sealed bottles remained unspoiled as long as the container remained unbroken. Appert won the prize in 1809. By 1820, the first commercial canning plants were operating in the United States, and by 1840 canning was common throughout the country.[19]

Considering the number of cans produced annually, the record of the American canning industry has been remarkably good. Commercially canned food may be stored almost indefinitely under proper conditions. Sealed cans are heated during the canning process to destroy undesirable organisms. Although acid foods may react eventually with the tin and iron in the can to cause off-flavors, such a taste is not an indication of spoilage. Canned foods should be stored in cool places to retard such reactions. There is a considerable loss of vitamins when the temperatures of canned vegetables and fruits are too high.[20]

FERMENTATION

Man has used microorganisms to aid him in the production and preservation of his food for a long time. Beer, cottage cheese, buttermilk, sauerkraut, bread, and wine are all examples. Fermentation is a process of decomposition of the carbohydrates in foods. It is easily distinguishable from putrefaction, which results from the action of microorganisms on protein materials.[21]

DRYING

Drying food to preserve it is as old as man's discovery that the sun could stop decay.

In the 1700's, people put their food near the fire to hasten drying it or else spread it in thin layers in direct sunlight to hasten the process. In 1795, two Frenchmen named Masson and Challet made an important improvement in the process of drying when they built a dehydrator in which air heated to about 105 degrees F. was blown over thinly sliced vegetables.

The first dehydrated instant foods, however, are credited to the United States Army Quartermaster Corps. In World War II, the Corps came up with instant mashed potatoes that tasted very much like wallpaper paste. During the war the Quartermaster Corps issued a contract to industry to improve dried potatoes. The improvement was made, and a host of other dehydrated products were developed, such as eggs, milk, and some vegetables. The processing reduced shipping weight, eased storage problems, simplified distribution, and enabled soldiers to carry their rations with less effort in the field. Though these World War II products still lacked quality, and were difficult to rehydrate, they were the forerunners of today's many dried convenience products.

Prior to 1950, most dehydration was in cabinets or tunnels with forced blasts of air at high temperatures to remove water. Such methods caused damage to the product. Today, vacuum drying in cabinets is used for prune flakes, apple powder, and potato granules. Spray-drying and drum-drying are also used for dehydration. Improvements in heating methods, water removal, and temperature control makes spray-drying and drum-drying techniques applicable to more foods in greater volume. Coffee, tea, soup mixes, fruit solids and vegetable purées may be spray-dried.

A fairly new method is puff-drying. The product is partially dehydrated by circulated hot air; then it is exploded (puffed) by a gun. The food is finish-dried in heated bins to withdraw the last traces of moisture. By using this method, the United States Department of Agriculture has puff-dried carrots, beets, blueberries, and apple pieces.

Studies on a significant number of samples of various dehydrated fruits and vegetables have shown very few, if any, of them to be sterile. Very little information is available concerning the significance of microbial populations found in these products.[22]

A combination of both the freezing and dehydrating techniques is "freeze-drying." This is a process in which moisture is removed from the food while it is in a frozen state. The advantage of freeze-drying is that the water is removed in a manner that does the least physical damage to the food itself. Freeze-dried foods now include soups, casserole dishes, fruits for cereals and coffee. They retain their flavor, aroma, and stability much better than air-dried foods.[23] One critical problem with freeze-dried foods is that they absorb water more rapidly than other dried foods. Therefore they require special packaging and handling. These facts, plus the higher cost for water removal, mean that the cost of freeze-dried products is usually high.

A new process using microwaves to hasten water removal may have good possibilities. When the microwaves pass through the food, the molecules in the food attempt to align themselves with the electrical field, creating friction and heat. As the microwaves uniformly pass through the food, water is removed by the heat generated within the food.

Concentrated, dry frozen baby food has been tested by the University of Missouri School of Medicine. Reporting their findings in the *Journal of Diseases of Children*, the researchers said that forty-nine infants were fed with the products. None developed signs of food poisoning or allergy. The researchers also said that, without exception, "the mothers stated that this new baby food appeared fresher and more appetizing." The processing included the application of heat, reduction of moisture, and freezing. No colors, flavors, preservatives, or fortifying nutrients were used in the process.

The Wisconsin Alumni Research Foundation reported studies of the frozen, concentrated baby food showed that the nutrients were effectively retained in processing and storage at freezing temperature. Bacteriological studies at the University of Chicago showed that no food-poisoning organisms were found and that the food could be safely stored in the deep freeze for about one year and in the refrigerator for about one month.[24]

MILDLY PROCESSED FOODS

Perhaps the most potentially dangerous of all convenience foods are the so-called "mildly processed."

Here is a quote from *An Evaluation of Public Health Hazards from Microbiological Contamination of Foods* by the Food Protection Committee of the Food and Nutrition Board, National Academy of Sciences and National Research Council:

"A variety of products in which microbial populations have been reduced in number by some mild bactericidal treatment—usually heat —is on the market. The final product is most commonly packaged in a metal can or a plastic bag, often under vacuum, and should be stored under refrigeration. Since these are not sterile products, there is an obvious danger associated with bad handling of the food either before or after processing. A few retailers still handle all canned goods as though they are sterile; consequently it is possible to see canned nonsterile products such as hams and bacon stored out of the refrigerated area.

"There are reasons for believing that the bacterial hazards associated with mildly processed products are greater than from corresponding unprocessed items. The principal objective of mild processing with most foodstuffs is to eliminate low-temperature spoilage micro-organisms which are in general highly sensitive to heating, smoking and irradiation. In untreated food, the normal flora serves two functions that concern the consumer; it quickly renders the food undesirable when storage conditions are poor, and in some cases it apparently competitively suppresses the growth of food-poisoning organisms. The former serves to warn the consumer of a potential danger. In pasteurized foods, the microbial balance is upset; the organisms that normally grow most vigorously on the stored foods are eliminated and conditions are probably made more favorable for growth and, perhaps, toxin production by potentially pathogenic organisms.

"If these pasteurized foods are packaged in vacuumized containers, an additional factor of risk exists where good refrigeration practice is not followed. The anaerobic conditions created are quite inhibitory to many of the surviving spoilage bacteria but may be suitable for the development of botulism."

The evaluation also said that the number of foods falling into this mild-processing category are increasing all the time, and already include poultry and meat products and party dips of various kinds:

"The potential hazards involved in long-term low-temperature storage (above freezing) are not at all well understood. The outbreaks of botulism due to *C. Botulinus* Type E. on smoked fish in 1960 and 1963, in which a number of deaths occurred, represents the particular hazard involved in mild processing and mishandling of the final product. The many uncertainties associated with the microbiology, etiology and epidemiology of these cases emphasize the inadequacy of our knowledge and understanding of the microbiological factors involved in certain mild-processing operations of the type involved here.

"In many such processes, the margin between a microbiologically satisfactory product and a potentially dangerous one is clearly very narrow, and its maintenance is almost entirely dependent upon proper control of storage and transportation conditions."[25]

IRRADIATION

Irradiation of food would seem to be the answer to all problems of foodborne disease and quality loss. The United States Atomic Energy Commission, Division of Technical Information, in a brochure describing "Food Preservation by Irradiation," said:

"Oranges as sweet and juicy as if just picked—strawberries firm and free of mold—yet all many miles and weeks away from harvest. How is it possible? They've been radiation-'pasteurized'—exposed to low levels of nuclear radiation.

"Bacon, ham and chicken that haven't been near a refrigerator in months are fed to hundreds of soldiers who find them the equal of normal fresh meat. How? They've been radiation-'sterilized'—exposed to levels of radiation high enough to kill bacteria."[26]

Other than canning, radiation processing is the only original—that is nonnatural—method of preserving food. The amount of radiation to be delivered depends upon the food itself and the result desired. If the goal is prolongation of shelf life, or storage time, a pasteurization dose, generally from 200,000 to 500,000 rads, is sufficient. If the food is to be sterilized for long-term storage without refrigeration, the required dose is between 2,000,000 and 4,500,000 rads.

Even lower doses of radiation—4,000 to 10,000 rads—stops potatoes or onions from sprouting. Twenty thousand to fifty thousand rads kills insects infesting food. Doses of 200,000 to 400,000 are highly effective in extending the refrigerated storage of fresh fish up to thirty days. Bacon and other pork products, chicken and beef can be packaged and then irradiated at 4.5 million rads, resulting in sufficient preservation to permit a year's storage at room temperature.

Irradiation could save us money by stopping food spoilage, help underdeveloped countries without adequate refrigeration and food distribution, and generally be the answer to worldwide needs.

On February 8, 1963, the FDA ruled that bacon preserved by radiation is safe and fit for unlimited human consumption. Later, the government agency approved radiation to inhibit sprouting in white potatoes and disinfestation of wheat and wheat flour in this country.

Such foods, however, are not for sale in the United States and chances are they may not be for a long, long time.[27]

In 1968, the FDA rejected the Atomic Energy Commission and Army's petition for clearance of canned irradiated ham. In addition, FDA officials said that all previous clearances of foods preserved by irradiation will have to be reevaluated to make sure the data justifies the approvals. In a letter to Army Brigadier General F. J. Gerace, Commander of the Army's Natick Laboratories, the then FDA Commissioner, Dr. James Goddard, said, "Our evaluation of these data [for use of gamma radiation in preserving ham] fails to establish that the proposed use of gamma radiation will be safe."

In a letter to AEC Chairman Glenn T. Seaborg, Dr. Goddard said he was "most disappointed" with Army data, and would have to have better data before new clearances are given. In discussing reasons for the denial of the petition, Dr. Goddard said that reported adverse effects on animal reproductive processes are "highly unlikely" to be due to chance. The FDA head cited a University of California at Los Angeles study on rats fed irradiated bacon and fruit compote which revealed that "the feeding of a diet containing irradiated bacon on the 1x level was associated with the reduction of 22 percent in weaned progeny and a 23 percent reduction in liveborn progeny." Others adverse effects included increased mortality rates in rats fed a diet of bacon irradiated at the 2x level. "There was consistently reported a slight but persistent depression of body weight observed both in dogs and mice that were fed irradiated diets," according to the UCLA study.

Dr. Goddard also expressed concern over the tumor-causing potential of irradiated foods. Rats fed a diet of irradiated bacon and fruit developed more tumors than a control group of animals. "One study of rats reported three carcinomas of the pituitary gland among 52 animals on irradiated pork diets versus none in the 26 animals on the control diet. Since this is a rarely occurring type of tumor, this could be very significant."

A study in the 1960's at Cornell University showed that eating irradiated sugar can produce the same results as irradiation directly applied to the cell. The scientists experimented with carrot tissue and coconut milk . . . both high in natural sugars. They bombarded them with cobalt 60, causing radiation-induced cell mutations in both foods. Moreover, the chemicals produced by sugar breakdown in the foods were seen in transfer radiation effects into the cells of fruit flies, resulting in stunted growth and chromosome damage. All living cells contain sugar, the report emphasized, and human beings may suffer similar consequences from long-term consumption of irradiated food.[28]

There are also many studies that maintain that irradiated food is wholesome. In the *FDA Papers,* May, 1967, Robert S. Roe, Associate Director of the Bureau of Science, summed it up:

"FDA scientists want to know if ionizing radiation causes radioactivity in the food, whether they produce toxic substances in the food or whether proposed treatments adversely affect the nutritive values of exposed food and whether the proposed treatments are effective for intended purposes.

"It is important that the greatest care be exercised, particularly at this stage of development, to insure that any regulations issued are scientifically sound and will, in fact, provide for safe and effective uses."[29]

Scientists kept up a running battle in the pages of *Science,* the publication of the American Association for the Advancement of Science, on the merits and dangers of food irradiation. The final consensus of opinion was that the burden of proof is on those manufacturers who want to irradiate food.

Perhaps radiation will prove to be the answer; perhaps we shall go back to older methods. In fact, United States Department of Agriculture researchers reported at the 1968 meeting of the American Institutes of Biological Sciences in Urbana, Illinois, that ultraviolet light (the same as that of the sun) can kill 99 percent of the harmful bacteria in maple syrup. They said control of bacterial growth by ultraviolet light irradiation is "simple, inexpensive, leaves no harmful additives, yet is 100 percent effective."

Actually, little is known about the microbiology of many of the newer foods and food-manufacturing processes.

The National Academy of Sciences and National Research Council report said: "Even as it concerns frozen foods, on which a considerable proportion of applied bacteriological research effort has been concentrated recently, there are many unexplained factors.

"The development of bacteriological guidelines is of the greatest urgency in the case of convenience and mildly processed foods. While there are strong public pressures in some areas for the regulation of the production of these products by the imposition of legal bacterial standards, the scientific basis for such standards has not yet been provided."[30]

THE SUPER-SUPERMARKET

When you go into a supermarket, what do you look for? The items on your grocery list? The special bargains for the day? Few of us look for signs of good sanitation in any of the nation's more than 28,000 modern food stores.

The average supermarket handles 7,000 to 8,000 items. Most invest $100,000 for temperature and humidity control to keep food in top condition.[31] Yet physical damage to food products from breakage, bruising, and other mishaps in warehousing, delivery to retail stores, and in the stores is estimated at more than $50 million annually. About three-fourths of this damage occurs in the store, with employees causing about 60 percent of it and customers about 40 percent. Some of the damage is not recognized until after the customer gets the product home.[32]

Most women do not select their supermarket; the market selects them by establishing a store in their neighborhood. Fortunately, the majority of stores do a good job in food protection; but all have a problem in maintaining quality, and a few harbor sickness and even death on their shelves.

Inspection of supermarkets, like inspection of restaurants, food-processing plants, caterers, and farms, is spotty and sometimes non-existent.

I went into a brand-new, luxurious super-supermarket with Dr. Paul LaChance, Associate Professor of Nutritional Physiology at Rutgers University, New Brunswick, New Jersey.[33] There were wide aisles with thousands of products invitingly displayed. It looked like a housewives' shopping heaven to me. Yet he showed me fish in broken plastic bags inadequately protected and refrigerated; chicken in packages that were perforated, with legs sticking out and juice dripping into the cabinet. (Women shoppers were handling the chicken with their bare hands, pushing aside the packages.) Sliced bologna, inspected by a local health department, was two months old; honey jars were leaking; hams were unrefrigerated; potatoes had heart rot; meat was packaged so that the underside and sides were hidden from the shopper; processed foods were piled high; and some, such as dough and cheese pirogis, were soft instead of frozen.

Dr. George Kupchik, Director of Environmental Health, American Public Health Association, said there is little doubt that some supermarkets sell over-age milk and do not handle meats and seafood properly.[34]

Dr. LaChance could read some of the mysterious codes on packages to determine their age.

"See this?" he said. "Women believe the stores put the older products in front and the new products in back. They usually reach toward the back to select a package."

The product that Dr. LaChance had selected from the back was much older, according to the code, than the product in the front.

A letter published in *Consumer Reports,* August, 1967, said:

"I've noted that you occasionally advocate dating of perishable food products. I don't think you go far enough.

"Last year I worked for a convenience-type grocery chain, and I know that people unknowingly purchased milk that was one and two days out of date, sandwiches that were a week out of date, and cartons of orange juice and lemonade that were two weeks out of date. Almost always a fresh package was available on the same shelf.

"I well remember one day when a young mother purchased a few cans and jars of baby food. I noted an old code on a jar of prunes and a can of meat and vegetables, and after she left I figured out how old those items were. Both had been on the shelves since the store first opened 32 months before. Perhaps the contents were perfectly safe, and good, but I lost my appetite for supper that day just thinking about it. . . .

"Most products are dated in code. I know that you cannot possibly explain all of the hundreds of systems used. But why don't you recommend a requirement that every grocer prominently display an explanation of all date codes used in his store?

"Orlando, Fla."   "F. C. W."

The editors of *Consumer Reports* answered: "Better yet, why don't food packers mark the labels with a clearly legible date indicating the reasonable shelf life of their products? Then the cake mixes wouldn't sit overlong on the shelf and the customers would have known whether those baby foods were perfectly all right after 32 months in the store."[35]

Today, good store management is really up to the owner's skill and conscience.

The career of Dave Fern, president of 230 Wakefern Food markets and honorary chairman of 78 Supermarkets General, spans the era from the time of the small neighborhood market to that of the giant chains of supermarkets. He began working as a grocery clerk in 1912.

"You used to greet the customers and chat with them. You knew what they liked," he said nostalgically. "Today, very few owners work in the store. It's big business." He explained that you need at least $500,000 just to open a store.

Mr. Fern, who sold Dave's Supermarket in Millburn, New Jersey, a number of years ago, still works there almost every day. "I like to be with people . . . give them some of the personal touch we had years ago," he said. Dave's Pathmark Supermarket now handles five thousand cases of products a week. Trucks pull up to the door at 6:30 A.M. and are unloaded automatically. The perishables are placed in a refrigerator. The nonperishables are stored off the floor on shelves. An exterminator services the store once a week. The Board of Health inspects at least once a week.[36]

Mr. Fern's supermarket, Dave's, was among the best I had seen on my tours of such establishments. Although not a trained inspector, in most other supermarkets I could observe defrosting frozen foods unrefrigerated hams, and obvious meat-processing violations.

Dr. LaChance and Weems Clevenger, District Director of the Food and Drug Administration, New York, are both food quality experts.

Dr. LaChance, who often shops in the supermarket for his wife, said he once saw a boy break open a crate of butter, put the butter on the floor, and then stamp the price on it. Dr. LaChance said he was so incensed at the breach of proper sanitation that he went and told the supermarket manager about it.

Mr. Clevenger said he saw unrefrigerated ham and other violations in a supermarket one day while shopping. He told the store manager about it, and the manager sloughed it off, not knowing the occupation of the shopper.

Dr. LaChance and Mr. Clevenger and other food experts with whom I spoke agreed that housewives and other shoppers who see a breach of sanitation in the store or who find they have spoiled food once they get home with their packages should report this to the store manager. If the situation is not rectified, then the customer should alert the local board of health.

Most store managers want to please their customers, and will go to great lengths to do so. Mr. Fern, for instance, said he had a refrigerated unit to hold produce.

"I had it in here for six months and then got rid of it because the men weren't changing the produce often enough. They left it in the unit too long. Now they have to carry all the produce to the refrigerator at night. In the morning, they must look it over and see if it is still right up to par. If not, we sell it for a few pennies. Actually, we would give it away, but the women wouldn't take it under those conditions. They would be suspicious."

Supermarket employees, in general, are paid better than many restaurant employees. At Dave's, the employees are unionized, and earn an average of $110 a week. Butchers earn as much as $150 a week. For Dave's and the other supermarkets in the chain there is an employee training program. Every department has a department manager, and there is an overall manager for the store.

Supermarkets are big business, and they make use of automation, mass buying and distribution, and even psychologists to lure the customer into buying more than he or she has on the shopping list. They are convenient, offer good prices, and generally do an excellent job. But there is much room for improvement.

Probably, the area that is weakest in all supermarkets is that of frozen foods. Most states do not have a frozen-food code that makes it unlawful to handle frozen foods at temperatures above 0 degrees F. But almost every item in a supermarket will deteriorate in time, regardless of whether it is merchandised in fresh or processed form.

Here are some hints on protecting your family's health when shopping in a supermarket:

SANITATION

Is the store clean? Are the floors dirty? Are the shelves messy? Are the people who work in the store untidy-looking?

Are there bathrooms available for customers? For the help? Are the bathrooms clean and properly equipped with soap and paper towels?

REFRIGERATION

Meat is supposed to be held at 28 to 38 degrees F.; produce and nonfrozen dairy products at 35 to 45 degrees; ice cream at −12 degrees.

Are hams and other processed foods that require refrigeration under refrigeration? How about eggs? They should be refrigerated too.

FROZEN FOODS

Check the condition and temperature of packages. Are they in cardboard cartons that interfere with cold air?

Are the products above the load line in the cases?

Does the thermometer in the box register 0 degrees or below? Remember, the thermometer is usually in the coldest spot in the case, so there should be a good margin of safety.

Is there evidence of leakage about the package of frozen food? Your purchase should be solid, with no material adhering to the outside of the package.

If large quantities of ice crystals are present on the inside walls of a package of frozen fruit or if the fruit is somewhat shriveled, it is suggestive of thawing and subsequent refreezing or longtime storage. If there is considerable ice on the bottom of the package of dry-packed fruit, the item may have been thawed and refrozen.

PRECOOKED FROZEN FOODS

Appearance and odor may help to tell you, once it is defrosted, that it is not of good quality. It will indicate that the product has fermented during processing by reason of a slow freeze or that it has been allowed to thaw. A dry, bleached surface is indicative of improper packaging, excessive storage periods, or widely varying temperatures in frozen storage.

CANNED FOODS

Don't look for bargains. Never buy an unlabeled or a dented can. Acid foods may react eventually with tin and iron in the can to cause an off-flavor. This undesirable flavor is not an indication of spoilage. However, it is better to be safe than sorry. The deadly botulinus sometimes causes off-odors and off-tastes. Canned food should be stored in a cool place to retard off-flavors. There is also a considerable loss of vitamins when the temperature of canned vegetable and fruit is too high.

JARS

Never buy a jar that is sticky or leaking.

PRODUCE

Check the bottom of the lettuce. If it has a brown instead of white ring, it is old, and may be an indication of the practices of the management.

THINK TWICE ABOUT BUYING SOMETHING NEW

According to Jean Judge, food-marketing specialist at Rutgers College of Agriculture and Environmental Science, "The customers who typically buy new products are usually those who most frequently reject the traditional housewife's role in food purchasing and preparation and thereby set the buying patterns for new products.

"They are most likely to be those who live in the urban areas of the Far West or Northeast, are well educated, represent families wherein the housewife is employed outside the home, have medium high incomes. Typically, families with young or school-age children are more likely to use new products, especially convenience items, than families without children."

Manufacturers of products know that an item is not profitable for more than two to five years, and for some, even less. Yet, the word "new" does not necessarily mean better.

Consumers Union found that a new food package which allowed the consumer to put a package of bacon into the toaster for instant cooking could cause a severe shock.[37]

Smoked fish that was packaged in vacuum-sealed envelopes turned out to be a wonderful medium for the growth of botulinus, and a score of persons died as a result.

This does not mean that food processors and vendors should stop trying to make improvements and developing conveniences for Americans. It does mean that each "new" product should be thoroughly tested for safety first. Like conservative doctors prescribing medicine, we should not rush out to buy something new, but hesitate long enough to see if it is really of good quality, and safe.

We should demand adequate inspection of food processors and supermarkets and other vendors of food.

Our best protection, however, remains our own skill and education as a buyer.

9 NOTES

1. Richard N. Collins, M.D.; Michael D. Treger, D.V.M.; James B. Goldsby, M.S.; John R. Boring, III, Ph.D.; Donald B. Coohon, D.V.M.; Robert N. Barr, M.D., "Interstate Outbreak of *Salmonella newbrunswick* Infection Traced to Powdered Milk," *Journal of the American Medical Association*, March 4, 1968, Vol. 203, No. 10.

2. *An Evaluation of Public Health Hazards from Microbiological Contamination of Foods*, National Academy of Sciences and National Research Council Publication 1195, 1964.

3. *The Sciences*, New York Academy of Sciences publication, May, 1965, Vol. 4, No. 12.

4. *Food Facts from Rutgers*, September, 1967.

5. Dr. Abel Wolman, Professor Emeritus of Sanitary Engineering, Johns Hopkins University, "Man and His Changing Environment," *Journal of Public Health*, November, 1961.

6. *FDA Papers*, July–August, 1967.

7. *Ibid.*

8. *FDA Papers*, April, 1968.

9. *Ibid.*, October, 1967.

10. *Ibid.*, June, 1967.

11. N. F. Insalata, J. S. Witzeman, J. H. Berman, and E. Borker, "The Incidence of *Clostridium Botulinum* in Frozen Vacuum Pouch-Pack Vegetables," meeting of the American Public Health Association, November 12, 1968, Detroit.

12. Author's tape-recorded interview with Dr. James Goddard, New Brunswick, N.J., 1968.

13. American Public Health news release, April, 1968.

14. Grace M. Urrows, "Food Preservation by Irradiation," U.S. Atomic Energy Commission, Division of Technical Information, April, 1968.

15. Horace K. Burr, Ph.D., and R. Paul Elliott, M.D., Albany, California, Council on Foods and Nutrition, "Quality and Safety in Frozen Foods," *Journal of the American Medical Association*, October 29, 1960, Vol. 174, No. 9, pp. 1178–1180.

16. William Dorsey, Chief of Richmond, Va., Public Health Laboratories, "Health Bulletin," June 6, 1964.

17. "Frozen Fruits, Vegetables and Precooked Frozen Foods," *Recommended Methods for the Microbiological Examination of Foods*, ed. J. M. Sharf (American Public Health Association, 1967), p. 97.
18. George P. Larrick, former Commissioner, U.S. Food and Drug Administration, before National Association of Frozen Food Packers, Chicago, Ill., March 20, 1964.
19. Grace M. Urrows, *op. cit.*
20. *Let's Talk About Food*, ed. Philip White (American Medical Association, 1967), p. 124.
21. Grace M. Urrows, *op. cit.*
22. *Recommended Methods for the Microbiological Examination of Foods*, p. 65.
23. *Food Facts from Rutgers*, January–February, 1968.
24. Gerard Van Leeuwen, M.D.; Emily J. Guyer, M.D.; University of Chicago, "New Concentrated Dry Frozen Baby Food," *American Journal of Diseases of Children*, January, 1961, Vol. 101, pp. 18–22.
25. *An Evaluation of Public Health Hazards, loc. cit.*
26. Grace M. Urrows, *op. cit.*
27. Reports in the press, July and August, 1968.
28. Dr. Richard D. Holsten, Cornell University doctoral thesis, 1965.
29. Robert S. Roe, *FDA Papers*, May, 1967.
30. *An Evaluation of Public Health Hazards . . . , loc. cit.*
31. Kermit Bird, Agricultural Economist, Marketing Economics Division, Economic Research Service, "Ketchup for a Small Boy: The Marketing Marvel," *The Yearbook of Agriculture*, 1966.
32. R. W. Hoecker, Chief of the Wholesaling and Retailing Research Branch, Transportation and Facilities Research Division, Agricultural Research Service, "Supermarket Safeguards," *The Yearbook of Agriculture*, 1966.
33. March, 1968.
34. Dr. George Kupchik, Director of Environmental Health, American Public Health Association, tape-recorded interview with author, February 26, 1968.
35. *Consumer Reports*, August, 1967, p. 454.
36. Interview with author, July, 1968.
37. *Consumer Reports*, February, 1967, p. 64.

10

Some Questions and Recommendations

IT IS NOT THE PURPOSE of this book to be sensational, nor is it to attack farmers, food processors, restaurants, government agencies, or any specific group. Its aim is not to point out that illness and death have resulted from what we eat, although this is certainly true. The author has no desire to hinder technology in its development of new and better means of preparing, packaging, and serving food.

The goal of this book is to raise questions.

Have we, like unsupervised children with beginners' chemistry sets, unrestrainedly poisoned ourselves and perhaps our descendants?

Have we allowed our technology to surpass our biological safeguards?

In a report to the Secretary of Health, Education, and Welfare by the Task Force on Environmental Health and Related Problems, dated June, 1967, it was pointed out:

"We know something of air pollution, but we know little about the potential hazard of 500,000 to 600,000 synthetic chemicals and other compounds on the market today. We know something of water quality but little of the effects of trace metals. . . .

"An individually acceptable amount of water pollution added to a tolerable amount of air pollution, added to a bearable amount of noise and congestion can produce a totally unacceptable health environment. . . .

"It is entirely possible that the biological effects of these environmental hazards, some of which reach man slowly and silently over decades or generations, will first begin to reveal themselves only after their impact has become irreversible.

"Not only have we overwhelmed many of nature's processes for environmental stability; we have misused, without knowing it, biological processes upon which the preservation of life depends. By allowing tiny amounts of pesticides to enter our waters, we have set in motion processes that can lead to the destruction of birds that feed on fish that feed on plants that draw the pesticides from the water. Our ignorance of the consequences of our deeds may be innocent, but it is ignorance we can no longer tolerate."[1]

Ironically, with all our supermethods of growth, processing, distribution, and variety, we Americans are not eating as well as we did only a decade ago. A survey released by Secretary of Agriculture Orville Freeman in 1968 showed that 21 percent of our households had poor diets compared with 15 percent in 1955. The ability to pay was not the criterion. One in every ten families with incomes of $10,000 and over had poor diets. The Department of Agriculture also found that families were consuming more soft drinks, instead of milk and milk products, and eating less vegetables and fruits.

As unbelievable as it may seem, we do not have accurate methods for determining what happens to the vitamins in our foods from the time they are harvested or processed until the time we eat them.[2]

We cannot answer the question of whether severe heat and dehydration processes in the preparation of precooked and easy-to-prepare "convenience" foods affect the nutritional quality of our food.[3]

We do not know the effect of a pregnant woman's diet on the fetus. Previously, scientists believed that the placenta, which provides nutrition for the growing embryo, protected it from harmful chemicals in the mother's system. Now it has been discovered that not only does the placenta not protect the child; it may even concentrate and increase the harmful substance delivered to the fetus.[4]

Infectious hepatitis appears to be directly related to contaminated drinking water, but how does the virus get into the water and how can it be removed or neutralized? No one knows![5]

The Food and Drug Administration has estimated that the American people are being exposed to some 500,000 different substances, many of them over very long periods of time. Yet, fewer than 10 percent of these substances have been catalogued in a manner that might provide the basis for determining their effects on man and his environment.[6]

For instance, do pesticides cause cancer? Rutgers University reported in 1968 that certain azo (nitrogen) compounds are formed as the result of microbial action in soil treated with pesticide. It has been proved that some azo compounds cause cancer in experimental animals; other compounds are suspect.[7]

Are there significant amounts of pesticides still in our food when we eat it?

Researchers from Washington and California state that commercial and home washing methods cannot remove parathion residues from vegetables; in fact, home methods of preparation may increase the level of residues.[8]

Can natural foods cause cancer? Increasing evidence that the cycad plant causes malignancy is being gathered. How many other plants that we eat may also cause cancer?[9]

What are the effects on the heart of nitrates and nitrites that we ingest with our food and water? Scores of deaths that have been proved to be from these chemicals are mentioned in the scientific literature; yet we continue to allow the deliberate addition of such substrates to food for babies.[10]

Questions about the effects on our health of what we eat and drink are almost endless. No one knows—and there are no figures available on—the true incidence of food poisoning in the United States because so many incidents are unreported or because deaths from food poisoning have been wrongfully attributed to other causes. Scientists at the National Center for Urban and Industrial Health, Cincinnati, Ohio, point out that more than half of the two hundred outbreaks of food poisoning reported annually in this country are caused by organisms that are not—but often could be—identified.[11]

Bernard Aserkoff, M.D., Chief of Salmonellosis Unit, National Communicable Disease Center, Department of Health, Education, and Welfare, Atlanta, Georgia, said in a letter to the author: "It is important to realize that this total [100,390] represents a small fraction of the number of cases of Salmonellosis that actually occur. Of the total cases each year, only a small percentage are ill enough to report to a physician. Of those who seek medical assistance, only a few have stool cultures taken to document the cause of their illness. We at the CDC estimate that only approximately 1 percent of all cases of Salmonellosis are ever reported. In fact, the Salmonellosis problem has been compared to an iceberg of which we can see only a small portion of the total magnitude of the problem sticking up over the surface."[12]

How well are our government agencies protecting us from harmful food or food of poor quality?

The Task Force on Environmental Health summed it up for the Secretary of Health:

"The Task Force finds that many products available on the consumer market, including food and household equipment and appliances, are processed or manufactured in ways that render them hazardous to human beings under normal use, and that at present there is no adequate means of protecting the consumer from such products.

"In 1965, a total of 711 firms suspected of producing harmful or contaminated consumer products refused to let the FDA conduct inspections. Some 515 refused to furnish quality or quantity formulas to the Administration; 26 denied the Administration the opportunity to observe a manufacturing procedure and 153 refused FDA personnel permission to review control records.

"The consumer was the victim.

"Unlike most government regulatory agencies, the FDA does not have subpoena authority either to summon witnesses or to require firms to divulge pertinent records. It has requested this investigative authority to allow it to do a better job of protecting the American public. To this date, the request has been denied [by Congress].

"With respect to foods, the Department must have considerably more authority to assure adequate protection of the public health. The Department must be able to evaluate the synergistic effects of food additives so that the consumer is protected from threats that cannot be detected by the separate analysis of the individual food additives. This means evaluating the sum total of the toxicological effects of a mixture.

"Furthermore, the Department must have, as it does not now, adequate authority to inspect and evaluate the processing of foods to make certain that their safety is not impaired through the effects of a process which may or may not involve the use of additives."[13]

In my tours of food-processing, handling, and retailing establishments, I learned that federal and local inspectors first sign in with the management. A health officer explained to me: "We do it out of courtesy. Most people have nothing to hide and if they do, they can do it so well, the notification of our presence wouldn't make one bit of difference."

The shortage of qualified personnel for the purpose of food protection, ranging from physicians to local inspectors, is acute. For instance, the FDA is desperately in need of "qualified specialists to review and evaluate scientific and clinical data." Unfortunately, our government is offering these physicians $17,953, when such persons could make from $20,000 to $100,000 in private practice or industry.

Some states have more positions open for sanitarians than they have positions filled. Again, pay is a factor. An Ohio city with a population of 80,000 advertised for a Category III sanitarian at a salary from $6,000 to $8,436. The requirements included a college degree, courses in sanitary and/or biological sciences, and experience in food-service vending, food establishments, and general sanitation.

A study of the characteristics of state food and drug employees showed that many have less than a high school education and that 41 percent of the state milk and dairy supervisors, 71 percent of food-inspection supervisors, and 84 percent of weights-and-measures supervisors have no degrees.[14]

This does not mean that they are not better at their jobs or sharper than many young college graduates with advanced degrees. However, inspectors without training in microbiological and chemical hazards, and who have inadequate salaries and are political appointees, are prime targets for corruption.

Just how prevalent corruption can be was demonstrated in New York when twenty-one milk firms, including most of the major milk distributors and suppliers in the metropolitan area, were indicted in 1968 for paying off sanitarians. One of the accused supervising sanitarians charged with graft had been on the job for more than forty years; another, for more than twenty-five.[15]

In *Public Health Hazards of Microbiological Contamination of Foods,* a report of the National Academy of Sciences and the National Research Council, it was pointed out:

"The food industries are highly competitive and tend to be concerned primarily with consumer acceptance of new products on the basis of appearance, flavor, texture and convenience. Their research and quality-control programs often do not delve deeply enough into the microbiological problems of food safety. For example, the incorporation of contaminated egg products into dry cake mixes and the packaging of nonsterile products under pressure or in a vacuum may permit the multiplication of, and toxin production by, food-poisoning organisms such as *Clostridium botulinum* or *Staphylococcus aureus*.

"Government agencies have also been hard pressed to keep abreast of new developments because the resources for food protection programs have not kept pace with the rates of technological change or population growth. Their programs are largely based on visual inspection for gross defects in products, facilities and procedures where food is processed, stored or prepared for serving. These techniques are not adequate to cope with centralized manufacturing, mass distribution, mechanical dispensing and commercial catering of prepared products."[16]

Dr. Walter Modell, Professor of Pharmacology at Cornell Medical College, recommended in 1968 that the FDA be separated from the Health, Education, and Welfare Department, where it "suffers from exasperations, insecurities, anxieties and the oscillations of department whims, and set up as an independent commission, responsible directly to the President."

"The job of the FDA is complicated by crucial overlapping of functions with the Department of Agriculture. Thus, the FDA does not deal with pesticides and herbicides and other toxic materials that contaminate food, apparently because Agriculture can force the issue as it chooses. The FDA, therefore, has ruled that this very toxic group of drugs are not drugs.

"The FDA lacks prestige and has such a modest salary ladder it has great difficulty attracting promising, well-trained junior members, especially physicians."[17]

Dr. William C. Grater, head of the Drug Committee of the American Academy of Allergy, believes the American public has been badly served by the FDA, Congress, medical experts, and food processors. Sometimes, he said, the FDA has approved chemical agents despite inadequate testing, only later to withdraw them "on the basis of new studies." Some of the pressure has come from other countries. (Oil of calamus, used for years in fruit, chocolate, root beer, vanilla, and so on, was withdrawn in 1968 because it was found to cause malignant tumors in animals. NGDA, used in shortening and other such products, was removed from the "generally safe" list after Canada banned its use there.)[18]

"And there are no ways for the consumer to know what has been added, Dr. Grater said. "The law requires only that labels say artificial coloring, flavoring or preservative added. The label does not have to list them. If a person is sensitive to those things, there is no way for him to know what not to eat.

"I think the less chemicals you put in a person's environment, the better off he is, whether he eats them or breathes them or soaks in them," Dr. Grater concluded.[19]

Though Dr. James Goddard, when he was FDA commissioner, concentrated on increasing the margin of safety in drugs, he admitted that food additives did not even receive the testing that drugs did. He said that FDA laboratories did thirty-seven thousand assays a year but that, in order to do adequate testing on the important drugs alone, they should do a million individual analyses a year.[20] He also admitted that the FDA could not adequately inspect the eight thousand drug plants in America. What about the hundreds of thousands of food and cosmetic plants?

The man who replaced Dr. Goddard, Dr. Herbert L. Ley, Jr., believes, as does Wilbur J. Cohen, Secretary of Health, Education, and Welfare, that the FDA's "policeman posture" is outmoded and should give way to a system of education and cooperation that relies more on state authority and industrial self-regulation.[21]

However, the man that preceded Dr. Goddard and Dr. Ley, George P. Larrick, in a speech before the National Association of Frozen Food Packers in Chicago, in March, 1964, said, "The extent to which some in industry adopt control methods is influenced by the attention given to the problem by federal, state and local officials."[22]

Although they are rare, there are criminals in the food business, from the shady buyers of contaminated foodstuff to truck hijackers to strong-arm vending-machine providers, and we are not being adequately protected from them.

Representative Benjamin Rosenthal, subcommittee chairman of the House Government Operations Committee, in a public hearing in March, 1968, offered proof that coffee, canned hams, and pre-cooked frozen dinners that the Army Supply Agency had classified as unfit for human consumption were being sold in supermarkets.[23] He did not learn this fact from an inspector but from one of his constituents who had noted a label on a can of coffee that said "procured under U.S. Government Specification and for Military Issue and Sale to Authorized Commissary Patrons Only." Laboratory tests showed that the coffee contained "a harsh type of coffee not permitted by specification, and some coffee contained dust particles."

Consumer Reports, in its August, 1968, issue, reported on tests of fresh pork sausages:

"Whether the sausage came from a Federally inspected packing plant or from the unchaperoned meat grinder of a local butcher, it was often sour or rancid and frequently contained an overabundance of bacteria. Some of it was contaminated with filth. Not one sample of 177 packages tested for quality and flavor could be judged really outstanding and only one national brand-name product was rated as high as good."[24]

But, according to Weems Clevenger, District Director of the Federal Food and Drug Administration, New York, imports form one of the weakest links in the chain of food protection. Of the $27 billion total of annual United States imports, nearly a sixth—more than $4 billion—is accounted for by foods, drugs, and cosmetics. The FDA is responsible for the same safety; wholesomeness, and purity of these imports as it is for domestic products.[25]

Unlabeled canned goods and canned goods without English labels are referred by Customs to FDA inspectors. In one case, a Customs inspector became suspicious of activities in an enclosure at the far end of a pier, and reported them to an FDA inspector. Investigation disclosed that floor sweepings of coffee beans were being picked up there and packed for sale. The sweepings were contaminated by assorted filth from the dock.

According to the *FDA Papers* of April, 1968, of vital concern to Customs officials and the FDA are the relatively new Customs Bureau procedures known as "Immediate Delivery," under which an importer can receive his shipment immediately upon arrival, and file the customs form within six days thereafter. The procedure is used at airports, seaports, and border ports, and is a boon to international traders, especially dealers in perishable commodities. But, without some means by which Customs can let FDA know about questionable merchandise, dubious goods may be in the hands of importers before FDA receives the necessary information.[26]

Mr. Weems Clevenger, New York District Director, said that FDA receives a list of imports, and selects the items to check. But he admitted that the FDA does not have sufficient manpower to do more than spot-check something its inspectors may think is hazardous. He recalled one questionable item, cheese with bits of salmon and bacon added. "When we asked the country of origin what inspection the cheese had received there," he related, "they replied that they smelled the cheese, and if it smelled all right, they passed it."

The rapid increase in containerization—the practice of shipping huge packages with many different items in each—is another new headache for food inspectors. For instance, when such containers arrive in the United States, should they be opened at the port of first arrival or be shipped to the inland point near the ultimate destination?

If this book raises many questions, it also presents some obvious answers. I asked Mr. Clevenger what he would do if he had unlimited power to improve the safety of our food supply:

"I would like to see more involvement of top management in industry," he said. "They spend more time dealing with money and promotion campaigns. We have been calling top executive officers of each drug firm now under intensified investigation, and laying out the whole sordid record before them.

"What happens in a food or drug plant is that an inspector goes in and gives the report to the plant manager. The plant manager doesn't want to be the bearer of bad tidings, especially when the boss holds him responsible. Many top executives do not know what is going on in their own plants."

From government experts like Mr. Clevenger, and from university scientists, physicians, and other concerned with what we eat, here are recommendations for steps that should and could be taken without delay:

INCREASED KNOWLEDGE ABOUT FOOD

We need research programs to produce new basic knowledge about both natural and processed foods in relation to health. This should include, but not be limited to, the study of new production, processing, and marketing methods as they may affect the public health.

We need more food science departments in institutions of higher learning in the nation. There are at present only about forty, and many of them are understaffed and underfinanced.

Physicians need to study nutrition, both in medical school and afterward. Although it has recently been reported that heredity probably plays a part in how an individual reacts to food, medical schools present very little in the way of nutritional studies. Food illnesses and allergies are poorly diagnosed. According to Dr. George Briggs of the Department of Nutritional Science at the University of California, most nutrition studies are "quite worthless because of inadequate experimental design in regards to diet composition and control groups."

IMPROVEMENT IN THE DETECTION, INVESTIGATION, AND REPORTING OF FOODBORNE ILLNESSES

There is a great need for more efficient techniques for finding, evaluating, and recording suspected foodborne illnesses. According to a report of the National Academy of Sciences and National Research Council, about two-fifths of the states typically report no outbreaks, and an additional two-fifths reports only one or two each year. Physicians do not see many of the persons involved in food-poisoning outbreaks, and the cases of those observed are apt to be diagnosed symptomatically as diarrhea, intestinal flu, or some equally vague condition. Public as well as private organizations are understandably reluctant to admit possible involvement in outbreaks of foodborne illnesses because they fear unfavorable publicity, legal action, or financial loss. They view investigations by health agencies as interference with internal operations rather than as practical efforts to help prevent future outbreaks.

Physicians, institutions, restaurants, and all food-handling establishments should be required by law to report suspected outbreaks.

Public health laboratories should have the personnel and equipment to detect specific organisms causing foodborne illness.

PESTICIDES

A reevaluation of the entire use of pesticides should be undertaken, and the use of hydrocarbons such as DDT should be outlawed.

Pesticides should be colored for identification, and laws should be created to govern their packaging and shipment.

Nonchemical methods of pest control should be encouraged by means of greater financial support.

CHEMICALS

Nitrites, which are salts or esters of nitrous acid, should be banned from all products immediately. Production of baby foods containing them should be forbidden.

Immediate efforts should be made to survey the true amount of nitrates, which are salts or esters of nitric acid, in our water and food, and immediate steps should be taken to reduce such residues.

There is no doubt that nitrates and nitrites are harmful, as the pitiful sight of the graves of tiny children across the country will attest.[27]

Vitamin D should be restricted and its dangers publicized.

All chemicals additives should be restudied by objective scientists —and that includes chemicals approved under the "grandfather clause." Just because something harmful may have been used by our ancestors is no reason it should poison us or our descendants.

All chemicals additives in food should be listed by name on the label.

CHEMICALS AND ANIMALS

The use of antibiotics and hormones in feed should be re-evaluated. Chances are, such practices should be abolished. Some control over the administration of medications to ill animals should be established. Since farmers are not trained in veterinary medicine, diagnosis and therapy should be left to veterinarians.

FROZEN FOODS

A complete survey of frozen foods, from the time of slaughter or harvesting to its preparation, packaging, sale, cooking, and appearance on the dining-room table, should be made.

No truck should be permitted to transport frozen food without adequate refrigeration and a graph to determine temperature control from the time of pickup to the time of delivery.

New safeguard devices, such as the strip of tape that shows whether a package has been defrosted, should be developed and used.

BETTER USE OF MANPOWER

There should be a coordinated inspection of food from growth and harvesting to the manner in which it is recommended that it be cooked. Overlapping and gaps in the use of manpower should be abolished.

Pay scales should be raised, and an effective, concerted effort should be made to interest young people in food-protection services.

FISH

Fish should be inspected under the law, and stricter standards should be made and enforced.

The American shipping industry should be revitalized by private and government subsidies for new equipment and by restrictions on imports.

SOME OBSERVATIONS

Our growing methods are not as efficient as those of the Japanese. If they were, California could feed the nation.

Our trucking is not as adequate as Britain's, where temperature graphs are required by law.

Our regulations governing pesticides are not as strict as Germany's.

Our food doesn't taste as good as French food does.

The food we eat on earth is not as safe as the food we provide for our astronauts, where upsetting the delicate balance between man and microbes could cause disaster.

But our supply is wondrous in its abundance and variety. Our sanitation is above that of countries where diarrhea kills off a large percentage of the child population.

For all-around quality, the American food supply is the best in the world—but it could be much better—and safer!

10 NOTES

1. *A Strategy for a Livable Environment,* a report to the Secretary of Health, Education, and Welfare by the Task Force on Environmental Health and Related Problems, June, 1967.

2. Paul LaChance, Ph.D., Associate Professor of Nutritional Physiology, Rutgers University.
3. United States Department of Health, Education, and Welfare, news release, July 31, 1965.
4. News from the National Institutes of Health, August 1, 1968; University of Wisconsin news release, June 12, 1968.
5. *A Strategy for a Livable Environment, loc. cit.*
6. *Ibid.*
7. News from the National Institutes of Health, June 15, 1968.
8. Richard Farrow, Frank Lamb, Edgar Elkins, Russel Cook, Margaret Kawai, Antoni Cortes, "Effect of Commercial and Home Preparative Procedures on Parathion and Carbaryl Residues in Broccoli," American Chemical Society Meeting, San Francisco, April 1–5, 1968.
9. National Institutes of Health *Record,* July 10, 1968.
10. Richard L. Woodward, Ph.D., Boston, in *Journal of the American Medical Association,* July 1, 1968, Vol. 205, No. 1. *See also* J. D. Orgeron, M.P.H.; J. D. Martin, M.D.; C. T. Caraway, D.V.M.; Rosemary Martine, B.S.; George Hauser, M.D., *Public Health Reports,* March, 1957, Vol. 72.
11. Herbert E. Hall, Ph.D.; Keith Lewis, Ph.D., in October, 1967, issue of *Health Laboratory Science,* American Public Health Association.
12. Correspondence with author, July 18, 1968.
13. *A Strategy for a Livable Environment, loc. cit.*
14. *A Study of State and Local Food and Drug Programs,* report to the Commissioner of the Food and Drug Administration, U.S. Department of Health, Education, and Welfare, 1965.
15. *New York Times,* January 27, 1968.
16. *An Evaluation of Public Health Hazards from Microbiological Contamination of Foods,* a report of the Food Protection Committee of the Food and Nutrition Board, National Academy of Sciences and National Research Council, Publication 1195, 1964.
17. *Medical Tribune,* March 21, 1968.
18. Correspondence with FDA, June 5, 1968.
19. Health Bulletin, March 9, 1968: correspondence with author, June 10, 1968.
20. James Goddard, M.D., Commissioner of the Food and Drug Administration, March and April speeches, 1967.
21. *Medical Tribune,* July 25, 1968.
22. George Larrick, Commissioner of the Food and Drug Administration, speech before the National Association of Frozen Food Packers, Chicago, March 20, 1964.
23. John Morris, *New York Times,* March 31, 1968.
24. *Consumer Reports,* August, 1968.
25. Weems Clevenger, District Director, FDA, New York, tape-recorded interview with author, July, 1968.
26. *FDA Papers,* April, 1968.

27. Richard L. Woodward, Ph.D., Boston, in the *Journal of the American Medical Association,* July 1, 1968, Vol. 205, No. 1. Donald E. Crane, Malco Chemical Co., American Society of Agricultural Engineering, Athens, Ga., 1965. J. D. Orgeron *et al.,* "Methemoglobinemia from Eating Meat with High Nitrite Content," *Public Health Reports,* March, 1957.

11

Home Fires and Freezers

No MATTER HOW WELL OUR food is grown, manufactured, inspected, warehoused, and retailed, if we don't handle and prepare it properly ourselves in our homes, we and those we love will suffer from food-borne illnesses.

Based on the advice of experts in all fields, here are methods for protecting the food you buy:

• Do your grocery shopping last, and head immediately for home.

• Always wash your hands before preparing food and after touching meat, and before touching produce that will not be cooked.

• Don't allow anyone with an infection, including yourself, to prepare food.

• Purchase—and use—an accurate thermometer in your refrigerator.

• Keep the inside of the refrigerator clean. Wash it at frequent intervals.

• Keep the areas around the motor and refrigerating unit clean. Lint and dirt on these parts cut off the supply of air, causing the motor and the refrigeration unit to overwork, thus reducing their efficiency.

• Check the gaskets around the doors. Be sure that they are flexible, and prevent the cold air from escaping.

• If your refrigerator is not self-defrosting, check the cooling area frequently, and defrost it. A buildup of ice on the cooling coils acts as an insulator, and the refrigerator will not work so well as it should. When the ice builds up to a fourth of an inch, it is time to defrost.

• Store foods in small, shallow containers. The more surface that is exposed to the cold, the faster the food will cool. Keep foods covered so that the food particles from the shelf above will not fall into the food stored below. Allow space between food containers and between all foods and the walls of the box.

• Never cover the wire shelves of the box with paper or foil, as this cuts down on the circulation of air within the refrigerator. Never stack foods on top of each other.

• Because bacteria grow between 45 F. and 120 F., refrigerate food immediately after it is cooked. This means all foods, including roasts, stews, leftovers, broths, puddings and so on. Any delay will allow bacteria to grow more rapidly.

• If much hot food must be refrigerated, precool it first. Place the food in a shallow pan, and set it in cold water. Be careful, of course, not to let the water mix with the food. Unless the cooling unit is overloaded, it is perfectly safe to put hot things in today's modern refrigerator.

• Keep hot things hot. Use a meat thermometer to check pork and other meats. In general, foods should be kept hot at a temperature above 140 degrees F.

• If you have been delayed in getting newly purchased food home to your refrigerator by a traffic jam or some other incident, be sure that temperatures reach 165 to 170 degrees in the center of the food that is being cooked.

• Keep eggs in the refrigerator.

• Store bread, in its original wrapper, in a breadbox or refrigerator. Bread keeps its freshness longer at room temperature, but in hot, humid weather, it is better protected against mold in the refrigerator.

• Store flours, cereals, spices, and other grains at room temperature in tightly closed containers that keep out dust, moisture, and insects. During the summer, buy such foodstuffs in small quantities only.

• Store butter, fat drippings, and margarine in tightly wrapped or covered containers in the refrigerator. These products should be used within two weeks. Don't let them stand for long periods at room temperature.

• Keep all homemade salad dressing in the refrigerator. Purchased mayonnaise and other ready-made salad dressings should be refrigerated unless used within a few days.

• Cold cuts should be stored in the refrigerator and used within three to five days.

• Store ham, frankfurters, bacon, bologna, and smoked sausage in the refrigerator in their original packaging. Uncooked cured pork may be stored longer than fresh pork, but the fat will become rancid if it is held too long. Bacon should be eaten within a week for best quality, a half a ham in three to five days, a whole ham within a week. Ham slices should be wrapped tightly and used within a few days.

• Ground meats, such as hamburger and fresh bulk sausage, are more likely to spoil than roasts, chops, or steaks because they have been exposed to contamination from air, food handlers, and mechanical equipment. Store them loosely wrapped in the coldest part of the refrigerator, and use them within one or two days.

• Although some food scientists say you can keep leftover stuffing from cooked fowl separate from the bird in the refrigerator for one or two days, it is best to throw it out.

• Fresh milk and cream should be stored in the refrigerator at about 40 degrees F. Milk and cream are best stored only three to five days. Keep them covered so they won't absorb odors and flavors from other foods.

Keep dry milk in a tightly closed container, and reconstituted dry milk in the refrigerator.

• Keep hard cheese in the refrigerator. Wrap it tightly to keep out air, and trim away any mold that forms on the surface of the cheese before use.

• Store soft cheeses in tightly covered containers in the coldest part of the refrigerator. Use cottage cheese within three to five days, and others within two weeks.

• Keep synthetic custards, milks, and puddings in the refrigerator.

• With few exceptions—such as potatoes, dry onions, hard-rind squashes, and eggplants—keep vegetables in the refrigerator.

Discard any vegetables that are bruised or soft or that show evidence of decay or worm injury.

• Wash all fruits and vegetables before eating them.

• Store honey and syrups at room temperature until opened. After their containers have been opened, honey and syrups are better protected from mold in the refrigerator.

• Store nuts in airtight containers in the refrigerator. Because of their high fat content, nuts require refrigeration to delay rancidity.

• After a jar of peanut butter has been opened, it should be refrigerated.

• When freezing food, package it so no moisture can enter. Containers should be leakproof.

• Records should be kept so that you know what foods are on hand and what foods need replenishing in the freezer. This will keep you from storing food too long.

• If a power failure develops in your freezer, or if the source of power is temporarily shut down, keep your freezer closed to retain the low temperature. Frozen foods in a fully loaded freezer will often stay frozen for as long as two days—in a half-filled freezer for about a day.

• Thawed fruits can be safely refrozen if they taste and smell good.

• Other foods that have thawed spoil more quickly. Special care is necessary in handling vegetables, shellfish, and cooked foods that have thawed or partially thawed.

• Once a food has been thawed, it is wise to use it as soon as possible, and not to refreeze it.

• Do keep frozen foods, especially poultry, in the refrigerator during thawing. If you have to speed up the defrosting of a turkey, place it under running cold water. Roasts, including turkeys, may go into the oven frozen; just increase the roasting time.

• Do keep meringues, custard-filled eclairs, synthetic custards, doughnuts, and pastries in the refrigerator. Take them out just in time to serve.

• Do chill main-dish salads for large groups in shallow bowls or on trays in the refrigerator, and keep an eye on their temperature during the meal.

• Do keep sandwiches or sandwich fillings in the refrigerator until served. Covering sandwiches with a damp cloth is not recommended, since bacteria grow especially well under such circumstances. In fact, sandwiches should not be made the night before. Cooked meat next to damp bread makes an excellent breeding place for bacteria.

• Do keep a separate pan for washing dishes. Dishwater should be 130 degrees F. or above. Be sure that the rinse water is clean and hot and that the towels are clean.

• Don't empty the turtle's bowl or clean the dog's dish in the same sink you use for washing dishes and preparing the family's food. The turtle's bowl is full of his waste, and your pet's dish may well be contaminated with harmful bacteria. In fact, avoid allowing pets in areas where food is being prepared.

• Don't use or buy canned foods if any of the following signs are present: bulging of the top or bottom of the can, dents along the side seams, or any sign of seepage, off-odor, or foaming when the can is opened; any unusual milky quality of liquid.

• Don't buy or eat salads, especially mayonnaise-base salads, that have not been or are not refrigerated.

• Don't use leftover food if discoloration, off-odor, or mold is apparent. Any food that has not been refrigerated below 45 degrees may be considered to be slightly spoiled. Recook any leftover food that has been kept in the refrigerator thirty-six hours or longer.

The cardinal rule of food safety at home is: When in doubt, throw it out!

Remember that we consumers have the weakest lobby in Washington. Our own education is our strongest safeguard against poisons in our food.

Appendix I

PAPAIN IS A MEAT TENDERIZER commonly used in homes and restaurants. An enzyme, it causes basic changes to occur in the rabbit's body when it is injected, according to researchers of The National Institutes of Health, U.S. Department of Health, Education, and Welfare. These changes result in the progressive collapse of a rabbit's normally erect ears.

Ordinarily, cartilage restoration takes place rapidly, and the ears stand up straight in three to five days. It was discovered, however, that the ears would remain collapsed—indicating interference with cartilage recovery—if daily injections of steroid drugs were given. The reason Federal authorities have not been alarmed over papain's effect on cartilage is that the papain is deactivated by heat used in cooking.

However, should the papain be put on steak tartar—uncooked meat—which is eaten raw or for some other reason not deactivated, the possibility of damage to the human body—especially in arthritics and asthmatics who take steroids—is not remote.

Dr. James W. Holsinger, Jr., Dr. Robert L. Fuson, and Dr. Will C. Sealy, all of the Division of Thoracic Surgery, Duke University Medical Center, described a death resulting from papain ingestion in the May 20, 1968, *Journal of the American Medical Association,* in an article entitled "Esophageal Perforation Following Meat Impaction and Papain Ingestion":

Papain has been given to people who have meat impactions in their esophagus (food pipe) after improperly chewing or bolting their food. In the case described, the meat, after being in place for a long time, caused necrosis or injury to the tissue of the esophageal wall. According to the physicians, the papain given to the patient "digested this area."

"Perhaps the products of protein digestion caused other areas of necrosis which in turn were digested by the papain," the doctors reasoned.

Earlier, experimental studies on fourteen dogs showed every animal receiving papain had some degree of damage to the esophageal wall, with reddening and thickening of the mucosal wall at the site of the lodged bolus. Advanced hemorrhagic pulmonary edema was found to be the cause of death in these animals.

The thirty-nine-year-old patient described by Dr. Holsinger and his group died of hemorrhaging. It was the second case reported in recent years of death after ingestion of papain, and thus raises the question of what effect papain may have on necrotic tissue in the mouth, throat, or stomach.

The experiments with the rabbits raise the question of the effect of papain when steroids are present either in the food eaten or in the person taking them therapeutically.

Photos courtesy of National Institutes of Health, Public Health Service, U.S. Department of Health, Education, and Welfare

Appendix II

TABLE I

FOOD CHEMICALS IN ALLERGY*

CLASSIFICATION OF INTENTIONAL ADDITIVES

1. Preservatives	33	8. Food Colors	34
2. Antioxidants Chelating Agents Metal Scavengers	28	9. Non-Nutritive and Special Dietary Sweeteners	4
3. Sequestrants Emulsifiers Stabilizing Agents	45	10. Nutritive Supplement	117
4. Surface Active Agents	111	11. Flavorings—Synthetic	1,610
5. Stabilizers, Thickeners	39	12. Flavorings—Natural	502
6. Bleaching and Maturing Agents	24	13. Miscellaneous Binders	Yeast Foods Firming Agent Texturizers 157 Anti-caking Agents Enzymes
7. Buffers, Acids, Alkalies	60		

Total Number of Additives 2,764

* From a lecture entitled "The Recognition of Food Additives as a Cause of Symptoms of Allergy," delivered by Dr. Ben F. Feingold, San Francisco, California, during the 24th Annual Congress, Scientific Program, American College of Allergists, Grand Ball Room, Denver Hilton Hotel, Denver, Colorado, Wednesday, March 27, 1968. Reprinted by permission of the author.

TABLE II

State Agencies Administering Consumer Food Protection Activities*

Interest code—other agency:

(1) Fluid milk.   (6) Poultry.
(2) Dairy products.   (7) Eggs.
(3) Meat.   (8) Fruits and vegetables.
(4) Fish.   (9) Other foods.
(5) Shellfish.   (10) Eating and drinking places.

Foods and associated processing and distribution

State	Principal agency	Other agency	Interests of other agency
Alabama	Agriculture	Health	1, 3, 10
Alaska	Health	Agriculture	3, 8
Arizona	Health	Dairy Commission	2
		Livestock Sanitary Board	2, 3
		Agriculture and Horticulture Commission.	8
		Egg Inspector	7
Arkansas	Health	Plant Board	8
California	Health	Agriculture	1, 2, 3, 6, 7, 8, 9
Colorado	Health	Agriculture	2, 6, 7, 8, 9
Connecticut	Consumer Protection.	Agriculture	1, 8, 9
		Health	5
Delaware	Health	Agriculture	2, 6, 7, 8, 9
Florida	Agriculture	Health	1, 5, 10
		Hotel and Restaurant Commission.	10
Georgia	Agriculture	Health	1, 5, 10
Hawaii	Health	Agriculture	3, 6, 8
Idaho	Health	Agriculture	1, 2, 3, 6, 7, 8, 9
Illinois	Agriculture	Health	1, 10
Indiana	Health	University	6, 7, 8
Iowa	Agriculture	Health	(†)
Kansas	Health	Agriculture	2, 7, 8
		Health and Restaurant Board.	9, 10
Kentucky	Health	Agriculture	7
Louisiana	Health	Agriculture	6, 8, 9
Maine	Agriculture	Health	10
		Sea and Shore Fisheries	5
Maryland	Health	Agriculture	2, 7
Massachusetts	Health	Agriculture	1, 6, 7, 8
Michigan	Agriculture	Health	1

	Foods and associated processing and distribution		
State	Principal agency	Other agency	Interests of other agency
Minnesota	Agriculture	Health	10
Mississippi	Health	Agriculture	2, 3, 7, 8
Missouri	Health	Agriculture	2, 7, 9
Montana	Health	Livestock Sanitary Board	2, 6
		Agriculture	2, 3, 7, 8, 9
Nebraska	Agriculture	Health	(†)
Nevada	Health	Agriculture	7, 9
New Hampshire	Health	Agriculture	6, 7, 8, 9
New Jersey	Health	Agriculture	6, 7, 8
New Mexico	Health	Agriculture	1, 7, 8, 9
New York	Agriculture	Health	1, 10
North Carolina	Agriculture	Health	10
North Dakota	Laboratories Commission.	Agriculture	1, 2, 9
		Health	1, 9, 10
		Livestock Sanitary Board	3
Ohio	Agriculture	Health	10
Oklahoma	Health	Agriculture	2, 3, 7, 9
Oregon	Agriculture	Health	10
Pennsylvania	Agriculture	Health	10
Rhode Island	Health	Agriculture	7, 8
South Carolina	Agriculture	Health	2, 9, 10
South Dakota	Agriculture	Health	10
Tennessee	Agriculture	Health, Conservation, and Commerce.	10
Texas	Health	Agriculture	8
Utah	Agriculture	Health	10
Vermont	Health	Agriculture	1, 7, 8, 9
Virginia	Agriculture	Health	1, 2, 4, 5, 10
Washington	Agriculture	Health	1, 4, 5, 10
West Virginia	Agriculture	Health	1, 9, 10
Wisconsin	Agriculture	Health	1, 10
Wyoming	Agriculture	Health	10

* "Protecting Our Food," in *The Yearbook of Agriculture,* U.S. Government Printing Office, 1966.

† No information available on specific interests.

TABLE III

ACCOMMODATIONS AND KEY EQUIPMENT IN STATE FOOD AND DRUG LABORATORIES*
(1964)

Key to Other Equipment Items:

A. Electrophoresis	D. Polarograph	G. Autoclave	J. Analytical balance
B. Cryoscope	E. Sacharimeter or polarimeter	H. Centrifuge	K. Thin layer chromatography
C. Flame Photometer	F. Refractometer	I. Kjeldahl	

State	Agency	Laboratory	(1) Food and Drug Work Load as Percentage of Total	(2) Total Floor Space (Sq.Ft.)	(3) Bench Space (Sq.Ft.)	(4) Bench Space Per Analyst (Sq.Ft.)	(5) Percentage Air-conditioned	(6) Microscopes (No.)	(7) Spectrophotometers and Allied Equipment[a] (No.)	(8) Gas Chromatographs (No.)	(9) Other Key Items
Alabama	Agriculture	Food and drug	80	7,730	—	—	100	b	2	0	—
	Health	c	—	—	—	—	—	b	—	—	H
Alaska	Not obtained	—									
Arizona	Health	Laboratory	20	10,000	—	—	100	18	6	1	H
	Agriculture	State chemist	65	5,400	750	125	100	—	2	—	H,I
Arkansas	State Plant Board	Chemical Laboratories	—	—	—	—	100	2	4	0	H,I,J
	Health	—	—	—	—	—	100	6	3	—	B,D,G,H,J
California	Health	Food and drug	95	4,250	480	40	100	6	10	8	H
	Agriculture	—	100	—	360	—	100	4	4	0	G,H
Colorado	Health	Food	100	1,500	—	—	100	2	3	2	B
		Standards	75	—	—	—	0	2	4	3	A,H,I
	Agriculture	Dairy	100	675	—	—	100	2	0	0	H

230

State	Agency	Laboratory	(1)	(2)	(3)	(4)	(5)	(6)	(7)	(8)	(9)
Connecticut	Agriculture Experiment Station	Analytical chemistry	90	2,700	790	—	0	3	4	1	E,F,G,H,I
	Health	Sanitary Microbiology	60	800	200	50	0				—
		Dairy chemistry	100	900	240	80	0				
		Chemistry and physics	10	2,400	560	80	0	b	5	2	B,D,G,H,I
		Radiology	60	400	240	80	0				—
		Research microbiology	20	760	200	50	0	b			
Delaware	Agriculture	Feed, dairy, other	—	1,535	300	60	75	3	1	0	H,I,J
Florida	Agriculture	Pesticide residues	100	4,630	200	20	100	0	5	6	H,K
		Pesticides	100	1,595	240	60	100	0	2	0	H
		Food	100	—	—	—	—	3	2	1	F,G,J
		Feeds	100	1,800	360	60	100	1	1	0	G,J
Georgia	Agriculture	Food	100	1,105	160	40	100	4	0	0	G
		Dairy	100	1,535	310	103	100	0	1	0	B,G,H,J
		Economic poisons	100	1,865	510	254	100	0	1	0	—
		Feeds	100	3,365	835	93	50	2	4	0	F,H,I,J
		Pesticide residues	100	1,565	430	108	100	0	0	1	H,K
	Health	Central	10	1,795	425	70	100	2	1	0	B,G,H
		Macon branch	10	385	125	62	100				B,H
		Waycross branch	10	385	125	62	100				G,H
		Albany branch	10	190	100	50	100				G,H
Hawaii	Health	Microbiology and chemist.	Minor	5,590	—	—	0	b	3	0	B,G,H,I
Idaho	Health	Central	20	2,800	300	—	100	4	2	1	B,E,G,H
	Agriculture	Dairy products	100	—	—	—	—	2	1	0	G,H
Illinois	Agriculture	Food and dairies	100	—	—	—	0	3	1		G
Indiana	Health	Food, drug, and dairy	100	2,895	623	56	100	16	3	1	A
Iowa	Agriculture	State chemist	75	—	—	—	0	3	3	1	F,I,J
		Bacteriology	100	—	—	—	0	b			B
Kansas	Health	Chemistry	—	—	—	—	100	3	4	0	H
	Agriculture		—	—	—	—	100	2	3	0	B,D,H,J

Key to Other Equipment Items:

A. Electrophoresis
B. Cryoscope
C. Flame Photometer
D. Polarograph
E. Sacharimeter or polarimeter
F. Refractometer
G. Autoclave
H. Centrifuge
I. Kjeldahl
J. Analytical balance
K. Thin layer chromatography

State	Agency	Laboratory	(1)	(2)	(3)	(4)	(5)	(6)	(7)	(8)	(9)
Kentucky	Health	Chemistry	—	—	—	—	100	1	4	2	D,H,J,K
	University of Kentucky	Feed and fertilizer	—	—	—	—	100	—	4	1	D,H,I,J
Louisiana	Agriculture	Chemistry	—	1,230	—	—	100	—	5	1	—
	Health	Food and drug	—	—	—	—	—	—	4	1	—
Maine	University of Maine	Biochemistry	65	3,620	950	25	0	3	—	0	F,G,H,I
Maryland	University of Maryland	Feed and pesticide	—	3,750	470	47	14	2	7	1	G,H,I,J
	Health	Central	—	—	—	—	—	2	6	0	—
Massachusetts	University of Massachusetts	Feed and fertilizer Amherst	100	3,760	610	476	50	2	6	1	G,H,J
	Health	Food and drug	90	1,700	460	51	0	2	2	1	F,G,H,I
Michigan	Agriculture	Laboratory division	90	9,415	2,195	105	95	22	8	1	B,F,G,H,I,J,K
Minnesota	Agriculture	Feed laboratory	—	—	—	—	0	2	2	—	H,J
		Chemistry	—	—	—	—	0	1	1	—	F,H
		Bacteriology and canning	—	—	—	—	0	4	1	—	—
Mississippi	Agriculture	Chemistry	—	—	—	—	—	—	8	2	D
Missouri	Agriculture	Feed	—	—	—	—	—	1	1	0	F,H,J
	Health	Headquarters	—	—	—	—	100	23	6	0	G,H,J
		District V	—	—	—	—	100	6	1	0	G,H,J
		District IV	—	—	—	—	100	6	—	0	—
Montana	Not obtained	—	—	—	—	—	—	—	—	—	—
Nebraska	Agriculture	Dairies and food	80	—	—	—	100	1	2	1	B,G,H,I,J
	Health	Laboratory	—	—	—	—	—	3	2	1	—
Nevada	Not obtained	—	—	—	—	—	—	—	—	—	—

State	Agency	Laboratory	(1)	(2)	(3)	(4)	(5)	(6)	(7)	(8)	(9)
New Hampshire	Health	Food and chemistry	45	905	210	35	0	6	4	1	E,F,G,H,K
	Agriculture Experiment Station		—	—	—	—	0	2	2	0	I
New Jersey	Health		—	920	120	60	0	2	2	0	F,G,H,I,J
	Agriculture Experiment Station		—	1,100	160	—	—	2	4	0	—
New Mexico	Agriculture	State chemist	—	950	—	—	—	2	5	2	D,G,H,I,K
	Health		—	1,800	260	50	100	2	3	0	B,F,H,I,J
			—	10,000	—	—	100	5	1	0	H
New York	Agriculture	Food	100	8,075	635	65	100	3	3	2	G,H,I,J
	Health	Central food laboratory	—	1,800	750	90	0	3	0	0	—
North Carolina	Health	Shellfish	25	200	60	30	100	0	0	0	—
	Agriculture	Dairy	100	2,560	305	61	100	1	0	1	—
North Dakota	State laboratory		—	—	—	—	—	4	2	—	—
Ohio	Not obtained		—	—	—	—	—	—	—	—	—
Oklahoma	Health		50	—	—	—	Work space	6	4	1	B,G,H
	Agriculture		75	1,700	800	—	—	3	2	0	B,H,I,J
Oregon	Agriculture	Laboratories division	20	4,000	—	—	0	2	4	1	A,K
Pennsylvania	Agriculture	Food and chemistry	—	—	—	—	100	2	4	3	B,F,G,H,I,J
Rhode Island	Health	Food and drug	100	450	95	32	0	2	—	—	F,J
South Carolina	Not obtained		—	—	—	—	—	—	—	—	—
South Dakota	State Chemist		—	—	—	—	—	—	—	—	—
Tennessee	Agriculture	Food, drug, and dairy	90	2,160	900	112	100	4	3	1	B,F,I,J
Texas	Health	Chemistry	25	5,915	1,530	85	100	—	—	—	B,E,F,G,H,I,J,K
		Food and drug	100	1,340	310	104	100	9	8	2	—
		Miscellaneous	25	860	230	76	100	—	—	—	—
		Sanitary bacteriology	55	860	230	114	100	—	—	—	—
Utah	Agriculture	State chemist	75	2,250	—	—	0	4	7	3	B,G,H,I,K
Vermont	Agriculture Experiment Station	Regulatory service	—	—	—	—	0	—	1	1	—

Key to Other Equipment Items:

A. Electrophoresis
B. Cryoscope
C. Flame Photometer
D. Polarograph
E. Sacharimeter or polarimeter
F. Refractometer
G. Autoclave
H. Centrifuge
I. Kjeldahl
J. Analytical balance
K. Thin layer chromatography

State	Agency	Laboratory	(1)	(2)	(3)	(4)	(5)	(6)	(7)	(8)	(9)
Virginia	Agriculture	Feeds	95	2,000	430	48	100	6	0	0	H,I,J
		Animal remedy	100	480	130	130	100	—	1	0	J
		Antibiotics	100	—	—	—	—	—	—	—	A
		Drug	100	335	75	75	100	0	5	1	D,H,J
		Food	100	1,480	410	137	100	6	3	0	B,E,F,G,H,I,J
		Pesticide residue	100	1,920	460	57	100	0	3	4	H
	Health	Shellfish	100	225	60	60	100	1	0	0	G
		Shellfish	100	450	60	60	100	1	0	0	G,J
		Shellfish	100	225	30	15	0	2	0	0	G
Washington	University of Washington	Food and drug	100	900	280	70	0	3	4	2	B,G,H,I
	Agriculture	Animal industry	40	4,800	—	40	100	1	4	2	—
		Grain and chemistry	—	4,150	—	—	100	—	—	—	I,J
West Virginia	Agriculture	General	70	2,500	650	80	100	3	2	1	A,F,H,J
	Agriculture	Pesticide residue	100	—	—	—	—	1	—	—	H,J
	Health	Hygiene	—	—	—	—	—	20	4	0	G,H,J
Wisconsin	Agriculture	General	90	17,325	2,385	95	100	8	4	1	B,D,E,F,G,H,I,J,K
Wyoming	Agriculture	State chemist	90	1,200	600	100	0	2	3	2	H,G

* *A Study of State and Local Food and Drug Programs*, Report to the Commissioner, Food and Drug Administration, US HEW, May, 1965.

a Includes, additionally, spectographs, colorimeters, and spectronics.

b Adequate number reportedly available.

TABLE IV

MEAN PESTICIDE CONCENTRATIONS IN ADIPOSE TISSUE OF HUMAN AUTOPSIES*

DISEASE	NO. OF CASES	DDT PPM	DDE PPM	DDD PPM	DIELDRIN PPM
Portal Cirrhosis	33	5.19	11.49	0.34	0.50
Carcinoma	40	5.65	15.97	0.34	0.55
Hypertension	8	6.54	17.91	0.40	0.73
Encephalamalacia	24	5.40	12.63	0.27	0.50
Brain Tumors	6	3.91	7.33	0.27	0.32
Atherosclerosis	54	5.10	12.01	0.27	0.37
Chronic Renal Disease	8	2.11	8.11	0.21	0.23
Control†	42	2.77	6.69	0.28	0.21

* Reprint of "Retention of Pesticides in Human Adipose Tissue," *Industrial Medicine and Surgery,* by permission of the author, Wm. D. Deichmann, Ph.D., March, 1968.

† These concentrations were found in adipose tissue of individuals who died accidental deaths.

Index

241

Johnson, Paul E., on food packaging materials, 67
Journal of Asthma Research, 65
Journal of Diseases of Children, 192
Journal of Environmental Health, 165
Journal of the American Medical Association, 14, 19, 20, 47, 122, 130, 155, 171, 184, 185, 224
Journal of the American Veterinary Medical Association, 91
Journal of Public Health, 185

Kelly, Dr. Margaret, on chemicals and cancer, 39
Kewick, Dr. A., on food preservatives, 64–65
Kota, Stephen, on meat processing, 80–81
Kupchik, Dr. George
  on monitoring of pesticides, 30
  on supermarkets, 198

Laboratory
  American Public Health Association, 187
  analysis of meat, 86, 90
  animals, 72
  Biological Sciences, Maryland, 115
  Chesapeake Biological Sciences, 115
  diagnosis of poultry disease, 92–93
  examination of dried milk, 183–184
  refrigerators for incubation of botulinuses, 131
  studies on fish, 115–116
  tests, 2, 23–24
LaChance, Robert, on supermarkets, 198–200
Lackey, Robert, on food handlers, 170–171, 175–176
Lancet, The, 24, 51
Larrick, George P., on frozen foods, 189, 211
Leake, Dr. Chauncey, 4
Lee, Dr. Philip R., on fisheries inspection, 102–103
Legator, Dr. Marvin, on Captan, 25–26
Leonard, Rodney E., on additives, 79

Leukemia, and insecticides, 9, 11
Levin, Dr. Morton L., on cancer, 60
Lijinsky, Dr. William, on cancer, 60, 64
Lindane, 17
  vaporizer, 11
Lockey, Dr. Stephen, on allergic reactions to hidden drugs, 40–41, 64
Lyons, Richard, on "Chinese food syndrome," 57–58

MacLinn, Dr. Walter, on natural food poisons, 142
Magnuson, Warren G.
  on processing of fish, 106
  on Fishing Products bill, 114
Malathion, 4, 23, 25
  See Pesticides; *see also* Insecticides
Maleic hydrazide, 41
Martin, Dr. W. Coda, on DDT and hepatitis, 21–22
Mastitis, treated by penicillin, 44
McCollum, Edward E., Jr., on Wholesome Fish bill, 112
Meat
  additives in, 82
  and poultry hazards, 77–96
  bacterial contamination of, 82 ff.
  examination by veterinarians, 88–89
  Federal Meat Inspection Act, 88
  "federally inspected," 89
  inspection procedures, 86 ff.
  lack of mandatory inspection of, 79 ff.
  mandatory state inspection of, 79 ff.
  storage and handling regulations, 87
  tenderizer Papain, 224 f.
  unsanitary packing conditions, 79 ff.
  unwholesome, 79 ff.
Meat Act, 1967, 87, 88
Medical Letter, on artificial sweeteners, 55
Medical World News, 23
Merck Index, The, 51
Metcalf, David R., on pesticides, 16
Methoxychlor, 17, 21
Methylparathion, 29

Michael, Dr. George A., vs. Fishing Products bill, 114
Milk
  contaminated with *Salmonella newbrunswick,* 183–184
  DDT in, effects of, 16–17, 21
  dried, 183–184
  laboratory examination of, 183 ff.
Modell, Dr. Walter, recommendations for FDA, 210
Mondale, Walter F., on meat processing, 82, 87–88
Mongolism, 58
Montoya, Senator Joseph, on unsanitary meat processing, 82, 86–88
Mucilages, synthetic, 62
Murray, T. Keith, on vitamin-A deficiency, 50
Mushrooms, poison in, 145
Mutagenicity
  due to packaging, 66–67
  of chemicals, 59
  of drugs, 59
Mutagens, 58–60
  pesticides as potential mutagens, 59

National Academy of Sciences, 42, 55, 61, 71, 72, 73, 140, 196
  Food Protection Committee, 2, 3, 61
National Advisory Cancer Council, on synergists, 20
National Biomedical Research Foundation, 57
National Cancer Institute, 3, 20, 49, 63–64
National Dental Institute, 49
National Health Surveys, 2
National Heart Institute, 49
National Institutes of Health, studies on vitamin D, 49
National Research Council, 71, 196
Nerve gas, effects on sheep, 24
Neutrapen, treatment for hives, 44–45
New England Journal of Medicine, 53, 54, 57, 122
New Jersey Allergy Foundation, 45
New York Academy of Sciences, conference on pesticides, 16
Nitrites, 51, 158, 215

Noridhydroguaiaretic acid (NDGA), 70
Nucleides
  Radium 226, 159–160
  Strontium 90, 159–160
Nutrition, Council on Foods and Nutrition of AMA, 52, 61

O'Connor, Dr. Richard G., on toxoplasmosis, 141
Oncology, 60
1, 4, 5, 6, tetrahydro-2-acetropyridine, 71
Orear, Leslie, on meat processing, 81
O'Rourke, Edward, on parathion, 10

Packaging, 66–68
  allergy, cancer, and mutagenicity due to, 66
  frozen food, 189
  of fish, 109
  requirements of meat, 79
Papain, 224
Parasites
  causing ulcers, loss of weight and dysentery, 140
  protozoa *Giardia,* 140
  tapeworms, 140
  Toxoplasma, 140
  Trichinella spiralis, 139
Parathion, 10, 15, 25
Parnate, effects of, 57
Pearson, Drew, on weakening of Federal Poultry Inspection bill, 90
Peck, Neil, on meat inspection, 91
Penicillin, 39
  allergic effects of, 39
  staphylococcus resisting, 43
  used to treat mastitis and hives, 44
Pest
  insects, 14, 32–33
  killer DDT, 13–17
Pesticides
  applied selectively, 33
  Aramite, 21
  arsenical, 46
  as potential mutagens, 59
  cancer-causing properties of, 20
  carbaryl, 4
  causing birth defects, 20

Typhoid-contaminated food, 2
Typhoid fever, 142

Ulcers
  duodenal, 6
  gastric, 6
  parasites causing, 140
Undulant fever, 142
United Nations Food and Agriculture Organization, on pesticides, 16
United States Department of Agriculture, 4, 80
Universal Seafood Company, Inc., and poisoned fish, 99–101
University of Pittsburgh School of Medicine, 3
Urethane, 4

Van Houweling, C. D., on animal feeds, 42
Vending machines, 176–180
Venereal disease, 169
Veterinarians
  inspection procedures for, 86
  meat examination by, 88–89, 91
Viruses
  and bacteria in contaminated waters, 115
  foodborne illnesses from, 137–138
Vitamins
  A and D, 49, 215
  defense of supplements of, 72–73
  in foodstuffs, 49
  intake of excess, 48

Wakefield, Lowell, on fish inspection, 116–117
Water
  containing detergents, sewage, and industrial wastes, 5
  disinfection processes, 162

pesticides in, 206
pollution affecting fish, 115
purification of, 162
standards for drinking, 153
supply and plumbing hazards, 154
tritium in, 160
viruses and bacteria in contaminated, 115
unfit for drinking, 151–162
Weatherwax, J. E., on pesticide residues, 26–27
West, Dr. Irma
  on insecticides, 12–13
  on pesticides, 25–28
"What the Consumer Should Know About Additives," FDA, 68
Wholesome Fish and Fisheries Act of 1968, 109–112
White, Philip L., on sodium content of baby foods, 52
Wilder, Arthur N., on processing of poultry, 85
Wiley, Dr. Harvey W., and pure-food law, 68
Wisconsin Alumni Research Foundation, on artificial sweeteners, 55
Withers, Dr. Orvil R., on allergic reactions to additives, 39
Wolman, Dr. Abel, on processed foods, 185
Woodwell, Dr. George, on pesticides, 31
World Health Organization, 16–17, 27, 50, 60
  Committee on Pesticide Residues, 16

Yeager, Dr. Leona, on sodium nicotinate, 79
Yearbook of Agriculture, The, 4
Yellow Number 5, tartrazine, 66